D0989752

VICTORIA AND ALBERT MUSEUM
CATALOGUE OF RINGS 1930

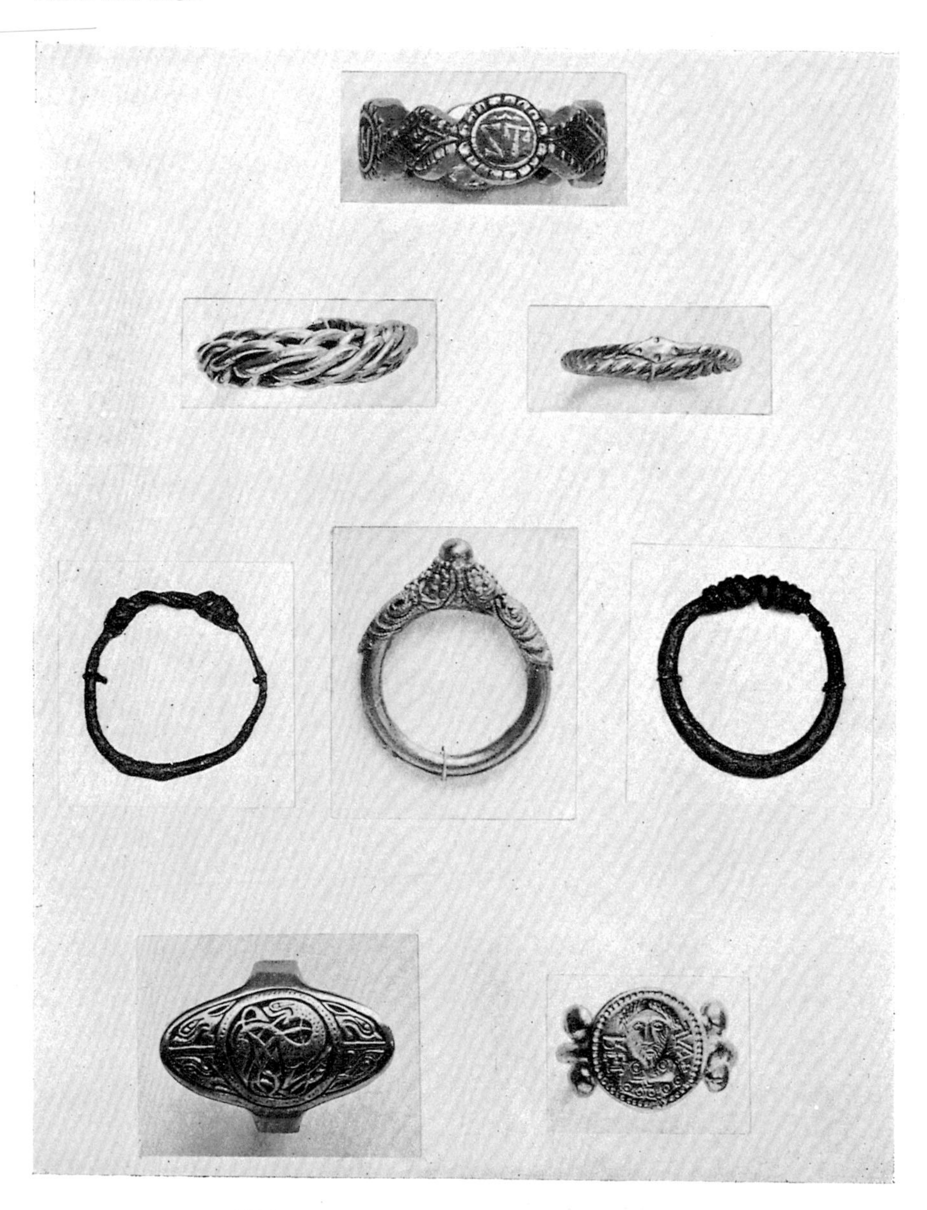

ANGLO-SAXON AND VIKING RINGS

227

230

229

224c

226

224a

225

228

VICTORIA AND ALBERT MUSEUM CATALOGUE OF RINGS 1930

By C. C. Oman, M.A.

1993

Anglia Publishing
Watts House
Capel St Mary, Ipswich
Suffolk, IP9 2JB

Published with the permission of
the Victoria and Albert Museum

First published in Great Britain under the authority of the United Kingdom Board of Education, London, 1930.

This edition published by Anglia Publishing, Ipswich, 1993.

Printed in Great Britain by The Ipswich Book Company.

ISBN 1-897874-02-2

Also in this series:

London Museum Medieval Catalogue 1940. ISBN 1-897874-01-4

British Museum Guide to Anglo-Saxon Antiquities 1923. ISBN 1-897874-03-0

Cover

A massive nielloed gold ring found at Llysfaen in
N.E. Carnarvonshire, previous to December 1773 and thought to have belonged to Alhstan, Bishop of Sherborne from 817 to 867 (see pages 63 and 64).

Publisher's Preface

"The most recent books dealing with British rings are over forty years old...... The specialist books on rings are now difficult to obtain, but although somewhat outdated, are still valuable." Thus wrote Charles Oman in the Preface to his "British Rings 800-1914" which was published in 1974. Included, of course, in that category of "over forty years old" was the original edition of this reprint, his own work, "A Catalogue of Rings".

Oman had been set the task of preparing this catalogue when he joined the staff of the Victoria and Albert Museum in 1924 as an Assistant in the Department of Metalwork. It was eventually published in 1930 at a price of nine shillings in soft covers or cloth-bound for ten shillings. It was sold out by 1945 and, in common with O.M. Dalton's scholarly work on the British Museum's Franks Collection published in 1912, was never reprinted.

Interest in finger rings has not diminished with the passing years. On the contrary, there is ample evidence that it has increased many-fold. The large attendances at sales of ancient and antique jewellery in London and in other major auction centres testify to this growing interest and much of the attention is focused on the rings. More than a few of the rings in these sales are recent finds and their provenances suggest that the advent of the metal detector is largely responsible. In any event there is much "new" material to be appraised and appreciated and more students searching for the appropriate reference books to assist them. Whereas such books were difficult to come by 20 years ago, now they are impossible to find at any price.

More recent books on rings do exist of course, but there is a marked tendency nowadays for catalogues and other books on the decorative arts to be less well-illustrated in the quantitative sense. Such illustration as there is may well be lavish, but will be concentrated on the rare and spectacular. Illustration is expensive now and such economies are understandable, but the results fall short of the needs of serious students, who seek more comprehensive guides. For this reason, "A Catalogue of Rings", albeit more than 60 years old, is deserving of this reprint.

Clearly, it was essential to consider whether any revision was necessary in the light of more recent research, technology and scholarship. It would appear that, in the main, the opinions expressed as to dates are still quite valid. Oman and his associates made good use of the information available from paintings, sculptures and literature from the 15th century onwards and hence there are very few rings which would now be placed more than half a century away from their stated dates. Among the earlier material we found three notable exceptions and it is possible that others exist:

No. 17 illustrated on Plate II
Far from being Sub-Mycenean and 9th century B.C., the style of this decoration with symmetrical curves forming a human face is typically Celtic, probably from Northern Italy and dating from the 3rd century B.C.

No. 223 illustrated on Plate VIII
Rather than 10th-12th century Byzantine this is most probably 9th century Saxon. This change in attribution had been effected before Oman wrote "British Rings", wherein it is acknowledged.

No. 625 illustrated on Plate XXVII
In "British Rings", Oman dates this as 13th century as opposed to 15th century in this catalogue.

This is the second in our series of reprints of classic museum guides. The first was the London Museum Medieval Catalogue, first published in 1940 and rushed to press after the outbreak of war and before the section on finger-rings was completed, which was thus omitted. In his Prefatory Note, R.E. Mortimer Wheeler promised a post war supplement to rectify this significant gap, but this and a section on coins were never forthcoming. We hope, therefore, that for the more general reader this catalogue will be a welcome aid in meeting that deficiency, but above all the purpose of this reprint is to provide a useful tool for the identification and dating of rings for all with an interest in this fascinating subject.

D Rowland
Ipswich
June 1993

PREFATORY NOTE

ALTHOUGH, in point of size, the collection here catalogued is greatly outnumbered by that at the British Museum, it may nevertheless justly claim to contain an equal proportion of important pieces. And even regarding it as only the second collection of its kind in London, it is very doubtful whether a museum in any other country can display a richer or more representative assemblage of rings of mediaeval and later dates.

In drawing up this Catalogue, extensive use has been made of the material in Mr. O. M. Dalton's invaluable catalogue of the British Museum examples; and the author wishes to express here, once and for all, his indebtedness to that work, instead of filling the text and footnotes with a tedious series of acknowledgments. While the freest use has been made of Mr. Dalton's researches and his scheme of arrangement in the main followed, a considerable amount of fresh material has been added and in some cases previous opinions modified. Nearly all the references reproduced from the previous work have been verified and fresh instances quoted where available.

Thanks are also due to Mr. F. N. Pryce, of the Department of Greek and Roman Antiquities in the British Museum, for his valuable aid in giving dates and attributions to the rings in the Classical section.

The Catalogue has been prepared, and the Introduction written, by Mr. C. C. Oman, an Assistant in the Department of Metalwork. The proofs have been read through by Mr. A. J. Koop, Keeper of the Department.

ERIC MACLAGAN.

January 1930.

Select Bibliography

The List of Principal Works of Reference, which appears on page 1, would still form the nucleus of a modern finger-ring bibliography. Much indeed has been written over the intervening years on all aspects of jewellery and a comprehensive listing of books and papers would run to several pages. Surprisingly little, however, has been published which is devoted exclusively to rings and, with the single exception of a more recent Victoria and Albert Museum catalogue, we have confined our supplementary bibliography to these. Those who wish to explore further may find what they seek in their comprehensive bibliographies:

Boardman, J. and Scarisbrick, D. — *The Ralph Harari Collection of Finger Rings,* London, 1978.

Bury, S. — *Jewellery Gallery Summary Catalogue, Victoria and Albert Museum,* London, 1982.

Deloche, M. — *La bague en France, à travers l'histoire,* Paris, 1929

Evans, J. — *English Posies and Posy Rings,* Oxford, 1931.

Fourlas, A. — *Der Ring in der Antike und im Christentum,* Munster, 1971.

Kunz, G.F. — *Rings for the Finger,* Philadelphia, 1917; new edition, New York, 1973.

Marshall, F.H. — *Catalogue of the Finger-rings, Greek, Etruscan and Roman, in the Departments of Antiquities in the British Museum,* London, 1907; reprinted 1968.

Oman, C.C. — *British Rings, 800-1914,* London, 1974.

Ricci, S. de — *Catalogue of a collection of ancient rings formed by the late E. Guilhou,* Paris, 1922.

Scarisbrick, D. — *Rings: Symbols of Wealth, Power and Affection,* London, 1993.

Ward, A., Cherry, A., Gere, C. and Cartlidge, B. — *The Ring from Antiquity to the Twentieth Century,* London, 1981.

A NOTE ON THE HISTORY AND ARRANGEMENT OF THE COLLECTION

THE history of the collection may be said to begin in the year 1864 with the gift by the Rev. R. Brooke of a quantity of family relics, amongst which were a number of rings—all typical of English workmanship in the 17th and 18th centuries. Four years later the Museum acquired the collection of Italian Peasant Rings displayed by Signor Castellani at the Paris Exhibition of 1867. In 1871 the opportunity was presented of purchasing the Waterton Collection of rings, and this was successfully negotiated by the Museum. Edmund Waterton, who held a high reputation in England as a collector and as an authority on rings, appears also to have spent a considerable time in Rome, where he held a post at the Papal Court. His collection seems to have been largely formed in England and Italy, but, as he aimed at making it as representative as possible, he did not confine himself to any country or period. The perusal of this Catalogue will suffice to show that the Waterton Collection, despite its amalgamation with previously acquired examples and with the subsequent additions of nearly sixty years, is still predominant in this section of the Museum.

Together with the Waterton rings was received a manuscript volume containing a considerable amount of interesting material about rings and a partial catalogue of the collection. Much use has been made of this work, but it is greatly to be regretted that Waterton's descriptions of his rings are often so vague as to prove useless for identification.

In 1888 was acquired a representative collection of English Mourning Rings, and in 1899 a number of important rings from the Waterton Collection, which had been withheld at the time of the original sale. It is not possible here to refer to the numerous acquisitions by gift, bequest or purchase, of single or small groups of rings since the collection was first started, though amongst these are a number of examples of primary importance.

On the reorganisation of the Museum in 1908 it was decided that attention should be concentrated on the art of the post-classical period and that for the future it should refrain from acquiring earlier antiquities. In consonance with this decision it will be found that in the preparation of this Catalogue the classical and post-classical rings have been kept entirely separate. The Early Christian rings, which are all of late date and merge naturally with the Byzantine and Frankish, are included in the second part. The classical rings, which constitute a comparatively small portion of the whole, have been arranged chronologically, the post-classical for the most part according to their uses, following the method adopted by O. M. Dalton in his catalogue of the British Museum rings, with certain modifications. Neither the collection of rings in the Indian section of the Museum nor a number of peasant rings of very recent date and scant artistic interest are included; and the same applies to gems mounted in modern "collectors' rings." The Introduction is confined entirely to the European rings of the post-classical period.

It is, of course, quite impossible to pursue to its logical extreme a classification according to uses. Some of the most important uses of rings to which reference is made in the succeeding pages have to be left entirely unrepresented in the Catalogue. No authenticated episcopal consecration ring is in the collection, though there are a number of examples which might well have served this purpose. Similarly, as it is the use and not the shape which distinguishes the wedding and betrothal ring, it is in every way probable that many unrecognised examples are here catalogued under other headings. Greater difficulty, however, is experienced in the case of rings uniting two or more distinct functions. Thus, a signet ring may also be engraved with a religious subject (compare Nos. 484, 485, 739) or a magical inscription (Nos. 582, 590), so that it remains a matter of opinion where it should be catalogued. For convenience the rule has been followed of entering each ring of this sort in the *first* group of the Catalogue to which it belongs and of giving cross-references in other places as required. Where, however, the interest of the ring is decisively such as to place it in a later category, this rule has been waived.

Two other classes of rings have also received exceptional treatment. The small but important categories of post-classical rings dating before the year 1000 A.D. have been catalogued together, as liable to be overlooked if distributed among the larger classes of later rings. Similarly, the peasant rings have all been kept together, instead of being distributed amongst the decorative, religious, or other groups. Many of them are exceedingly difficult to date, and it is also felt that to place, for instance, 18th-century traditional imitations of 16th-century types among the fashionable rings of their own time would merely lead to confusion.

It has not been thought necessary to give measurements. The size of the ring, being conditioned by that of the human finger, varies very slightly, and here and there a word or two added to the catalogue description indicates that the example under notice is of abnormal dimensions, one way or another. Moreover, nearly all the rings of exceptional proportions are shown in the illustrations, which are full-size.

CONTENTS

INTRODUCTION

CATALOGUE

PART I. CLASSICAL RINGS

PART II. EARLY CHRISTIAN AND POST-CLASSICAL RINGS

LIST OF PLATES

LIST OF THE PRINCIPAL WORKS REFERRED TO BY ABBREVIATIONS IN THE INTRODUCTION AND CATALOGUE

Arch. Journal	*Journal of the Royal Archaeological Institute of Great Britain and Ireland.*
Brit. Archaeol. Assoc. . . .	*Journal of the British Archaeological Association.*
Cabrol	*Dictionnaire d'archéologie chrétienne et de liturgie*, edited by Dom Fernand Cabrol and Dom Henri Leclercq, Paris, 1907 and after.
Cancellieri	*Notizie sopra l'origine e l'uso dell' Anello Pescatorio e degli altri anelli ecclesiastici e specialmente del cardinalizio . . . raccolte da Francesco Cancellieri*, Rome, 1823.
Dalton	*British Museum, Catalogue of the Finger Rings, Early Christian, Byzantine, Teutonic, Mediaeval and Later*, by O. M. Dalton, M.A., 1912.
Deloche, *Anneaux Sigillaires* .	*Étude historique et archéologique sur les anneaux sigillaires et autres des premiers siècles du moyen âge*, by M. M. Deloche, Paris, 1900.
Deloche, *Le Port des Anneaux* .	*Le port des anneaux dans l'antiquité romaine et dans les premiers siècles du moyen âge*, in *Mémoires de l'Académie des Inscriptions et Belles-Lettres*, xxxv. 2e partie, 1896.
Du Saussay	*Panoplia Episcopalis, seu de sacro episcoporum ornatu*, by A. du Saussay, Paris, 1646.
Evans, *Magical Jewels* . .	*Magical Jewels of the Middle Ages and the Renaissance, particularly in England*, by Joan Evans, B.Litt., Oxford, 1922.
Ironmongers' Hall Exhibition, 1861	*Catalogue of Antiquities and Works of Art exhibited at the Ironmongers' Hall, London, May* 1861.
Jones, *Finger-ring Lore* . .	*Finger-ring Lore, Historical, Legendary, Anecdotal*, by William Jones, F.S.A., London, 1877.
Kirchmann, *De Annulis* . .	*De annulis liber singularis*, by Johann Kirchmann, Leyden, 1672. (First Edition, 1623.)
Marquet de Vasselot . . .	*Musée National du Louvre : Catalogue Sommaire de l'Orfèvrerie, de l'Émaillerie et des Gemmes du Moyen Âge au XVIIe Siècle*, par J.-J. Marquet de Vasselot, Paris, 1914.
Marshall	*British Museum, Catalogue of the Finger Rings, Greek, Etruscan, and Roman, in the Department of Antiquities*, by F. H. Marshall, M.A., 1907.

Proc. Soc. Ant. . . . . *Proceedings of the Society of Antiquaries of London.*

Smith and Cheetham . . . *A Dictionary of Christian Antiquities*, edited by William Smith, D.C.L., LL.D., and Samuel Cheetham, M.A., London, 1875-80.

Waterton MS. . . . . . *Dactyliotheca Watertoniana : A Descriptive Catalogue of the Finger-rings in the Collection of Mrs. Waterton*, by Edmund Waterton, K.Ch., F.S.A., M.R.I.A., dated 1866. (In the Library of the Victoria and Albert Museum.)

INTRODUCTION

THE WEARING OF RINGS

IF the changing fashions of the last half-century seem to have worked consistently towards the elimination of jewellery, there does not seem as yet to be any danger of the ring falling into disuse, if only because of the usages with which it is associated. It requires, likewise, little imagination to realise that in the course of time there should have been many changes of fashion both in the number and manner of wearing rings.

The decline and fall of classical civilisation caused no break in the use of rings. But, although stray facts are recorded here and there with regard to the wearing of rings in the early Middle Ages, archaeological and literary evidences are not sufficient to give any adequate picture of the usages of that period. More satisfactory information becomes available only with the rise of a realistic school of painting, sculpture and literature. A considerable amount of material is to be obtained from these sources for the 15th and 16th centuries, but a change in artistic conventions in the 17th forbade the illustration of jewellery in painting or sculpture. Rings are rarely shown in portraits from the middle of the 17th till nearly the end of the 18th century, when under the influence of Sir Thomas Lawrence they began to appear again. One ring depicted by this artist is in the collection (No. 958).

As it was formerly customary to use a greater number of rings than is now usual, it is only natural that there should have been a greater variety of ways of wearing them. Rings have been worn on all fingers and on the thumbs, though on some fingers more frequently than on others. The thumbs were certainly commonly used by men for their rings from the 14th to the 16th century.[1] In the 17th and 18th centuries women appear to have commonly worn their wedding rings on their thumbs.[2]

[1] A few examples shown in readily accessible pictures may be quoted :—Henry V. (1413-1422), Edward IV. (1461-1483), Richard III. (1483-1485), all in the National Portrait Gallery.

[2] See p. 18.

The first or index finger, contrary to modern custom, was formerly much used by both sexes. The heavy signet rings of the 16th century were frequently worn on this finger.[1]

The second finger, the *digitus infamis* of the Romans, seems still to have remained unpopular.[2]

The third finger has always been the finger most commonly used, though the little finger has also been popular.

Rings are now worn normally on the bottom joint of the finger, but in the past the upper joints were also used, the top joint probably only by ladies. It will be seen, therefore, that small rings must not necessarily be considered as having been made for children, although these also shared in this prevailing form of luxury.

Early pictures and monumental effigies often depict ecclesiastics wearing rings over their gloves. *Per contra*, laymen are sometimes shown in 16th-century pictures wearing gloves slashed to reveal the rings worn underneath them.[3]

The wearing of rings was not confined to the hands either in the Middle Ages or the Renaissance. In the 15th century they seem to have been sometimes strung on rosaries.[4] Elizabethan portraits show rings worn on a string suspended from the neck,[5] tied round the forearm.[6] They were sometimes also worn threaded on a hat-band.[7]

Gifts and bequests of rings were made not only to famous shrines like

[1] See examples depicted in the portraits of Archbishop Cranmer (1489-1556) and Sir Nicholas Bacon (1510-1579) in the National Portrait Gallery.

[2] Ecclesiastics, however, seem to have worn rings over gloves on this finger. See the brass of Archbishop Cranley (d. 1417) at New College, Oxford, the effigies of Archbishop Langham (d. 1376) at Westminster Abbey, of Benozzo Federichi, Bishop of Fiesole (d. 1540), in Sta. Trinità, Florence, of Rudolf von Scherenberg, Bishop of Würzburg (d. 1495), in Würzburg Cathedral, and of Ernst, Duke of Saxony and Archbishop of Magdeburg (d. 1513), in Magdeburg Cathedral (plaster casts of the last three are in the Museum). The following examples amongst laics may be quoted :—the effigies of King John in Worcester Cathedral (Crossley, *English Church Monuments*, 225) and of Sir Reynold Cobham (d. 1446) at Lingfield, Surrey (*Arch. Journal*, lxxx. 1923, Pl. XXXVII.); and two rings on both the middle fingers of Lady Elizabeth Fitzherbert (ca. 1480), at Norbury, Derbyshire (Crossley, *ibid.*, 198). A ring is also shown on the middle finger of the left hand in the portrait of Henry VII. in the Jones Collection in this Museum (No. 572–1882).

[3] See the portrait of a lady by Lucas Cranach in the National Gallery (No. 291).

[4] *Bury Wills and Inventories*, Camden Society, 1850, pp. 36, 42, 98.

[5] See the picture of Sir Henry Lee, painted about 1560, and of Robert Cecil, Earl of Salisbury (d. 1612), in the National Portrait Gallery (Nos. 2095, 107).

[6] See the portrait of Sir Henry Lee, quoted above.

[7] See the portrait in the Pinakothek, Munich, of Bernard IV., Margrave of Baden (d. 1536), by Hans Baldung Grien (*Classical Picture Gallery*, x. 32).

St. Albans [1] and Walsingham,[2] but also to small parish churches.[3] In the case of the abbeys some of the rings were retained for the abbot's use on high occasions; [4] otherwise they were probably attached to the figure of a saint [5] or some devotional object.[6]

DECORATIVE RINGS

It may be argued that very nearly all the rings in this collection were worn originally with an idea of personal decoration, but it is proposed to deal here only with those which have no obvious practical use. If some of them were worn as love tokens or wedding rings, as badges of office, or for superstitious purposes, there is nothing by which such use can now be recognised.

The great majority of decorative rings are of gold, silver, or bronze, though at various times other fancy materials have been employed. The silver and bronze examples of mediaeval date were all probably gilt, though in many cases all trace of this has disappeared. At almost all periods gem rings have outnumbered those not set with stones and decorated merely with niello, enamel, granular work, or simple chasing. Most mediaeval gem rings were set with stones cut *en cabochon*—that is to say, of rounded form without facets. Sliced garnets were very popular in the early Middle Ages, and from at least the 12th century stones were cut in simple pyramidal forms or with longitudinal facets. More elaborate types of gem-cutting only began to appear in the 16th and 17th centuries. The use of glass pastes in place of gems has been continuous since Roman times, and the practice of placing coloured foils under inferior gems and pastes, in order to enhance their appearance, has been equally prevalent.

It is not, of course, possible to do more than allude to some of the

[1] Matthew Paris, *Chronica Majora VII.*, *Additamenta*, Rolls Series, pp. 383-5.

[2] *Bury Wills and Inventories*, 98.

[3] For bequests, see *Somerset Mediaeval Wills*, 1901, vol. i. pp. 178, 245, 384; see also under Alford, Ash, Godstone and Wonersh in the *Inventories of Church Goods of Surrey in the time of Edward VI.*, Surrey Archaeological Collection, iv. 1869; also *passim* in the *Edwardian Inventories* published by the Alcuin Society.

[4] See reference to Matthew Paris above.

[5] Some rings will be found on the hands of the demi-figure reliquary of St. Lambert in the cathedral treasury, Liége.

[6] A 14th-century devotional tablet of wood in the Waddesdon Bequest at the British Museum has a ring attached to it (*Catalogue of the Waddesdon Bequest*, 1927, p. 48, No. 231).

most characteristic techniques and forms displayed by rings at various periods, with special reference to those in this collection.

As might be expected from the heterogeneous character of the Eastern Empire, Byzantine decorative rings show no very remarkable artistic unity. Though a considerable number of examples have survived, it is hardly feasible to distinguish any as belonging to common types, though many minor technical mannerisms are found recurring. Some, like the peacock ring (No. 220), are clearly of oriental inspiration, whilst others are closely related to the work of the western nations and are not improbably of Italian or Sicilian workmanship. The use of cloisonné enamel in the decoration of rings is doubtless peculiar to this period and to a very few examples, of which one (No. 223) is in the collection. Niello was used extensively, both on gold and silver, whilst granular decoration (filigree), so characteristic of all the European peoples of the period, is also common.

A very large proportion of Frankish rings were engraved with monograms and were therefore probably intended for signets, though many examples must have been worn for ornament rather than for use, as the engraving is often so shallow as to make it impossible to obtain a recognisable impression. The most common form of gem ring amongst the Teutonic nations of the Continent had a circular bezel set with slices of garnet in a wheel pattern (Nos. 237, 238). Other forms that should be noted are the high-projecting cup-shaped (Nos. 239, 240) and "architectural" (No. 235) bezels, both extremely unpractical. An attempt to imitate cloisonné enamel by an easier technique is shown in one example (No. 240), where the bezel is set with a blue-and-red glass mosaic.

The rings used by the Anglo-Saxons in the early period were of the most primitive sort, consisting of mere spirals or hoops formed by twisting together the ends of a piece of wire (Nos. 224*a-c*). The rings of the Christian period, however, include examples which were probably unsurpassed by any produced in other parts of Western Europe at this time. The surviving specimens are few in number, and, though often sharing certain technical peculiarities, bear very slight resemblance to each other in point of form. The Alhstan ring (No. 227) is of a design which has probably never been repeated, whilst the Chelsea ring (No. 225) is an anticipation of the "marquise" pattern so popular in the 18th century.

The rich use of niello on the Alhstan ring can be paralleled by the two royal rings in the British Museum bearing the names of King Ethelwulf and Queen Ethelswith, with which it is probably contemporary. The Meaux Abbey ring (No. 226) affords a spirited example of the use of granular ornament. Although the sliced garnet decoration commonly found on Continental rings of this period was used by the Anglo-Saxons on their other types of jewellery, no sort of gem ring seems to have been popular in England.

A peculiar type of ring composed of plaited gold wire diminishing in diameter towards the back must also be noted. These rings appear to have been found all round the coasts of the British Isles, from the Orkneys southwards, and also in the districts overrun by the Vikings, who were doubtless responsible for making them.

It is only necessary to examine some richly-jewelled piece of 12th or 13th-century goldsmith's work, such as a textus-cover, to notice the variety of different gem-settings used at the same time. Such settings are, of course, very similar to the bezels of rings and are useful as aids in dating unusual examples. During these two centuries stones were still frequently used in a practically uncut state, so that the bezels in which they were set had necessarily to be of most irregular shapes.[1] The stone is usually held by four claws applied to the outside of the bezel, whilst the shoulders are sometimes moulded or chased in the form of dragons' heads. When set with cut stones or pastes, the bezels are often rectangular and are with or without claws.[2] Some of the " pontificals," or rings worn by bishops and other ecclesiastics over their gloves at great ceremonies, appear to have been of very large dimensions and set with numerous stones.[3] Perhaps the commonest type of gem ring in use during the 12th, 13th and 14th centuries was the " stirrup-shaped," of very simple and graceful design.[4]

During the 14th and 15th centuries the rounded cabochon gem in a plain setting maintained its popularity and it became less usual to set practically uncut stones in rings. The bezels tend to become much more

[1] Compare the rings of Bishops Manassé (d. 1190) and Hervée (d. 1223) in the cathedral treasury, Troyes (illustrated in Rohault de Fleury, *La Messe*, viii., Pl. DCLXXX).

[2] Compare No. 243, the ring of Bishop Flambard (d. 1128), in Durham Cathedral Library (*Archaeologia*, xlv. 1880, Pt. I. p. 387), and three rings found at Lark Hill, Worcester, in conjunction with coins of Henry II. and David I. of Scotland (British Museum, Dalton, 1743-5).

[3] Compare two presented to St. Albans Abbey by Dom Hamon and Cardinal Henry de Blois described and illustrated by Matthew Paris (Rolls Series, *Chronica Majora VII.*, *Additamenta*, frontispiece and pp. 383, 386-7).

[4] Compare Nos. 249-253, and the ring from the so-called grave of Bishop Hilary (d. 1169) in Chichester Cathedral (*Arch. Journal*, xx. 1863, p. 235).

regular in shape and the stone is usually held in a plain collet, but sometimes this is fringed with teeth.[1] Among the common types of settings in the 15th century may be noted the grooved quatrefoil used with rectangular gems.[2] The passage from the early to the later Middle Ages is marked by an increased tendency to decorate more elaborately the shoulders and hoop of the ring, though simple examples still, of course, predominated. Many 15th-century rings are fully equal to the best of their Renaissance successors in delicacy of design and decoration. It is very much to be regretted that whilst 16th-century rings which retain the full splendour of their enamelling are still common, it is rare to find mediaeval examples that retain any but the slightest traces of their former colouring. The loss is the greater from the national point of view, as the beauty of a large proportion of the English 15th-century rings depended in whole or in part on a very characteristic decoration of enamelled flowers.[3] Niello decoration was at this period very much used in Italy on silver rings [4] and as a side-line to a large trade in love rings and tokens which are alluded to elsewhere.[5]

The increasing love of display which swept over Europe in the first half of the 16th century was responsible for the growth in the popularity of the richly-decorated ring, as well as for considerable progress in the art of gem-cutting. The publication of printed books of designs for jewellery helped to maintain the comparative uniformity displayed by the rings of each successive period of the Middle Ages, despite the rejection of Gothic ornament in favour of the Classical or pseudo-Classical. Great as was the reputation of the Italian and German goldsmiths who were undoubtedly responsible for a very large output of jewellery at this time, it is seldom possible to postulate a nationality with any probability for a ring the provenance of which is unknown.

It is not possible here to do more than refer to a few of the commonest types of ring in use during the 16th century. In some cases a type can be traced through several stages of development. In this collection is a

[1] Compare the " Founder's Ring " of Winchester College, connected traditionally with Bishop William of Wykeham (d. 1404) and of the period.

[2] Compare the middle gem of No. 265. This type of setting is also seen in the portrait of Henry VII., in the Jones Collection (No. 572-1882) in this Museum, and in that of Elizabeth of York, d. 1503, in the National Portrait Gallery (No. 311), and is often depicted in pictures of the early Flemish school.

[3] Compare No. 262, and the ring of Bishop Stanbery, d. 1474, in Hereford Cathedral (illustrated in *Archaeologia*, xxxi. 1846, p. 249).

[4] Compare Nos. 272-274.

[5] p. 22.

plain gold ring (No. 276) set with a rounded turquoise.[1] The edge of the setting is embossed with a double row of scalloping, the points of every second of the inner row of scallops coinciding with those of the outer and larger band. The outer scalloping on this ring suggests the appearance of a flower with four petals, and it is not difficult to see in this example an early stage in the development of the well-known Renaissance type having a bezel set with a table-cut gem and with sides like four well-developed petals.[2] It will be noticed that even in the later examples both the inner and outer bands of scalloping remain. It is possible, indeed, that another equally characteristic type of Renaissance ring, which has a rectangular bezel resting on what may be described as a cushion,[3] may also be related to it, as the inner border of scalloping certainly appears.

Of the numerous other types of 16th and 17th-century rings with rectangular bezel it is only necessary to draw attention to those set with a pointed " writing diamond " (half a natural crystal), so called from its being occasionally used for writing on window-panes.[4]

The decoration of the more gorgeous rings of this period was not confined to the bezel, but was continued on the shoulders, which were chased and enamelled with equal richness. In the less elaborate rings of the late 16th and 17th century the shoulders were often left unchased, but the whole of the hoop was enamelled. From the end of the 16th century may be noticed a tendency to set rings with a number of small gems, instead of a single large stone as previously. The change in fashion, which was accompanied by technical progress in the use of more elaborate methods of cutting stones, gave the jeweller greater freedom in the development of his designs. The increasing varieties of forms were accompanied by a general movement away from the heavy magnificence of the 16th century.

From the lighter forms of the late 17th century developed the " giardinetti " rings of the succeeding century, so called from the representations of flowers in many coloured stones which formed the bezels. In the " giardinetti " and other rings of similar types the bezels are usually of openwork, and the settings of silver, although the hoops are gold. Con-

[1] This stone, though by no means a novelty, seems to have been particularly popular during the first half of the 16th century. Compare the portraits of Thomas Cromwell, Earl of Essex, d. 1540, and Thomas, Lord Wentworth, d. 1551, in the National Portrait Gallery (Nos. 1727 and 1851).

[2] Compare Nos. 278-284. This development was noted by Dalton, p. 268.

[3] Compare Nos. 285-294.

[4] Compare Nos. 307-308, also a ring shown in the portrait of Sir Henry Lee in the National Portrait Gallery (No. 2095).

temporary with the "giardinetti" was the "marquise" ring, with a vesica-shaped (pointed oval) bezel. The "marquise" type seems to have been more popular abroad than in this country, where it was chiefly used for a variety of mourning ring. The appearance of the decorative rings of the 19th century is still so familiar as to make description unnecessary.

PEASANT RINGS

DESPITE the comparative modernity and small intrinsic value of most examples, the importance and interest of what are usually called peasant rings should not be under-estimated. In the present group are included rings dating from the 17th century onwards which reproduce contemporary styles in cheaper materials, or continue those of a previous age which had generally fallen into disuse. Those rings of an earlier date which would otherwise have fallen under one or other of these headings have been kept in the main collection. Despite the low-grade gold usually employed and the use of pastes and semi-precious stones, the workmanship is often good, whilst the tendency to reproduce vanished types makes it possible to make good in part the deficiencies of the main collection by showing traditional imitations. Few of the examples here catalogued are earlier than the 18th century and the majority belong probably to the 19th.

SIGNET RINGS

(1) MATERIALS

SIGNET rings have been used continuously since the Classical period, though their popularity has at times been affected by the use of other forms of seal—and latterly by the adhesive envelope.

The characteristic part of the signet ring is, of course, the bezel; the hoop, for the most part, merely follows the prevailing fashion for decorative rings. The bezel may either be set with a stone intaglio or engraved with a device directly in the metal, but otherwise only slight varieties of form may be noted.

Allusion may be made to one further type, although its use in post-Classical times has never been more than occasional. The signet ring with a revolving bezel may be traced back to the Egyptian scarab ring and was known to most of the peoples of the ancient world. A ring of this type was used by Avitus, Bishop of Vienne,[1] in the 6th century, and is exemplified in this collection by two examples of 16th and 17th-century date (Nos. 494, 739).

The art of engraving directly on the metal has seen many vicissitudes, and at every period good and bad work has been produced. As is natural, less trouble was usually expended on bronze rings than on those in the more precious metals. The Early Christian rings, which are mostly of bronze, show much the same workmanship as the contemporary pagan rings in the same material. During the Byzantine, Frankish and Anglo-Saxon periods the signet devices were usually of a simple description, but often carefully executed, whilst some examples—like the lost ring of the Frankish king Childeric once in the Bibliothèque Nationale, and the Anglo-Saxon AVFRET ring in the collection (No. 228)—are the works of artists of considerable ability.

By the 14th century a much higher standard of technical skill had been reached, as is shown in the Italian heraldic ring, No. 509; and from this time till the middle of the 17th century a continuous sequence of craftsmen were producing work of the highest order. A large proportion of the English 16th-century signet rings are especially worthy of mention.

In the second half of the 17th and first half of the 18th century much of the best metal intaglio work was directed towards the production of small pendent seals (of which the Museum possesses a representative collection). Although a revival in the demand for this type of signet occurred in the 19th century, the standard of workmanship generally remained low.

The practice of setting antique engraved gems in signet rings has been consistently popular since the fall of the Roman Empire. The repugnance felt by Clement of Alexandria and other early Christians for signets bearing the figures and emblems of pagan deities, disappeared at an early date. Rings discovered in what were judged to be the tombs of Archbishop Hubert Walter (d. 1205) in Canterbury Cathedral, and of a bishop in Chichester Cathedral, are both set with undoubted Gnostic gems, whilst that found in the tomb of Bishop Stephen Gardiner (d. 1556) in Winchester Cathedral bears a head of Minerva.

Since the Renaissance, Classical gems have been prized purely for their

[1] Described in a letter to Apollinaris, Bishop of Valence, who had offered him the gift of a ring. See *S. Aviti Epistol.*, lxxviii., in Migne, *Patrol. Lat.*, lix. 280-1, quoted with a translation by Babington in Smith and Cheetham, ii. 1804.

artistic and historic value. During the Middle Ages, however, the belief was held that the inherent magical properties of certain stones might be enhanced when found engraved with the appropriate symbols.[1] There can be no doubt that many antique gems set in mediaeval rings must have been chosen for this reason, though owing to the wide range of subjects recognised in Classical times many must have been re-used in the Middle Ages without such a secondary purpose.

Great obscurity prevails with regard to the engraving of gems in the early Middle Ages. There seems no reason to doubt that this art was practised, at any rate intermittently,[2] between the fall of the Roman Empire and the Carolingian period, during which a decided revival took place.[3] Little further work of this description appears to have been done in the West before the Gothic period was well advanced, but in the Byzantine Empire no break seems to have occurred. In this collection is a gold ring (No. 224) set with a bloodstone intaglio of St. John the Evangelist probably of 11th-century date.[4]

The later mediaeval revival of gem-cutting is represented by some splendid signets in this collection. Among them is a gold ring (No. 534) found in a well at Hereford in 1824. It is set with a sapphire engraved with what appears to be the head of a monk, and has a marginal inscription TECTA LEGE LECTA TEGE, the motto used by Matthew Paris (d. 1259), the historian monk of St. Albans. It is certainly an early example of its kind and can hardly be later than the first quarter of the 14th century. Next comes a fine 15th-century gold ring (No. 535) engraved with flowers and set with a spinel intaglio of a crowned head with the marginal inscription TEL IL NEST (there is none like him). It seems probable, however, that the intaglio may be a representative of the great 14th-century school of French

[1] Lists of antique gems with the peculiar property of each device are given in two MSS., Bodleian Digby 79, fols. 178*v*-179*v*, 13th century, English, and B. M. Sloane 1784, fol. 8, 14th century, French, both printed as appendices in Evans, *Magical Jewels*, pp. 235-246. The whole subject is fully treated in Chapters IV.-VI. of the same work.

[2] Deloche, *Anneaux Sigillaires*, pp. xviii-xxi, gives the following instances :—the ring of Agilbert, Bishop of Paris (ca. 670), set with an agate engraved with St. Jerome (d. 470) before a crucifix, and that of Ebregisilus, Bishop of Meaux (ca. 660), set with a stone engraved with St. Paul the Hermit before a crucifix, both unfortunately lost ; also the ring of Avitus of Vienne (see above).

[3] Compare an intaglio of the Crucifixion set in the 13th-century reliquary of the True Cross in this Museum (7947–1862).

[4] Two fine examples of Byzantine cameo-work of rather later date, depicting the Annunciation (7552–1861) and St. Theodore (779*c*–1891), are shown in the Department of Architecture and Sculpture.

gem-cutting. A fine garnet intaglio of Italian 15th-century work, showing a head with flowing hair to right, is set in a gold ring (No. 606) which is itself probably French or English.

The imitation of Roman gems of the best period is illustrated by two splendid Italian Renaissance rings (Nos. 612, 613), each set with an intaglio of Hercules. From the 16th century onwards gem-engraving has been practised with varying success all over Europe. The decline in merit noticeable amongst 17th-century intaglios was to a certain extent remedied by a revival in the succeeding century. The skill of the intaglio-cutters of the late 18th century was not, however, long maintained, so that elaborate designs have seldom been successfully executed since.

A peculiar class of signet ring used principally in the 16th century must be especially mentioned. In this the bezel was set with an engraved crystal over foil coloured so as to show the device in its proper tinctures. The earliest recorded ring of this sort belonged to Jean Sans Peur, Duke of Burgundy, assassinated in 1419.[1] In this case, however, the ring was set with a white sapphire engraved with his arms, instead of with a crystal. A similar use of white onyx is mentioned by the German mineralogist Georgius Agricola (d. 1480). The most historic ring of this sort is the signet of Mary Queen of Scots, in the British Museum. A considerable number of fine examples are in this collection, amongst which the ring of Sir Richard Lee, of Sopwell, is especially noteworthy (No. 486).

(2) Devices

(a) *Portraits*

The custom of engraving a signet with a representation of its owner, or his patron, goes back to Classical times. Several examples of the Roman period are in this collection. At no time has this been a very common type of device, as it is obviously much more difficult to engrave even a passable representation of a head or bust, than to cut a monogram, merchant's mark, or set of initials. In the period after the development of heraldry the rich, who were also the armigerous, usually preferred a signet engraved with their arms or crest to one bearing a conventional representation of the owner almost devoid of individuality.

It is not surprising that a considerable proportion of the "portrait"

[1] Waterton MS., 249.

signets should belong to the early Middle Ages. A number of examples from Frankish sites are enumerated by Deloche.[1] Nearly all are of gold and may therefore be inferred to have belonged to wealthy persons. They range artistically from the purely barbarous to the highly accomplished workmanship of the lost ring of Childeric I. (457-481). The splendid ring bearing the name AVFRET in this collection, probably Anglo-Saxon work, is perhaps the finest example of this type of signet made before the year 1000 A.D. Other examples, discovered in Italy, may be seen in the Ashmolean Museum, Oxford,[2] and the Bargello, Florence.[3]

A number of later mediaeval gem-rings are engraved with conventional portrait heads and busts probably intended to represent the owners.[4] In this collection may be instanced the ring conjecturally connected with Matthew Paris and another bearing a crowned head, both already mentioned.

Few portrait signets were produced by the gem-engravers of the Renaissance, though decorative rings, like the Essex ring with its cameo portrait of Queen Elizabeth, are known.

During the 18th-century revival of the gem-engraver's art a considerable number of signets set with portrait busts were produced. Most of these were after the antique and were not representations of the owner, or of any one of whom he was a supporter.

A curious iron ring (No. 791) has a silver bezel engraved with the heads of the princes who participated in the Family Compact of 1761.

(b) *Inscriptions*

Signets bearing inscriptions without any form of accompanying device have been used at various periods, but were especially common during the later days of the Roman and the Byzantine empires. The inscription might merely be the name of the owner, but was often an acclamation such as LIBERI VIVAS (No. 132), VIVAS IN DIO (No. 199), *κύριε βοήθει τὸν φοροῦντα* (No. 222). As the principal function of a signet is to serve as a means of identification, types with more easily recognisable individuality have more often been preferred.

[1] Deloche, *Anneaux Sigillaires*, p. xxiv, with references in footnotes.
[2] Fortnum Colln., 341.
[3] In the collection of seals, No. 819.
[4] The 14th-century signet inscribed S. CRISTINE ALMARICI in the British Museum (Dalton, 220) is, however, set with an intaglio of what appears to be a male head with pendent hood.

(c) *Monograms*

Monograms in which all the letters of a word or of an inscription are disguised in the form of a single character were well known in the ancient world before the Christian era. It was only, however, in the later years of the Roman Empire that they became popular as devices for signets.

Amongst the Early Christians, signets bearing the monogram for VIVAS IN DEO were extensively used, and two examples are in the collection (Nos. 200, 201). More personal signets were engraved with the monogram of the owner's name, often in the form of a cross.

These devices retained all their popularity amongst the inhabitants of the Eastern and the inheritors of the lands of the Western Roman Empire, but gradually disappeared as the Middle Ages advanced.

Except in the case of very simple examples or a few well-known formulae, it is seldom possible to read a monogram with any real degree of certainty. That this difficulty is not peculiar to an age when monograms have fallen into disuse is shown by a letter from Symmachus (d. between 395 and 410) to his brother Flavian, of whom the writer asks whether he has received all his letters, sealed with his ring, where his name is more easy to recognise than to read.[1]

(d) *Initials*

The use of initials as the principal device of signet rings began to be common in the 14th century, though they had appeared in subsidiary positions at a much earlier date. The mediaeval rings of this type seem to have been used principally by those who were not entitled to coats-of-arms. They are common in bronze and silver, but rare in gold. A very fine example in the last metal is, however, in the collection (No. 551). The usual design consisted of a single initial or two, beneath a crown or surrounded by a wreath. The use of the crown has clearly no significance. The initials are frequently shown linked, sometimes in such a manner as to make them difficult to distinguish.

In the 16th and 17th centuries a fashion arose for showing two initials bound together by a true-lover's knot. The most interesting and historic

[1] "Non minore sine cura cupis cognoscere an omnes obsignatas epistolas meas sumpseris eo anulo quo nomen meum magis intelligi quam legi promtum est" (Symmachi, *Epistolae*, ii. 12).

example is the Darnley ring (No. 559), which bears inside his name and the year of his betrothal and marriage, and has on the bezel H (for Henry) and M (for Mary Queen of Scots), both letters bound together by a knot. From the 17th century the use of linked initials has been continuous, the most reliable material for dating being the alterations in the script.

(e) *Heraldic Devices*

Although armorial seals were one of the evidences of the spread of heraldry, the use of signet rings engraved with coats-of-arms, crests, and badges seems hardly to have begun till the 14th century. A large proportion of the earlier examples are Italian, and it would seem that this type of signet did not become common in other countries till the 15th century.

Since the wearers of these rings belonged to the wealthier classes, the standard of workmanship from the 14th to the 17th century was exceptionally high. Some excellent examples of the realistic treatment of heraldic subjects on rings are to be found amongst the 16th and 17th-century English signets in this collection.

Heraldic signet rings of 18th-century date are comparatively rare. Though much of their popularity was recovered in the 19th century, the standard of workmanship remained low.

(f) *Merchants' Marks*

Though there was in most countries during the later Middle Ages a limited class of rich burgesses who possessed merchants' marks as well as coats-of-arms, the former were, as a rule, used by tradesmen and merchants who could not aspire to heraldic distinctions. Great obscurity exists as to the time of origin of these marks, but they do not seem to have begun to appear on signet rings till the 14th century. Though the owners of such rings would themselves usually be able to read, it was a convenience for them to possess a signet engraved with the emblem with which they marked their goods, so as to be easily recognised by any illiterates with whom they might do business. Signets of this type were widely used until the 17th century, when they gradually fell out of fashion partly owing to the change in business methods, partly to the increase in the number of those who could read.

(g) *Rebuses*

The rebus, a device in which a name is expressed by a combination of objects whose names when pronounced give the same sound, was known in antiquity. The use of such devices on signet rings was popular chiefly in the 15th and 16th centuries, and was not confined to the less wealthy classes, as is shown by some of the magnificent examples in the collection. Amongst these may be mentioned the gold ring of R. Wylmot expressed by " R Wy (an elm) ot " (No. 552). Another example giving the name Vincent by means of part of a vine and CENT, is finely executed, though only of gilt bronze (No. 555).

(h) *Miscellaneous Devices*

The use of a device which makes no direct reference to the owner has always been popular. Amongst these may be classed signets set with engraved gems, Classical and post-Classical, and a number of bronze rings bearing hands held in various postures, probably of secret significance.

Another type of device refers to the owner's sentiments, such as the French 15th-century silver ring (No. 589) bearing a couchant hound with IAME S'GEEIN (*j'aime songeant*), a German ring of gold (No. 602) set with a foiled crystal showing the date 1572 with forget-me-nots and V M N (*vergiss mein nicht*), and an Elizabethan gold ring (No. 560) engraved with a cradle and inscribed inside " my wille were."

(i) *Religious Devices*

As has already been remarked, it is impossible to divide a collection such as this into clearly marked classes without a certain amount of overlapping. Thus, allusion must be made to the category of signets engraved with devices or inscriptions of a religious character which were in use from the 5th to the 17th centuries. A large number of Early Christian rings belong to this class. Clement of Alexandria considered that the signet was the only type of ring admissible for a Christian and advocated the abandonment of all others. The interesting passage in which he enumerates the suitable devices for such rings will be quoted in the section dealing with religious rings.

The religious signet maintained a somewhat decreased popularity during the existence of the Byzantine Empire. Most examples belong to one or other of two types: those bearing invocatory inscriptions such as "Lord, help the wearer" (No. 222), and those with representations of saints such as No. 224.

In the West many Early Christian types, especially the more easily engraved, persisted into the Merovingian period, but at later dates the signet ring engraved with a religious subject became unusual, although the purely religious ring long retained its popularity. The ring of Jacques Bouchier (No. 588), engraved with the figure of his patron St. James, is a fine example of a 15th-century ring of this class. A number of 16th and 17th-century "memento mori" rings (Nos. 566-567) seem to mark the end of this group.

BETROTHAL, WEDDING, AND LOVE RINGS

It will be convenient to attempt first to trace the historical development of this class of rings, before arranging them according to their forms and types.

Though in modern ideas the betrothal, wedding, and love rings suggest each a definite purpose, this has not always been so. The history of the wedding ring is confused with the betrothal ring, and that of the betrothal ring with the simple love ring.

The use of a betrothal ring is well attested amongst the Romans. At the betrothal (*sponsalia*) the father or guardian of the future bride made a solemn promise of marriage on her behalf to her future husband, who in return presented her with a ring (*anulus pronubus*) as a pledge.[1] Betrothals could always be broken off without trouble in Classical times.

The betrothal ring continued in use amongst the Early Christians. St. Ambrose records in his sermon on St. Agnes, that when solicited in marriage by a noble youth, she replied that she was already betrothed with a ring to another lover (*i.e.* Christ) more worthy in every way. Isidore of Seville (d. 636) has a most interesting passage[2] on the betrothal ring. "The ring," he says, "is given by the espouser to the espoused (*a sponso sponsae*) either for a sign of mutual fidelity or still more to join their hearts

[1] The principal authorities for this section are H. Leclercq, in Cabrol, col. 2188-91, C. Babington, in Smith and Cheetham, ii. 1807-8, Father Herbert Thurston, S.J., in *St. Peter's*, iii. 1899, pp. 356-367, *Jewish Encyclopaedia*, x. 428, and Sir John Evans, *Posy-rings*, 1892.

[2] *Ecclesiastical Offices*, ii. 20.

by this pledge, and therefore the ring is placed on the fourth finger [1] because a certain vein, it is said,[2] flows thence to the heart."

Pope Nicholas I., writing in about 860, gives an account of the ceremonies connected with marriage in his day, from which it is clear that the betrothal, at which the ring was given, and the subsequent marriage ceremony, which took place in the church, were still considered as being quite distinct, and the possibility of a lapse of time between the two functions was envisaged.

It would seem that the increasing reverence with which succeeding generations regarded betrothal was responsible for the conversion of the *anulus pronubus* into the wedding ring by the amalgamation of the ceremony of the plighting of troth with the celebration of the marriage itself. Till the end of the Middle Ages the plighting of troth and the giving of the ring usually took place at the church door,[3] and not at the entrance to the chancel, but, though this trace of the existence of two ceremonies still remained, the ring definitely became the symbol of an unbreakable contract.

Rituals for the blessing of the ring and for putting it on the finger of the bride can be traced back to the 11th century. It is not necessary to go into the mediaeval ritual regarding the wedding ring, but it should be noted that it appears to have been usual to place the ring on the right hand of the bride. This is clearly shown in nearly all pictures of marriage from the 13th to the 16th century.[4] The rubric in the Sarum Manual prescribes that the ring at the marriage should be left on the third finger, and gives as explanation the supposed existence of the vein flowing to the heart, to which allusion has already been made.

The first sign of the change of practice in placing the ring on the third finger of the left hand appears in the Book of Common Prayer of Edward VI. (1549). The reason for this change is not specified, but it is possible that it had been discovered that Aulus Gellius (d. about 180), the authority on whom Isidore of Seville, and other writers who had followed him, relied for the statement about the vein flowing to the heart, had spoken of the left hand and not the right. The change in the English usage was followed

[1] The thumb used to be treated as the first finger.

[2] Aulus Gellius, *Noctes Atticæ*, x. 10, Macrobius, *Saturnalia*, vii. ch. 13.

[3] W. Maskell, *Monumenta Ritualia Ecclesiae Anglicanae*, i. 50.

[4] Besides a few pictures which show the wedding ring being placed on the left hand, it may be mentioned that John Burchard in his Diary (ed. Thuasne, Paris, 1883, v. 488) describing the marriage of Louis of Aragon to Battistina Cibo, in the reign of Innocent VIII., speaks of the placing of the ring on the left hand of the bride. Father Thurston supposes this may have been a Spanish custom.

by the *Rituale Romanum* in 1614, though previous liturgical works printed as late as 1584 had still prescribed the right hand. This alteration was not observed by English Catholics till about the middle of the 18th century.

Serious attempts were made by the English Puritans to do away with the wedding ring, but without success. The Lutherans, though not insisting on the use of rings, favoured the practice already prevalent at betrothals in Germany of exchanging rings.[1] The practice of the Orthodox Church is for the bridegroom to give the bride a gold ring and to receive a silver ring. Both rings are worn on the right hand.

There does not seem to be any record of the use of marriage rings by the Jews till about the 7th or 8th century, when it became, as among Christians, the most important part of the service. The bridegroom placed the ring on the middle finger of the right hand of the bride, saying " Be thou hallowed to me through this ring, according to the laws of Moses and Israel." The ring was used only at the service and not worn afterwards.[2]

Though Christian custom gradually prescribed that the wedding ring should be placed on one particular finger at the actual ceremony, the habit of wearing it always on the same finger is of comparatively recent date.[3] It appears to have been quite usual to wear the wedding ring on the thumb in the early 18th century.[4]

The modern betrothal or engagement ring, like the ancient *anulus pronubus*, is the sign of a voidable contract to marry at a future date. With the incorporation of the solemn plighting of troth in the marriage service the *anulus pronubus* appears to have become the wedding ring. The obvious advantage of some sort of previous understanding before marriage ultimately resulted in the giving of a separate engagement ring, but it is difficult to trace at all clearly the origin of this custom. The diversity of the forms of betrothal in use in the Middle Ages and the varying degrees of voidability ascribed to them is paralleled by the different practices in the

[1] Thiers (*Traité des Superstitions*, 1704, ii. 512) quotes a ritual of Bordeaux of 1596 and Father Thurston one of Passau of 1774 in which both the bride and the bridegroom received a ring, but there does not seem to be any indication that this practice was ever widespread in Catholic countries.

[2] *Jewish Encyclopaedia*, x. 428-30.

[3] A passage in the will of Ann Barrett (d. 1504) shows that wedding rings were sometimes worn on rosaries : " Item I bequeath to Our Lady of Walsingham my corall bedys of thrys fifty, and my maryeng ring, with all thyngs honging theron " (*Bury Wills and Inventories*, Camden Soc., 1850, p. 98).

[4] Jones, *Finger-ring Lore*, 288-9; *British Apollo*, i. 1711, p. 226; Butler's *Hudibras*, pt. ii., canto 2, v. 303.

giving and receiving of rings, which certainly seem to have formed a common though unessential part of an engagement from an early date. Betrothals varied from ceremonies considered as almost tantamount to marriage to mere agreements between lovers, or children's parents, and it is not possible now to discover a clear definition of what was then considered a true betrothal ring or a lover's token.

In former times, when it was fashionable to wear more rings than now, gifts of rings were a common means of showing regard or repaying a service of any sort. As the wearing and the possession of numerous rings became less usual, the custom of giving rings away declined and the ordinary love ring implying no formal engagement gradually disappeared.

Despite the undoubted antiquity of the modern usage with regard to the giving of an engagement ring, it would seem that the present uniformity of practice is of comparatively recent date.

Several distinct customs can be recognised besides that of the giving of a ring by the future bridegroom to his betrothed. An exchange of rings between betrothed appears to have been an early and long-continued practice. When in 1235 Pier di Vinea, ambassador of Frederick II., came to make formal request on behalf of his master for the hand of Isabella, sister of Henry III., he presented her with a ring acclaiming her as Empress of the Holy Roman Empire. She in return sent a ring to the Emperor in token of the acceptance of the troth.[1]

The signet ring (No. 559) in this collection, which was found at Fotheringay and bears on the bezel H M in monogram bound by a true-lover's knot, and inside the hoop HENRI L DARNLEY 1565 with a coat-of-arms, is usually accepted as a ring given by Mary Queen of Scots to her future husband at their betrothal.

Gimmel rings (*gemellus*, a twin) were a 16th-century elaboration of the same idea. These rings had two hoops fitting closely together so as to appear as one. When the ring was separated into two, each lover could wear half until the promise was redeemed by marriage, when the two hoops could be rejoined and worn as one ring. It seems doubtful whether this troublesome ritual was often performed in actual practice, for the more common variety of gimmel consisted of two interlacing hoops which could only be parted and rejoined by a jeweller, and it is rare to find any trace of this having happened on an extant example. This objection does not, of course, apply to the variety with pivoted hoops, but in either case the sharp

[1] T. Rymer, *Foedera*, i. 355.

edges of the divided ring must have been a constant and unpleasant reminder of the plighted troth !

In dealing with some of the other principal types of love rings it is necessary to abandon any attempt to arrange them according to their uses as wedding rings, betrothal rings, or love tokens. It should be remembered that many rings which have been used for the above purposes must be scattered unrecognised among the other parts of the collection, especially among the decorative rings, simply because there is nothing in their appearance to show the special purpose which they have served. It is not possible, for instance, to distinguish any separate class of wedding rings, as the present uniformity of use belongs only to recent centuries. It does not, however, appear to be true that the use of a plain gold wedding ring was due entirely to the spread of Puritan ideas in the 17th century. In accounts of the marriage of Queen Mary in 1554 it is specially mentioned that " the Quene's mariage ring was a plain hoope of gold without any stone in it : for that was as it is said her pleasure, because maydens were so maried in olde tymes," [1] which seems to prove that plain rings were considered unfashionable, but were not unknown. Plain silver rings without gems or inscriptions were in use in the diocese of Paris,[2] and the use of this metal is attested in several other French dioceses.[3] The use of wedding rings set with gems during the Middle Ages and Renaissance is well authenticated. Durandus, Bishop of Mende (d. 1296), speaking of the wedding ring, implies that in his day it was usually a gold ring set with a gem.[4] In a will dated 1503 of Marion Chambers, of Bury St. Edmunds, the testatrix mentions her " marying ring having a dyamond and a rubie therein." [5] The wedding ring of Mary of Modena was also of gold set with a diamond.[6]

In the time of Pliny (d. A.D. 79) the *anulus pronubus* was of iron and without a gem, but by the time of Tertullian (d. about 230) gold rings had come into use. Roman love rings both of gold (No. 125) and silver

[1] John Elder's Letter published as Appendix X. to *Chronicle of Queen Jane and of Two Years of Queen Mary*, Camden Society, 1850, p. 141. An almost identical phrase appears in *Wriothesley's Chronicle*, Camden Society, 1877, i. 120.

[2] Du Saussay, p. 208, quoting from *Manuel des prêtres de l'Église de Paris*.

[3] Martène, *De antiquis ritibus ecclesiæ*, ii. 365-74.

[4] " Postmodum vero pro ferreis sunt aurei constituti et pro adamante gemmis ornati, qui sicut aurum cetera metalla, sic amor universa bona praecellit " (*Rationale Divinorum Officiorum*, i. 41).

[5] *Bury Wills and Inventories*, Camden Society, 1850, p. 252.

[6] Strickland, *Queens of England*, ix. 56, quoting from MS. memorials of Mary of Modena in the Archives Nationales, Paris.

(No. 131) are in this collection, but there is, of course, no evidence that any of them were used at betrothals.

Only the Jewish wedding ring, indeed, can be recognised by its external appearance. The earliest examples of this appear to date from the 13th century, but the majority belong to the 16th and 17th and are of Venetian or South German workmanship. Their chief characteristic is their unwieldy size, which renders them quite unsuitable for daily wear, for which they were not intended. The building which forms the bezel of many of them is thought to represent either a synagogue or Solomon's Temple. Most examples bear the Hebrew words *Mazzāl tōb* (" good luck "), either in full or in an abbreviated form, and are ornamented with filigree bosses. The variety which is decorated with scenes from the Old Testament is unfortunately not represented in the collection. The later examples of these rings are often of gilt bronze and show a very marked decline both in size and workmanship.

The most common type of love ring in use since the Middle Ages bears an amatory inscription, usually in rhyme, referred to variously as a " chançon," " reson," or " posy " (poesy, poetry).[1] Though these rings were widely used in the Middle Ages, they reached the period of their greatest popularity in the 16th and 17th centuries. Many of these rings are ordinary gem rings inscribed to suit an occasion, but the majority are plain gold or silver hoops obviously intended for inscriptions. The posies on mediaeval examples are mostly engraved on the outside of the hoop ; in later times they were usually inside. There can be little doubt that most of the 17th and 18th-century examples were used as wedding rings.

Though a certain number of the posies may have been the spontaneous efforts of the givers of the rings, there seems to have been a number of standard inscriptions which could be bought already engraved on the rings. This is clearly indicated in *As You Like It*,[2] where Jaques says to Orlando, " You are full of pretty answers ; have you not been acquainted with goldsmiths' wives, and conned them out of rings ? " In 1674 was published a small book entitled *Love's Garland, or Posies for Rings, Handkerchers, and Gloves and such like pretty Tokens that Lovers send their Loves.*

The type of love ring which has the longest history is the " fede " (for the Italian " *mani in fede* "), having a representation of two clasped hands. There are in the collection several Roman examples of these rings, which enjoyed an unbroken popularity till the 19th century.

[1] Compare Sir John Evans, *Posy-rings*, 1892. [2] Act III., scene 2.

A considerable number of mediaeval " fede " rings have magical inscriptions engraved on the hoop. A variety which was produced in great quantities in Italy during the 15th century is of nielloed silver with a circular bezel depicting a woman's head and a " fede " at the back of the hoop.

The gimmel ring has already been mentioned. The most common variety of this has a hand on each of the two interlacing or pivoted hoops, so that a " fede " is formed when the ring is closed. An example (No. 662) in the collection which is inscribed QVOD DEVS CONIVNVIT HOMO NON SEPARET must presumably have been used as a wedding ring. Later examples often have three or more hoops, and it is clear that the symbolism was not exactly observed. Rings with many hoops can only be classed as love rings when there is some positive evidence of such a use, for many examples were made merely as puzzles in the 16th and later centuries.

A very considerable number of types of love rings have been used besides those already mentioned, especially in the 16th and 17th centuries, but it is not possible to detail them here. The symbolism of the cupid or the heart requires no commentary, but it is perhaps necessary to remark that rings engraved with initials bound by a true-lover's knot must not be presumed to be love tokens. This knot became a mere decorative *motif* and was often used to bind the initials of the same individual.

RELIGIOUS AND MAGICAL RINGS

THE idea of the religious ring is very ancient—the earliest examples in this collection being Egyptian,—but it is proposed to exclude from this section all but Christian examples. At an early date the pagan practice of engraving rings with the emblems or representations of gods and heroes was imitated by the Christians.[1] The majority of these rings are signets and do not date before the 4th century. Most examples are of bronze or gold, silver rings being less common.

In an interesting passage Clement of Alexandria details some of the devices which he considered suitable for Christian rings. " But let our signet devices," he says, " be a dove or a fish, or a ship running before the wind, or a musical lyre, which Polycrates employed, or a ship's anchor,

[1] For Early Christian rings see C. Babington in Smith and Cheetham, pp. 712-22, 1792–1803 ; H. Leclercq in Cabrol, cols. 2191-2208 ; E. Drury Fortnum in *Arch. Journal*, xxvi. 1869, pp. 137-47, xxviii. 1871, pp. 278-91 ; Abbé Barraud in *Bulletin Monumental*, xxx. 1864, pp. 354-64.

which was the seal of Seleucus, or if it be a fisherman it will remind us of an Apostle and of boys saved from the water." Of these devices the dove (Nos. 204, 204*a*) and the ship (No. 205) are represented in this collection, as are also the lamb (No. 203) and the acclamation VIVAS IN DIO (No. 199).

It will be seen that the two principal divisions of religious rings can be traced back to the Early Christian period. The first consists of those engraved with religious emblems or representations of Our Lord, the Virgin, or Saints. The second comprises rings inscribed with acclamations, prayers, or quotations. Some examples, of course, possess the characteristics of both classes. Though much used by the Byzantines, the zenith of the popularity of the religious ring was probably reached in the 15th and 16th centuries, and most of the examples here catalogued are of this date.

The majority of the rings engraved with religious subjects in this collection belong to a class of very distinctive appearance and of English workmanship of the 15th and 16th centuries. The name " iconographic " has been applied to this particular type of ring, though it should properly refer to any ring bearing representations of religious personages. A few examples are of gilt bronze, a fair proportion are of gold, but the majority are of silver-gilt. Many were originally enamelled or had the engraving filled in with black, but usually few traces remain of either of these. The number of subjects depicted on these rings is comparatively small, but it comprises most of the saints who enjoyed popularity at this time.[1]

Many early decade rings have bezels engraved with figures of saints and belong to the class just described. These rings were formerly used in the same manner as a rosary. The name decade was applied to them because their hoops usually had ten knobs, with an eleventh larger one to form the bezel. An *Ave* was repeated as each of the smaller knobs was touched, and a *Pater Noster* at the bezel. The use of these rings appears to have begun about the 15th century and to have been continued down to the early 19th. It has been suggested that they may have been used especially in England, during the time when the penal laws were enforced, as they were more easily concealed than rosaries.[2] According to Barbier de Montault the popularity of these rings was increasing in the 19th century

[1] The following are typical subjects (those marked * being represented in the collection) : —Annunciation, *Virgin and Child, Crucifixion, *Pietà, Five Wounds, *Trinity, SS. *Anne, Anthony, *Barbara, *Christopher, George, *John the Baptist, *John the Evangelist, *Joseph (?), Margaret, Thomas Becket, and *the Magi.

[2] *Brit. Archaeol. Assoc.*, xiv. 1858, p. 271.

until checked in 1836, when the Sacred Penitentiary announced by order of Gregory XVI. that they could not receive the benediction and therefore could not communicate the indulgences accorded to rosaries.[1]

Though the symbolism of the skull and skeleton has been familiar since classical times, it remained for the popular religion of the later Middle Ages and Renaissance to emphasise the fact of human mortality in art and literature. The Memento Mori ring, bearing the emblems often accompanied by an admonitory inscription, was an expression of the sentiment of the time. A silver-gilt ring of 15th-century date in this collection (No. 718), having a bezel formed of two skulls and the hoop inscribed IOH'ES GODEFRAY, is an interesting and rather early example.

The 16th and 17th centuries saw a very much more extensive use of these rings on the Continent, and also in England, where most other types of religious rings fell into disuse after the Reformation. A number of examples were engraved as signets, but the majority bear merely the device in enamel, sometimes set with gems and accompanied by appropriate inscriptions.

As time progressed, the use of these rings as a warning to the wearer of his own approaching end seems to have become confused with the idea of them as memorials of the dead. At first, doubtless, the two ideas were combined, but by the close of the 17th century the presence of complete obituary inscriptions and a general uniformity of design prove that these last Memento Mori rings were no more and no less than mourning rings, as which they are here catalogued.

The use of rings as reliquaries is attested by a considerable amount of literary evidence both for the early and later Middle Ages, but there are no examples in this collection. St. Gregory of Nissa mentions in his life of his sister St. Macrina, that she wore a piece of the True Cross set in an iron ring suspended from her neck.[2] In 1378 Philippa, Countess of March, bequeathed to her son "a gold ring with a piece of the True Cross with this writing: *In nomine Patris et Filii et Spiritus Sancti*," and in 1427 Elizabeth, Lady Fitzhugh, left her son a ring containing a "relick of St. Peter's finger."[3]

In dealing with almost every type of mediaeval religious ring it is necessary not to overstress the devotional sentiments seemingly implied

[1] *Le costume et les usages ecclésiastiques*, 176-7.
[2] Migne, *Patrol. Graec.*, xlvi. 990.
[3] Nicolas, *Testamenta Vetusta*, 1826, pp. 137, 213.

in them. Popular thought drew no sharp distinctions between religion, natural science, and magic, and a similar confusion can be traced in the rings of the period. Some even of the rings engraved with the figures of saints were worn for reasons which according to modern ideas would be magical. St. Christopher, who is commonly depicted on rings, enjoyed an immense popularity during the 15th century from his supposed ability to give immunity from sudden death for the day to all who had looked at any representation of him.

It is with the inscribed rings that the confusion of religion and superstition is most apparent. It is unsafe to presume that any ring bearing a prayer, invocation, or biblical quotation was worn for a purely devotional purpose, as so many are known to have been regarded as charms against specific evils, the appeal for deliverance from which could not possibly be deduced from the text of the inscription. Thus a ring in this collection (No. 765) combines the last words of Our Lord on the Cross with some unintelligible words, the former being considered efficacious for quelling tempests, the latter probably being formulas for curing epilepsy and toothache.[1]

The transition from rings of a real or superficially religious complexion to those of an avowedly magical character is neither abrupt nor difficult and is justification for their inclusion under the same heading in this catalogue. The history of amuletic and magical rings is no less ancient than that of the religious. Whilst, however, the spread of Christianity imposed a new iconography for devotional rings, the charms and superstitions of the Ancient World formed to a great extent the core of those of the Middle Ages and Renaissance.

It is difficult nowadays to realise the extent to which superstitious beliefs affected the daily life of all classes from the Classical period down to the end of the Renaissance, when true scientific study began slowly to shatter popular beliefs, not by challenging the propriety of their use, but by exposing their inefficacy. The history and literature of magic is a study in itself, and it must suffice here to differentiate between some of the more important varieties of rings supposedly endowed with magical powers.

[1] It is interesting to note that St. Thomas Aquinas when questioned about the use of inscribed charms (*Utrum suspendere divina verba a collo sit illicitum* ?) decided that they were only permissible if no evil spirits were therein invoked, no incomprehensible words used, no deceit or belief in any other power than the power of God, no character used other than the sign of the Cross, and no faith placed in the manner of the inscription. See Thiers, *Traité des Superstitions*, 1704, i. 352, quoting from the *Quaestiones*.

Reference has already been made to a large class of rings to which a special efficacy was attributed through their inscriptions. The sources of these inscriptions are diverse. Some are thought to go back to the " words of power " of the Gnostics, others are prayers or invocations, sometimes reduced to an abbreviated form and often so altered by illiterate copying as to become almost unrecognisable. A certain number contain Greek and Hebrew words, whilst the derivations of a great many are now entirely beyond the realm even of conjecture.

Rings which owed their supposed efficacy to the material of which they were made form a large but ill-defined class. Though the results anticipated from their use were sometimes merely the cure or prevention of ordinary diseases, the border-line of magic is seldom very distant. The elaboration and completely fantastic foundation of some of these beliefs is perhaps best illustrated in the toadstone, which is one of the commonest charms found set in rings. Rounded and convex and of a brownish colour due to long burial, it is really the palatal tooth of the fossil ganoid fish called *Lepidotus*. As is indicated in the well-known quotation in *As You Like It*, it was supposed to be carried in the heads of toads—especially in those that were large and old. It was said that it would change colour and sweat when brought into contact with poisons, and was therefore sometimes set in drinking cups. It was also considered efficacious against kidney-disease, and in the protection of new-born infants. Two principal methods for obtaining the stone are usually mentioned. It might be cut from the head of the toad, or if the animal was placed on a red cloth it would throw it out of its mouth. An illustration of a man performing the former operation is given in a treatise of about 1490 entitled *Hortus Sanitatis*, whilst Anselm de Boot,[1] afterwards physician to the Emperor Rudolph II., records that he once attempted the second method in his youth without any success, despite the sacrifice of a whole night's rest. The method for testing the genuineness of the toadstone was to place it in front of a toad. If it was a genuine toadstone, the toad would attempt to snatch it up.[2]

The most remarkable feature of the story of the toadstone is that there is in fact no connection between the fossilised tooth and the toad. The belief in the toadstone was both of ancient origin and long endurance. It

[1] A. Boetius de Boot, *Gemmarum et Lapidum Historia*. Revised edition, Leyden, 1636, pp. 301-3.

[2] T. Lupton, *A Thousand Notable Things*, London, 1586. *Notes and Queries*, 4th Series, 1871, pp. 324, 399, 484, 540.

appears fairly completely in the *Kyranides*,[1] a work of Gnostic tendencies, probably written at Alexandria. Rings set with toadstones dating from the second half of the 17th century are not uncommon, and their use is recorded in the 18th century.

The use of toadstones in rings is paralleled by that of other curious objects for similar purposes. The medicinal and prophylactic powers of rings set with stone intaglios has been alluded to elsewhere, and it is only necessary to add that almost every variety of gem was supposed to be endowed with some special efficacy. Many ordinary gem rings in this collection were probably worn for superstitious purposes. Though the curative and protective powers of gems were discredited by a few early writers, the belief as a whole remained practically unchallenged till well into the 17th century. Even de Boot, whose scepticism with regard to the toadstone had been aroused by the experiment already related, was the author of a lapidary published in 1634, in which the effects attributed to stones are little less amazing than those detailed in earlier works.

Though sometimes written in the form of a medical treatise the mediaeval lapidary went far beyond mere curative lore. The sapphire would not only cure diseases of the eye but would prevent poverty, betrayal and wrongful conviction, and preserve the chastity of its wearer. The onyx gave protection from melancholy, fear and law-suits, and the turquoise from a fall from horseback.

One further type of prophylactic ring must be mentioned, although no extant examples are known. As early as the reign of Edward II. it seems to have become a custom for the coins given by the King on Good Friday at the offertory at Westminster Abbey to be fashioned into rings. After being hallowed by him at a special service, the rings were distributed as a protection against cramp.[2] The origin of this custom is obscure, but it is probable that it was in some way connected with the ring of Edward the Confessor, which was also supposed to have curative properties and was one of the principal relics of Westminster Abbey. The rings appear to have attained quite a European reputation, as Lord Bernars, when Ambassador to the Emperor Charles V., requested that some should be sent to him, as he knew recipients who would appreciate them. No details of

[1] Where the stone is recommended for curing dropsy and the spleen. See Evans, *Magical Jewels*, p. 19.

[2] Crawfurd, *The Blessing of Cramp Rings*, in *Studies in the History and Method of Science*, ed. C. Singer, 1917, p. 166. E. Waterton in *Arch. Journal*, xxi. 1864, p. 218.

these rings are recorded beyond that they were of both gold and silver. Their distribution was discontinued after the reign of Mary.

OFFICIAL RINGS

(1) Ecclesiastical

(a) *Episcopal*[1]

The ring conferred on a bishop at his consecration and worn by him as the emblem of his office appears to be the most ancient of the several varieties of ecclesiastical rings. The date when this ritualistic use of a ring became usual is not known, but it is probably significant that the Apostolic Constitutions make no mention of it, although they give a detailed account of the consecration of a bishop.

Rings had been in general use amongst the Christian community from the earliest times, and there is no reason to think that bishops ever abstained from their use. The position of a bishop naturally entailed much correspondence, and for this purpose a signet was almost a necessity. No details are available of the ring of Pope Caius (d. 296) which was found in his tomb in 1622,[2] but signet rings appear to have been in the possession of a number of early bishops, including Augustine, Bishop of Hippo[3] (d. 430), and Avitus, Bishop of Vienne[4] (d. 525). Clovis, King of the Franks, when writing to some bishops in 511, promises to give recognition to letters under their signet rings.

Positive evidence of the use of the true episcopal ring suddenly becomes plentiful at the end of the 6th and beginning of the 7th century. The Sacramentary of Pope Gregory the Great[5] (590–604) definitely prescribes the use of the ring and pastoral staff, whilst a decree of Pope Boniface IV. at the Third Council of Rome (610) refers to monks raised to the episcopate

[1] The principal authorities for this section are :—H. Leclercq, in Cabrol, col. 2181-2186 ; C. Babington, in Smith and Cheetham, pp. 1803-7 ; W. W. Watts, in *Transactions of the Scottish Ecclesiological Society*, vi. 1921, pp. 143-53 ; Francesco Cancellieri, *Notizie sopra l'origine e l'uso dell' Anello Pescatorio e degli altri anelli ecclesiastici*, Rome, 1823 ; O. Morgan, in *Archaeologia*, 1855, xxxvi. 392-9 ; and Kirchmann, *De Annulis*, ch. xx.

[2] Aringhi, *Roma Subterranea*, vol. ii. p. 426, and lib. iv. c. 48.

[3] Babington, in Smith and Cheetham, col. 1804.

[4] Migne, *Patrol. Lat.*, lix. 280-1.

[5] Muratori, *Liturg. Rom. Vet.*, ii. 442 (Venice, 1748).

with the phrase "monks sworn to the pontifical ring." At the Council of Toledo in 633 it was ordained in the 28th canon that a bishop who had been deposed and was subsequently found to be innocent, could only be reinstated by receiving once more his stole, ring, and staff. Isidore of Seville (d. 636), in his *Ecclesiastical Offices* (lib. ii. cap. 5), describes the episcopal ring as a "mark of the pontifical honour and for the signing of documents."

Pope Gregory IV. (827-844) decreed that the episcopal ring should be worn on the right hand, with which blessings are given, and not on the left, despite the popular belief that a vein flowed from the third finger of that hand direct to the heart.[1] As early as the time of Hincmar, Archbishop of Rheims (845-852), it was usual to wear the ring on the third finger of the right hand,[2] but it would seem that in the 16th [3] and 17th [4] centuries the first finger was also used. The reason for this is sometimes stated to be that this was the finger with which the sign of silence was given.

It is necessary to insist on the point that the episcopal ring is merely the ring used at the consecration ceremony, and is not of a type the purpose of which is apparent at a glance. The only definite regulation with regard to the form of the episcopal ring was made in the 7th century [5] by the Synod of Milan, which decreed that it should be of pure gold set with a gem that had not been engraved. Previous to this date, as is suggested by the words of Isidore of Seville already quoted, it is probable that signet rings had been so used. It seems that this regulation was observed fairly strictly. Rings set with antique intaglios have been found in this country in the graves of three mediaeval bishops, but it is extremely doubtful whether these were ever the actual "episcopal" rings, rather than rings added for burial; so that the only certain exceptions seem to be the rings of certain 19th-century English bishops.[6]

Though it is probable that several of the rings in this collection belonged

[1] *De Cultu Pontificum*, quoted by J. Martigny, *Dictionnaire des Antiquités chrétiennes*, 1865, p. 60.

[2] Migne, *Patrol. Lat.*, cxxvi. col. 188.

[3] J. E. Duranti (d. 1589), *De ritibus Ecclesiae Catholicae*. In the portrait of Stephen Gardiner, Bishop of Winchester (d. 1556), at Trinity Hall, Cambridge, a ring set with a sapphire is shown on the first finger of the right hand. As this is the only ring shown, it may perhaps be the episcopal ring.

[4] Georgius Longus, *Tractatus de Annulis Signatoriis*, Leyden, 1672, p. 41.

[5] But perhaps recorded in words only at a later date (H. Leclercq, in Cabrol, col. 2185).

[6] Another possible exception is the ring of Bishop Bitton (d. 1307) found in his grave at Exeter Cathedral. It is of gold set with a sapphire engraved with a hand in benediction.

to bishops, it is not possible to claim any of them definitely as episcopal, seeing that not even the rings found in the graves of bishops can safely be so regarded. It is difficult, for instance, to regard so paltry a ring as that found in the grave of Lawrence Booth, Archbishop of York (d. 1480), at Southwell Minster, as one that could have been used at a consecration. It seems, moreover, to have become an established custom in England for the ring of a deceased bishop—presumably his consecration ring—to be handed over to the royal treasury. The same usage seems to have obtained in Germany before the Emperors were defeated in the Investiture Contest,[1] and perhaps in France.[2] An inventory of the year 28 Edward I.[3] shows the rings of three archbishops, five bishops and three abbots in the royal treasury. Similar instances can be traced at later dates, but it would rather seem that either the king's right was not always enforced, or else that he was content with some other ring of equal value, for the majority of the rings found in the graves of English bishops agree closely with those described in the Edwardian Inventory and are remarkably uniform in essentials, though each example follows stylistically the contemporary patterns for gem rings.[4]

[1] Kirchmann, *De Annulis*, p. 183, quoting from the Life of St. Otto, Bishop of Bamberg, gives instances of the return to the Emperor Henry IV. of the rings and pastoral staves of the bishops of Bremen and Bamberg.

[2] A number of " anneaulx pontificaulx à prélats " are mentioned in an inventory of Charles V. of France (J. Labarte, *Inventaire . . . de Charles V.*, p. 136) and have been presumed to be relics of a similar usage. The descriptions of the rings show them to have been set with a large variety of stones, one with a cameo, and in default of other evidence it would seem safer to treat these as " pontificals " and not consecration rings.

[3] *Liber Quotidianus Contrarotularius Garderobiae anno regni regis Edwardi I. vicesimo octavo*, published by the Society of Antiquaries of London, 1787, pp. 343-8.

[4] The following is a fairly complete list of extant examples of the rings found in the graves of English mediaeval bishops, excluding only those detailed above, which do not fulfil the injunctions of the Synod of Milan.

Gold, set with an unengraved sapphire :—

Bishop Ralph Flambard, d. 1128. Found in the Chapter-house, Durham.
Bishop Geoffrey Rufus, d. 1140. Chapter-house, Durham.
Bishop William de St. Barbara, d. 1152. Chapter-house, Durham.
Archbishop Wytlesey, d. 1374. Canterbury Cathedral.
Bishop William of Wykeham, d. 1404. Winchester Cathedral.
Bishop John Stanbery, d. 1474. Hereford Cathedral.
Unknown bishop. Chichester Cathedral.

Gold, set with an unengraved ruby :—

Archbishop Sewell, d. 1258. York Minster.
Archbishop Greenfield, d. 1315. York Minster.
Bishop Richard Mayo, d. 1516. Hereford Cathedral.
Unknown bishop, 13th century. St. Davids.

The evidence as regards England certainly appears to suggest that the sapphire and the ruby were the normal stones for episcopal rings, if we can accept the rings mentioned in the note on p. 30 as such. A number of foreign examples which are regarded as the episcopal rings of certain bishops seem on the whole to confirm these results,[1] though abroad the material for consideration is still more scanty than in this country.

Even before the Reformation English bishops do not appear to have worn their episcopal rings habitually. In the portrait of Archbishop Warham (d. 1532), in the National Portrait Gallery (2094), no ring at all appears, whilst in that of Archbishop Cranmer (d. 1556), in the same collection, only a signet ring set with a foiled crystal is shown. It is hardly necessary to say that this tendency was accentuated during the 17th and 18th centuries.

Before leaving the subject of episcopal rings it is necessary to allude to the class of " pontificals," which must not be confused with them. The pontifical ring is used by bishops and certain other privileged ecclesiastics at High Mass, and as it is worn over a glove it is of especially large size.

Gold, set with an unengraved sapphire with four small emeralds at the angles :—
Unknown bishop. Chichester Cathedral.
Gold, set with an unengraved amethyst :—
Bishop Richard of Carew, d. 1280. St. Davids.

The ring found in the grave of St. Cuthbert in 1537 and preserved at Ushaw College, Durham, is of gold set with a sapphire ; it does not appear to be contemporary with the Saint, but several centuries later.

In the Edwardian Inventory the rings of the archbishops of Dublin and York and of the bishops of St. Asaph and Salisbury are each set with a single sapphire, those of the archbishop of Canterbury, and the bishops of Bath and Wells, and Exeter, with rubies, and that of the bishop of Coventry and Lichfield with a single ruby. In addition, among the jewels captured with Piers Gaveston (d. 1312) was the ring of a bishop of Bath and Wells, which was set with a sapphire (T. Rymer, *Foedera*, 1706, iii. 389).

[1] See, for instance, the collection of rings from the graves of bishops in the cathedral treasury at Troyes. Among them are two gold rings each set with a sapphire, found in the graves of Bishop Manassé (d. 1190) and Bishop Hervée (d. 1223) ; whilst a gold ring set with a ruby was found in the grave of Bishop Nicolas de Brie (d. 1269).

The rings found in the graves of Bishops D'Arci (d. 1395) and Malier de Houssay (d. 1678) were respectively of gilt copper set with a paste and of silver-gilt set with a crystal, and cannot be regarded as possible episcopal rings. In the cathedral treasury at Sens is the " Bague de St. Loup " (d. 623), of gold set with a sapphire, but the rings found in the graves of Archbishops Gilan I. Cornu (d. 1254), Pierre de Charny (d. 1274), and Guillaume de Melun (d. 1336), were of copper-gilt or silver-gilt set with crystals, and therefore too unimportant for consecration rings. The ring of Archbishop Absalom (d. 1201) at Soro, Denmark, is of gold set with a sapphire ; and the ring said to have been found in the grave of an archbishop at Mainz is of gold set with a ruby surrounded by small stones. The ring found in the grave of Giraldus, Bishop of Limoges (d. 1022), at Charroux (Vienne) is of gold, but without any stone.

A mediaeval bishop appears usually to have had several " pontificals," whilst certain cathedrals seem to have had such rings amongst their treasure. It would appear that the Archbishop of Canterbury had a right to the second-best pontifical of all deceased bishops of his province.[1] The essential characteristics of the " pontifical " appear to have been exceptional size and magnificence. One left by Archbishop Reynolds (d. 1327) to Canterbury Cathedral was set with rubies and a large oblong emerald between twelve smaller gems,[2] whilst that bequeathed by William of Wykeham (d. 1404) to his successor and described as his larger pontifical, was set with a sapphire surrounded by balas rubies, two small diamonds and eleven pearls.[3] The collection of Pope Paul II. (d. 1471) contained seven " pontificals," all set with a large variety of mixed stones.[4] Pontificals set with single stones appear in inventories,[5] but it would seem that the use of varied stones was usual.

(b) *Abbots and Abbesses*

The use of an official ring by abbots appears to have been of comparatively late introduction and was supposed to be the result of a special papal concession. This usage was of course imitated from the episcopal and appears to have aroused considerable jealousy amongst bishops in early days. A letter of Pope Innocent III.[6] (1198-1216) makes mention of an abbatial ring, but still as a special privilege. Mention of the benediction of abbots' rings does not occur in rituals till the 15th century. According to the rule of Popes Clement VIII. and Urban VIII. the abbatial ring was worn on the third finger of the right hand.[7]

The ring discovered in the grave of Henry of Worcester, Abbot of Evesham (d. 1263), was of gold set with an amethyst.[8] It would appear that the custom of surrendering the ring of a dead bishop to the royal

[1] *Arch. Journal*, xi. 274.

[2] Woodruff and Danks, *Memorials of Canterbury Cathedral*, p. 142.

[3] N. H. Nicolas, *Testamenta Vetusta*, ii. 767.

[4] E. Müntz, *Les arts à la cour des papes*, ii. 187-8.

[5] An "Account of Church Plate, etc., delivered to King Henry VIII.," quoted in *Memoirs of the Antiquities of Great Britain, relating to the Reformation*, 1723, refers to " a Pontifical of Golde, wherein is set a Great Sapphire . . . from Winchester," and to " two Rings of Golde with two Sapphires Therein set . . . from the Cathedral of Lincoln."

[6] H. Leclercq, in Cabrol, col. 2187.

[7] W. W. Watts, *op. cit.*, p. 148.

[8] *Archaeologia*, 1824, xx. 566-8.

treasury applied to certain abbots also, as the rings of three abbots are found in the inventory of 28 Edward I. The ring of the abbot of Abingdon was of gold set with a topaz, those of the abbots of St. Albans and Glastonbury are merely described as of gold. The ring of the abbot of Abingdon taken with Piers Gaveston was of gold set with a sapphire.[1]

Abbesses appear to have assumed an official ring late in the Middle Ages, but the practice was prohibited by Gregory XIII. in 1572.[2] Rings depicted on the hands of abbesses must not be presumed to be worn because of their office, as it had been a custom from a remote period for Christian virgins and nuns to take a ring on making their profession.[3] Such rings were regarded as symbols of a betrothal to Christ.

(c) *The Ring of the Fisherman* [4]

The Ring of the Fisherman (*Anulus Piscatoris*), which has become the investiture ring of the Pope, is so called from the representation engraved on the bezel of St. Peter in a ship letting down a net into the sea ; above is the name and title of the Pope. Though the date of its adoption is not known, it is clear that it cannot claim as great antiquity as the episcopal ring. The earliest mention of it is in a letter dated 1265 from Pope Clement IV. to his nephew Pierre Grossi de St. Gilles, in which he says, " Greet my mother and brothers ; we do not write to you or to your familiars under the Bull, but under the Seal of the Fisherman, which the Roman Pontiffs use for their private letters." [5] It is clear, therefore, that by the middle of the 13th century the ring was well established and that its use was then confined to one particular purpose. By the beginning of the 15th century this restriction appears to have fallen into disuse, for in 1417 Pope Martin V. is found issuing briefs under the Fisherman's Ring. In a confirmation of some capitulations relating to the commune of Todi, dated 1448, the ring is still called the Pope's private seal, though attached to an official document and used by a papal secretary of Nicholas V. From

[1] T. Rymer, *Foedera*, 1706, iii. 389.

[2] H. Leclercq, in Cabrol, col. 2187.

[3] St. Ambrose in a sermon on St. Agnes has been taken to imply that the custom was known in his day. He says : *Hinc est quod anulo fidei Agnes se asserit subarrhatam* (Sermon XLVIII., in Migne, *Patrol. Lat.*, xvii. col. 701).

[4] The principal authorities for this section are E. Waterton, in *Archaeologia*, 1856, xl. 136, and Cancellieri (*see* Bibliography).

[5] Platina, *De Vitis Pontificum*.

the reign of Pope Calixtus III. it would seem that the use of the ring was confined to the sealing of briefs. When Pope Innocent XI. reduced the number of Apostolic Secretaries from twenty-four to two, one was called Secretary of Briefs Apostolic and given the use of the Ring of the Fisherman, the other, the Secretary of Briefs ad Reges et Principes, using a seal bearing the Pope's arms. Actually an iron stamping die, which gives an impression in ink, is used to seal all briefs "*sub anulo piscatoris.*"

After the official recognition of the death of a Pope the Ring of the Fisherman with the other papal seals is given into the custody of the Cardinal Chamberlain. At the first public meeting of the cardinals the ring and seals are broken. This ceremony can be traced back as far as the death of Pius IV. in 1565 and has been observed since except on the occasion of the death of Pope Pius VI. at Valence in 1799, when the ring was merely re-engraved with the name of Pius VII. In 1809 Pius VII. was forcibly deprived of the Ring of the Fisherman by the French general Radet, who held him prisoner. Before surrender the ring was mutilated, so that although it was afterwards restored to the Pope by Louis XVIII., a new one had to be engraved. A temporary iron seal was used in the meanwhile.

Before the conclave for the election of a Pope a new *Anulus Piscatoris* is prepared with the space for the name of the Pope left blank. After the election the Cardinal Chamberlain places the ring on the Pope's finger and enquires what name he will take. The Pope replies, and gives the ring to the master of the ceremonies to have the name engraved.

Nothing is known of the circumstances under which the Ring of the Fisherman in the Museum (No. 781) came into existence. It is probable that it was prepared for a conclave and accidentally mislaid. It can hardly be dated earlier than the second half of the 18th, and might perhaps belong to the first quarter of the 19th century.

(d) *Cardinals' Rings* [1]

The earliest mention of the ring which is given by the Pope to a new cardinal at the conclave at which he is appointed occurs in the Ordo Romanus XIV., dated about 1300 and attributed to Cardinal Jacopo Gaetani, nephew of Boniface VIII. A considerable number of references to cardinalitial rings have been found in 14th-century records, but none of these

[1] The principal authority for this section is Cancellieri (*see* Bibliography).

seems to give any indication of their appearance or the stones with which they were set. According to Müntz, who has found amongst the accounts of Pope Eugenius IV. the payments for the stones set in the rings of the cardinals created in 1439, the use of a sapphire appears general.[1] The value of the stone varied considerably, probably according to the importance of the recipient or the esteem in which he was held by the Pope. Cardinal Alberto degli Alberti received a ring which was set with a sapphire worth only twelve florins ; Cardinal Giovanni Tagliacozzi, Archbishop of Taranto, received one with a sapphire worth fourteen florins ; but some others received rings set with stones worth eighteen or twenty florins. In more modern times the cardinalitial ring has usually been set with a sapphire and the inner side of the bezel is decorated with the arms of the reigning Pope. The hinged hoop of the example in the Museum (No. 782) is exceptional.

Though the cardinalitial ring is a gift from the Pope, the new cardinal has to pay a heavy fine in return for receiving the right of making a will and several other minor privileges. The fines were originally paid to the Camera Apostolica, but in 1555 Pope Paul IV. gave this source of income to the Arch-confraternity of St. Anne at Rome, since when it has been transferred at different times to various religious institutions, but since 1622 it has been held by the College de Propaganda Fide. In sign of mourning, cardinals do not wear their rings on Good Friday.

(e) *Rings of Lesser Ecclesiastical Dignitaries*[2]

A constitution of Pope Innocent III. at the Council of the Lateran prescribes that no priest shall wear a ring except those whose dignity entitles them to it, and that such should wear only one ring. Certain dignitaries, such as protonotaries apostolic and doctors, are permitted the use of a ring which must, however, be set aside when celebrating mass.[3] Certain cathedral chapters, especially in Southern Italy, have the privilege of using " pontificals " when celebrating, but though a decision of the Congregation of Rites in 1663 permitted canons the use of a plain gold ring, this right was annulled in the 18th century.

[1] E. Müntz, *Les arts à la cour des papes*, i. 154 ; but he does not quote his authority nor indicate whether the sapphires may have been mixed with other stones.

[2] See Barbier de Montault, *Le Costume et les Usages Ecclésiastiques selon la Tradition Romaine*, i. 163-74 ; Waterton MS., pp. 189-90.

[3] Protonotaries may use a " pontifical " instead when celebrating.

Though the wearing of rings by the ordinary priesthood was forbidden, and often sternly inveighed against, the rule appears to have been very scantily observed till a comparatively late date. A 16th-century silver signet ring in this collection, probably of French workmanship, is inscribed S. EGIDII SACERDOTIS, and references to priests' rings may be found in mediaeval English records. Thus, the Bishop of Chester had the right to the best horse, saddle, bridle, bit and spurs, the best signet or other ring of every priest who died in the archdeaconry of Chester.[1] In the will of Martin de Sancta Cruce, dated 1259, bequests of rings were made not only to certain bishops, but also to the dean and canons of York and the Vicar of Auckland.[2]

Like nuns, widows appear often to have received a ring if they took a vow of perpetual chastity, the symbolic meaning of the ring being the same.[3] A testator who wished to safeguard the interests of his children against loss arising from the re-marriage of their mother sometimes made the extent of his bequests to his widow dependent on whether she was prepared to take the ring and mantle of a vowess or not.[4]

(2) SECULAR

Investiture by the ring was by no means confined in the Middle Ages to ecclesiastics, but is found likewise in connection with secular offices. The ring seems to have been a usual feature in the coronation service of most European princes. The Emperor was invested with a ring as King of Germany, and when Henry IV. was deposed he was bidden to surrender the crown, ring, mantle, and the other things pertaining to the imperial dignity.[5] The ring appears equally in the coronations of kings of France. When Henry III. of England accepted from the Pope the crown of Sicily for his son Edmund, the Bishop of Bologna was sent to invest him and conferred upon him a ring.[6]

[1] *Arch. Journal*, 1854, ix. 273.

[2] Surtees Society, *Wills and Inventories*, 1835, p. 7.

[3] Lady Alice West, in her will dated 1395, left to her son " a ring wherwith I was yspoused to God " (H. Nicolas, *Testamenta Vetusta*, p. 137).

[4] Sir Gilbert Denys, Knight, of Syston, in a will dated 1422, devises as follows : " If Margaret my wife will after my death vow a vow of chastity, I give her all my movable goods, she paying my debts and providing for my children, and if she will not vow a vow of chastity, I desire that my goods may be distributed or divided into three equal parts." Quoted by Henry Harrod, *On the Mantle and Ring of Widowhood*, *Archaeologia*, xl., 1866, p. 308.

[5] Kirchmann, *De Annulis*, 196-7.

[6] Matthew Paris, *Chronica Majora*, Rolls Series, v. 515.

In England the coronation ring appears in the Benedictional of Robert of Jumièges, Archbishop of Canterbury in the time of Edward the Confessor, but it is not mentioned amongst the " ornamenta " in the coronation service of the Pontifical of Egbert, Archbishop of York (d. 766).[1] Accurate descriptions of early coronation rings do not appear to exist, but the ring intended by Richard II. for the coronation of his successors was of gold set with a ruby. The same stone was used in the rings of Charles II. and James II. The ring of Mary II. is set with a ruby between two diamonds, that of Charles I. has the same stone surrounded by diamonds. The rings of William IV. and Queen Victoria were set with a sapphire surmounted by a ruby cross and surrounded by diamonds. It has also been the custom for some time past for queens-consort to be invested with rings. The investiture of the Prince of Wales with a ring can be traced back to the grant of the title to the Black Prince in 1343,[2] and a similar custom seems also to have been used in connection with certain foreign princes.

It is not possible to detail the numerous investiture ceremonies in which a ring was used, but it is worthy of note that it seems to have been used at admissions to the doctorate at all mediaeval universities.[3] Its use at Oxford survived as late as 1669,[4] and it is said to have continued in use at Coimbra and Upsala, and to have been revived at Louvain.

COMMEMORATIVE RINGS

THE usages and sentiments connected with the commemorative rings in this collection show considerable variety. If mourning rings be excluded, it will be found that political rather than personal sentiments seem to be expressed in most of the examples. Though some of the wearers were probably friends of the persons depicted on their rings, in general no more is implied than loyalty to some political hero, or to his memory. The list of the personages thus celebrated in the collection is enough to show how widespread this practice had become in the 17th and 18th centuries.

During the same period a considerable number of rings were set with portrait miniatures of private persons, who unfortunately now often remain

[1] J. Wickham Legg, *Arch. Journal*, 1897, liv. 1-9.
[2] Selden, *Titles of Honor*, 1672, p. 495.
[3] Rashdell, *Universities of Europe in the Middle Ages*, i. 231, 289.
[4] Diary of John Evelyn, June 10, 1669.

unidentifiable. Amongst the non-political rings will be found an example (No. 794) presented to a guest at the wedding of Frederick Duke of York in 1791. The custom can be traced as early as the time of Sir Edward Killey, a friend of the celebrated Elizabethan astrologist Dr. Dee. He is said to have presented four thousand pounds' worth of gold rings at the marriage of one of his maid-servants.[1] The custom appears never to have become general, like the distributing of mourning rings, and it probably ended in this country with presentations made at the marriage of Queen Victoria.

MOURNING RINGS

THE development of a separate class of mourning rings had its origin in the natural desire to bequeath to friends and relations some small object which would serve as a personal memorial. This practice can be traced well back into the Middle Ages, and as long as the list of destined recipients was carefully restricted it was possible to fulfil the testator's wishes with the rings which had been his personal property. Such rings, however, even as in the example (No. 938) inscribed with the date of the death of the deceased, though by use they have become mourning rings, must obviously for our purposes be treated as belonging to the classes to which their original purpose intended them.

The desire to bequeath these memorials to a larger number of persons and to avoid the discrimination involved in the distribution amongst them of rings of different values, gave rise to the practice of leaving injunctions in the will for the purchase of rings of some specified type or value. The earliest known instance of this custom appears in the will,[2] dated 1487, of Sir John Shaw, Alderman of the City of London, who directed that gold rings engraved with the Five Wounds of Our Lord should be given to sixteen of his friends. It will be noted that these rings belonged to the ordinary " iconographic " class and were not specially designed for memorial purposes. Similar bequests occur in other wills of the 16th and first half of the 17th century, but no distinct form of mourning ring appears to have been evolved, although a general preference seems to have been shown for the " memento mori " type. Although some of the " memento mori " rings of this period bear names and initials, there is usually

[1] Recorded by Anthony Wood and quoted in Jones, *Finger-ring Lore*, p. 296.
[2] *Notes and Queries*, 3rd Series, iii. 1863, pp. 328, 416, 460, 516.

nothing about them, such as the age and date of death, which makes it possible definitely to distinguish them from rings worn with a purely religious motive. A late 15th-century ring of silver-gilt, bearing the name IOH'ES GODEFRAY (No. 718), may be cited as an example.

By the second half of the 17th century bequests of rings had ceased to be tokens of special friendship and had become hardly more than a fee which all acquaintances and most of those who attended the funeral might expect. Thus, at the funeral of John Evelyn's daughter (d. 1685) 60 rings [1] were given away, at that of Samuel Pepys (d. 1709), 123,[2] at that of Dr. Thomas Gale, Dean of York (d. 1702), 200. The wealth and ostentation of the testator was indicated by the number of rings bequeathed, and not usually by their intrinsic value. Money for the purchase of expensive rings was left only by those who restricted their lists to a few friends.[3] What are described as "fashionable" rings [4] costing one guinea are frequently mentioned in wills. Fashion, indeed, played a great part in the trade of supplying mourning rings, and it is not difficult to make out a regular sequence of types with the aid of a collection such as that here catalogued. It may be observed that, though not quite unknown on the Continent, the custom of giving mourning rings was practically confined to the English-speaking peoples.

The earliest definite type of mourning ring was in use from the reign of Charles II. till about 1720. It consisted of a hoop engraved inside with the name and date of death of the deceased, and decorated outside with foliage or a skeleton reserved in the metal on a ground of black enamel. The bezel was of oval or circular form set with a crystal covering either the representation of a skull or else the initials of the deceased worked in gold thread on a ground of plaited hair or coloured silk.[5] As the middle of the 18th century

[1] Diary of John Evelyn, March 16, 1685.

[2] *Memorial Rings, Charles II. to William IV., in the possession of F. A. Crisp*, 1908, p. 2.

[3] Extract from the will of George Washington: "To my sisters-in-law Hannah Washington and Mildred Washington, to my friends Eleanor Stuart, Hannah Washington of Fairfield and Elizabeth Washington of Hayfield, I give each a mourning ring of the value of one hundred dollars. These bequests are not made for the intrinsic value of them, but as mementoes of my esteem and regard" (C. Edwards, *History and Poetry of Finger-rings*, New York, 1855, p. 222).

[4] F. A. Crisp, *op. cit.*, p. 169. Extract from the will of Sir Samuel Prime (d. 1777): "I recommend it to my son to consider of delivering fashionable Mourning Rings of the Value of one Guinea each unto every such person as I shall mention or describe in a list of Names for his better attention in that behalf."

[5] Some other 16th and 17th-century mourning rings bore inscriptions chosen by the testator with or without his initials. Thus Sir T. Beaumont (d. 1507) left to each of his

was approached, bezels became rarer and the inscription was transferred from the interior to the exterior of the hoop, where it was reserved in the metal on an enamelled ground. The hoop was either quite plain, with slightly waved outline, or divided into small scrolled compartments each bearing part of the inscription. A popular convention prescribed that those who died unmarried should be commemorated with rings enamelled white, whilst the rings of those who had been married should be decorated with black enamel. An exception may be noted in the ring (No. 812) commemorating Rachel Brain, died 1746, aged 3, which is black, but it is possible that this may be merely a jeweller's error.

Towards 1770 a new design, more in keeping with the sentimentalism of the time, made its appearance. The hoop was of plain gold, spreading towards a large pointed oval bezel set with a crystal covering a painting. The subject depicted usually comprised a weeping figure standing beside an urn bearing a lugubrious inscription and overshadowed by a willow-tree. In many cases the design was wholly or partially executed with the hair of the deceased, whose name, age, and date of death were inscribed on the back of the bezel. Concurrent with this type, which lasted down to the end of the century, was another, in which the hoop was formed of several strands of gold wire joined at the back and spreading towards the bezel, the latter having single or double border of seed pearls, or jet, surrounding a crystal which covered some plaited hair of the deceased.

After 1800 less uniformity is apparent, but the use of black-and-white enamel became more common. The mourning ring (No. 909) for Captain James Newman Newman, R.N., lost at sea in 1811, is an interesting example, showing more genuine sentiment than usual; it has on the bezel a Union flag surrounded by the serpent representing the engulfing ocean. The early 19th century saw a very general decline in the output of this type of memorial, which hardly survived into Victorian times. This change appears to be due to an alteration in the sentiment towards death, rather than to a reaction against excess, for extravagant expenditure on the

six nephews and nieces " a hope of golde to the value of 20s. with this scripture to be made within everyche of the same hoopes 'Ye shall pray for Sir Thomas Beamonde'" (*Somerset Mediaeval Wills*, 1501-30, p. 112). Sir Henry Wotton (d. 1637) left to each Fellow of Eton " a plain gold ring enamelled black, all save the verge, with this motto within, *Amor unit omnia*." Speaker Lenthall (d. 1682) bequeathed 50 gold rings inscribed *Oritur non Moritur*. Isaak Walton (d. 1683) left rings bearing " A friend's farewell. I. W. obiit," " Love my Memory. I. W. obiit," " A mite for a million. I. W. obiit." (Jones, *Finger-ring Lore*, pp. 357, 359, 360.)

memorials does not seem to have been at any time greater than in the early days of mourning rings.

SERJEANTS' RINGS [1]

From the first half of the 15th century it appears to have been the custom for all those called to the dignity of Serjeant-at-Law to present rings of gold to the King, Princes of the Blood, the chief lords spiritual and temporal, and certain officials.[2] Though the rings varied in value according to the rank of the recipient, the total cost was always considerable. Sir John Fortescue expended £50 on his call in 1429, Sir John Wynne with thirteen others shared £773 for 1409 rings in 1776, whilst Mr. Peckwell and Mr. Frere paid £53, 19s. 6d. for 60 rings in 1809. At a call in 1559, King Philip and Queen Mary received rings costing £3, 6s. 8d., the Lord Chancellor and other high officials £1, the judges and Barons of the Exchequer 16s., and so down to the filacers whose rings were worth 2s. 6d. The rings were all plain hoops inscribed with an appropriate motto varied at each call, the earliest known being "*suae quisquis fortunae faber*" in 1485. The motto on the single example in the collection, "*Rex legis tutamen,*" was used in 1669 (No. 916). Occasionally individual serjeants seem to have used separate mottoes on their rings. The presentation of rings continued until the Judicature Law of 1875 made it unnecessary for new judges first to become serjeants; but even before that date several judges had refused to accept rings from those newly appointed.

"PAPAL" RINGS

The class of so-called "Papal" rings presents a problem which has so far remained unsolved. This name is applied to a very distinct group of rings bearing the names or insignia of popes, cardinals, bishops, and secular princes. They are characterised by their extreme massiveness [3] and small intrinsic worth, as they are made of gilt copper or bronze and are set with glass pastes, crystals, or stones of very little value.

[1] The authorities for this section are *Notes and Queries*, 1st Series, v. 1852, pp. 110, 564; 6th Series, x. 1884, pp. 29, 132; Jones, *Finger-ring Lore*, pp. 186-90; Society of the Inner Temple, *Catalogue of the Paintings, Engravings and Serjeants' Rings*, 1915.

[2] This custom finds an interesting parallel in a practice which obtained at the University of Bologna, where each candidate on becoming a doctor presented a ring to the Prior of the Doctorial College (Rashdell, *Universities of Europe in the Middle Ages*, i. 231).

[3] An example (No. 922) in the collection weighs over thirteen ounces troy.

A very considerable number of these rings remain scattered all over Europe, but though they can be traced back in inventories to the period of their manufacture [1] no record has been discovered which indicates the manner of their use. The great majority of them can be safely dated within the 15th century; the papal arms seemingly refer to the popes from Martin V. (1416-31) to Innocent VIII. (1484-91), and the secular monarchs referred to appear also to belong to much the same period.[2] The bishops and cardinals are less easily identified, as most of the arms on the rings are those of important families which have produced more than one high ecclesiastical dignitary.

A number of conjectures have been made to explain the existence of these rings. The only thing which can be regarded as certain is that such clumsy and tawdry objects cannot have been worn by the important personages whose arms they bear. Even if such a use were credible, a further difficulty arises from the fact that several identical examples exist of some of these rings, especially those of Pius II. and Paul II. A few of the more popular theories are perhaps worth mentioning, though not one of them can be said even to suggest a probable use for these rings. It has been said that they were rings of investiture given at the transference of fiefs or dignities. No evidence has been adduced that such usages were known at this period with regard to secular fiefs, whilst, as has been shown, the rings given with the higher ecclesiastical dignities were very different. The presence of the arms of both a king and a pope on the same ring adds another difficulty, but if indeed these rings were given as badges of office it would seem wise to search amongst the minor rather than the major dignities.

It has been suggested that the rings were given as credentials to an envoy sent by a pope to a king (hence the two coats-of-arms), but a ring of more intrinsic worth and convenient proportions might be expected to be used for such a purpose. The weight and form of these rings are often so abnormal that they could hardly have been worn on the finger except as a

[1] One is mentioned in an inventory of the year 1494 of the Este family: *Un annello di ottone dorato cum vedro rosso quadro grande ligato dentro cum le mitra et chiave et quatro Evangelisti dintorno tagliati* (G. Campori, *Raccolta di Cataloghi ed Inventarii inediti*, Modena, 1870, p. 27).

[2] Out of about ninety examples of "Papal" rings known to the writer, probably only two belong to a period earlier than the 15th century. One, in the British Museum (Dalton, 1690), has been dated stylistically to the 14th (the attribution to Robert the Wise of Naples is entirely conjectural), the other, which is published in the *Arch. Journal*, iii. 269, bears the inscription ROGERIVS REX and has been connected with Roger II. of Sicily (1130-54).

formality at some brief ceremony. If they were indeed badges or credentials, then it may be supposed that they were worn suspended from the neck on a cord. A theory which attempts to explain the proportions and cheap gorgeousness of this type suggests that they may have been symbolic gifts to sacred images. The gift of a ring of real value might invite burglary whilst one of gilt bronze might be used to represent a more substantial gift too precious to be recklessly exposed.

FANCY RINGS

THE rings included in this section fall into two distinct groups. The first consists of rings the primary use of which was decorative, but which are of such unusual shapes and sizes that they would seem out of place elsewhere.[1] The second group consists of rings having other than decorative uses, but of such diverse sorts as to defy any closer classification.

Fancy rings of both groups were well known in Classical times and are represented by several examples of Roman date in this collection. The 16th century ushered in a fresh period of popularity, which continued through the 17th and 18th centuries.

It may be remarked that the utility of many of the rings in the second group must have been more imaginary than real. The armillary sphere (No. 943) and the dial ring (No. 942) can have been of little practical use. In others the non-annular use is predominant. The tobacco-stopper (Nos. 949-951) and pugilists' rings (Nos. 952, 955) might be excellent for their respective purposes, but ill-suited for ordinary wear. It is not, unfortunately, possible to pronounce the ring with a locket-bezel (No. 946) a poison-ring, as it may well have been used to contain a perfume.

[1] Some of the larger rings must have had some ceremonial use, but there is no indication of what sort.

CATALOGUE

PART I.—CLASSICAL RINGS

A. *ANCIENT EGYPTIAN*

1. SILVER; revolving oval bezel set with a steatite scarab engraved with a symmetrical scroll device; tapering hoop.
XIth to XVIth Dynasty.[1] *Plate I.*
(Waterton Colln.) 411–1871.

2. GOLD; revolving oval bezel set with a plain scarab of lapis-lazuli; the shoulders bound with wire.
XIth to XVIth Dynasty.
(Waterton Colln.) 410–1871.

3. GOLD; revolving oval bezel set with a glazed steatite scarab (illegible inscription); thick tapering hoop, the shoulders bound with wire.
XIth to XVIth Dynasty. *Plate I.*
(Waterton Colln.) 407–1871.

4. BLUE-GLAZE; oval bezel moulded with an oryx antelope (?).[2]
Late XVIIIth Dynasty (reign of Khu-en-Aten).
(Waterton Colln.) 405–1871.

4*a*. BLUE-GLAZE; oval bezel moulded with a spray of lotus.
Late XVIIIth Dynasty. 2245–1900.

4*b*. BLUE-GLAZE; with applied figure of Ta-urt, the Hippopotamus Goddess.
Late XVIIIth Dynasty. 2042*j*–1877.

[1] The Middle Kingdom of Ancient Egypt, covering the XIth to the XVIth Dynasties, is variously computed to have extended from the 30th to the 18th, or the 22nd to the 16th century B.C. The XVIIIth Dynasty, similarly, lasted from the 17th to the 15th, or from the 16th to the 14th century.

[2] The glazed-ware rings were probably intended for funerary use only, and not for ordinary wear.

5. PURPLE-GLAZE; oval bezel inscribed NEB-KHEPERU-RĀ (the throne name of Tut-ankh-amen), between uraei, and, below, AMEN-RĀ.
Late XVIIIth Dynasty. *Plate I.*
(Waterton Colln.) 402–1871.

Ironmongers' Hall Exhibition, 1861, ii. 490.

5*a*. UNGLAZED WHITE EARTHENWARE; rounded oblong bezel merging into hoop. C. 776–1923.

6. RED-GLAZE; oval bezel inscribed NEB-KHEPERU-RĀ (the throne name of Tut-ankh-amen).
Late XVIIIth Dynasty.
(Waterton Colln.) 406–1871.

7. GLAZED WARE; the bezel blue, in the form of a right *utchat* (sacred eye); plain yellow hoop.
Late XVIIIth Dynasty (?). *Plate I.*
(Waterton Colln.) 403–1871.

8. BLUE-GLAZE; the bezel in the form of a right *utchat* (sacred eye).
Late XVIIIth Dynasty. *Plate I.*
(Waterton Colln.) 404–1871.

9. GOLD; the bezel a revolving scarab of green jasper, engraved with two deities; the shoulders bound with wire.
Plate I.
(Waterton Colln.) 409–1871.

10. GOLD; revolving oval bezel set with a bloodstone scarab engraved with Isis nursing Horus; the hoop of fine wire plait. *Plate I.*
(Waterton Colln.) 408–1871.

11. GOLD; pointed oval bezel engraved with Isis enthroned, nursing Horus.
Plate I.
(Waterton Colln.) 412–1871.

12. GOLD; long oval bezel engraved with a hawk-headed deity (Horus ?) holding the sign for life (*ānkh*).
(Waterton Colln.) 413–1871.

13. WHITE METAL; revolving rounded oblong bezel engraved with Isis enthroned nursing Horus in the marshes (represented by papyrus stems); unread inscription below; tapering hoop.
Plate I.
(Waterton Colln.) 414–1871.
Ironmongers' Hall Exhibition, 1861, ii. 490.

14. SILVER; revolving cornelian bezel in the form of a right sacred eye (*utchat*), engraved at the back with the sign for life (*ānkh*); plain tapering hoop; the shoulders originally bound with wire.
Plate I.
(Waterton Colln.) 401–1871.
Ironmongers' Hall Exhibition, 1861, ii. 490.

15. BRONZE; oval bezel engraved with a seated figure of Ptah.
(Waterton Colln.) 416–1871.

16. SILVER; long oblong bezel with rounded ends, engraved with human figures, some of which are winged.
(Waterton Colln.) 415–1871.

B. *ANCIENT GREEK*

17. GOLD; cast and chased with a grotesque mask and scrolls.
9th Century B.C. (Sub-Mycenean).
Plate II.
(Waterton Colln.) 418–1871.
Found during excavations in Sardinia. Waterton MS., p. 44.

18. SILVER; pointed oval bezel decorated with filigree (one pellet in gold); tapering hoop; the shoulders bound with wire.
8th to 7th Century B.C. *Plate II.*
(Waterton Colln.) 420–1871.
Compare a very similar ring in the British Museum (Marshall, 1026).

19. GOLD; a mortuary ring; the hoop with overlapping ends, widening to form the plain convex bezel.
About 7th Century B.C.
Given by Mr. Walter Child, A.R.S.M.
643–1906.
Said to have been found at Novi, twenty miles south of Catania, Sicily.

20. ELECTRUM; revolving bezel set with a composition; the shoulders bound with wire.
6th Century B.C.
(Waterton Colln.) 421–1871.
Found by Auguste Salzmann in the necropolis of Camirus, Rhodes.

21. GOLD; openwork bezel chased with two winged demons, with foliations between.
Greek or Phoenician, 6th or 5th Century B.C. *Plate II.*
(Waterton Colln.) 419–1871.

22. IRON; circular bezel engraved with a head of a winged demon.
About 5th Century B.C. (?).
(Waterton Colln.) 422–1871.
Found in 1864 in a tomb outside the city of Rhodes, on the road leading to Chioschino, by Signor Giuseppe Panni, Swedish Vice-Consul, from whom Waterton bought it in the following year. Waterton MS., p. 22.

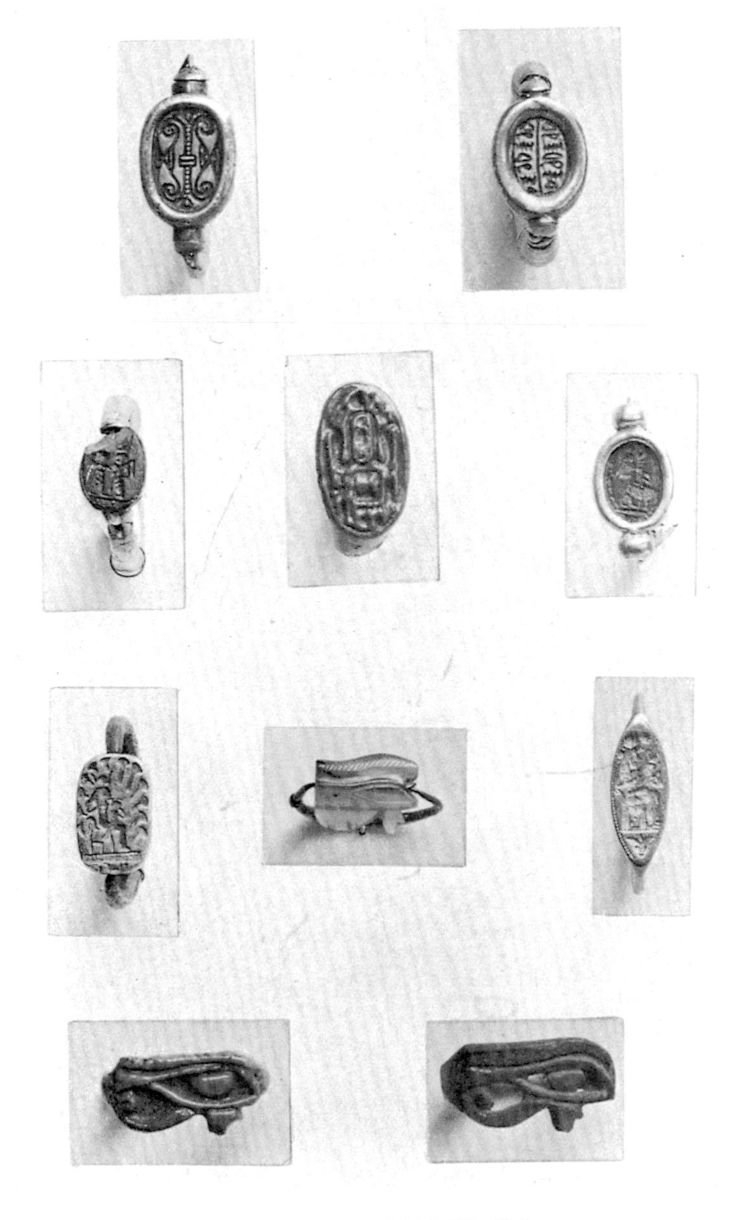

ANCIENT EGYPTIAN RINGS

1		3
9	5	10
13	14	11
7		8

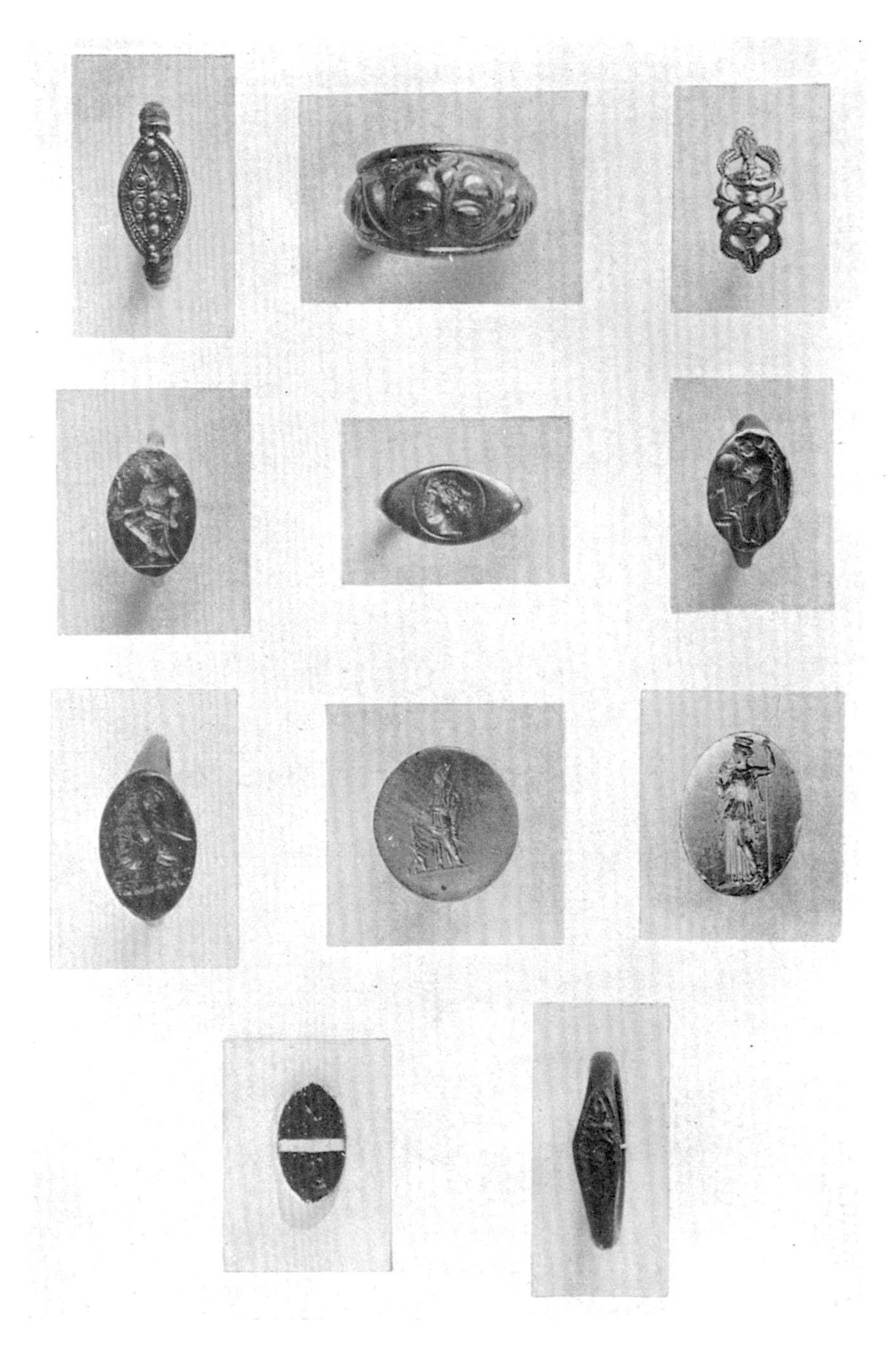

ANCIENT GREEK RINGS

18	17	21
26	24	23
27	32	28
31		34

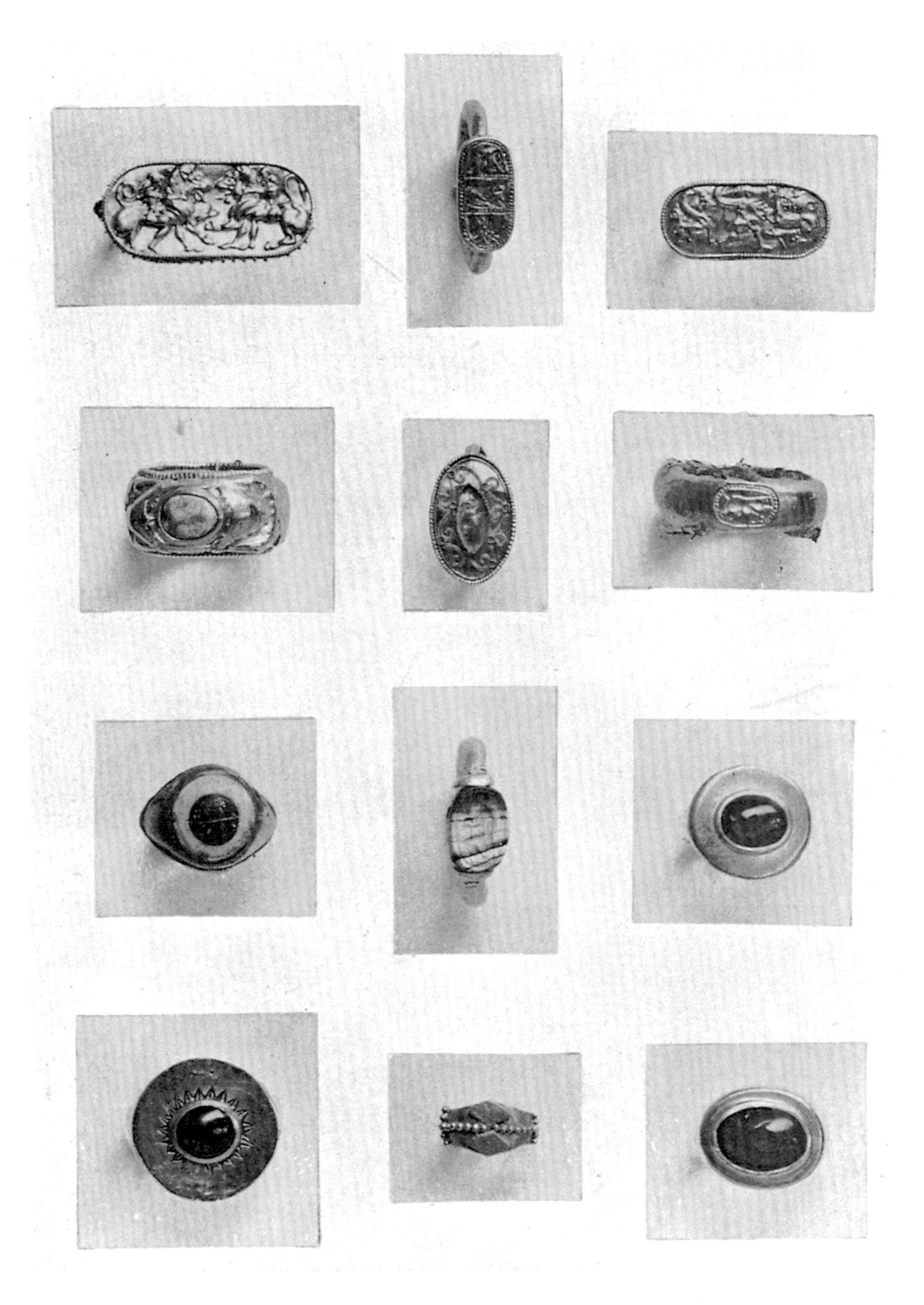

ANCIENT ETRUSCAN RINGS

40	38	39
47	42	48
57	51	53
58	235*a*	60

PLATE IV

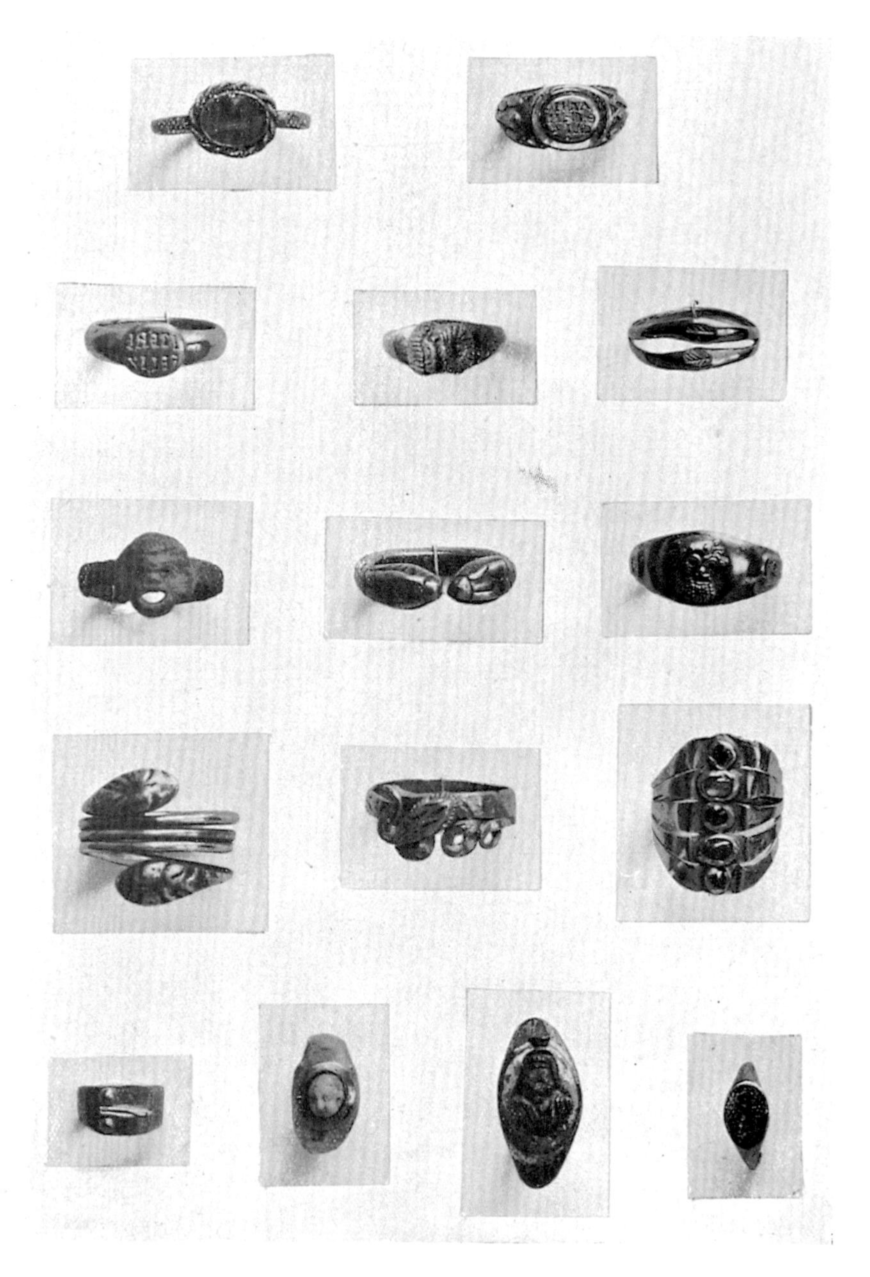

ANCIENT ROMAN RINGS

	71			103	
102			76		89
94			84		77
88			87		104
80		82		105	88

23. SILVER; oval bezel engraved with a Victory fastening her sandal; a circular plug of gold inserted in front of the figure.
5th Century B.C. *Plate II.*
(Waterton Colln.) 434–1871.

24. GOLD; pointed oval bezel engraved with a female head in profile to left.
Late 5th or 4th Century B.C. *Plate II.*
(Waterton Colln.) 431–1871.

25. GOLD; lozenge-shaped bezel, with filigree border, set with an opaque paste; the hoop ribbed.
5th or 4th Century B.C.
(Webb Colln.) 8773–1863.

26. GOLD; pointed oval bezel engraved with a seated female figure holding a Victory who is crowning her.
Early 4th Century B.C. *Plate II.*
(Waterton Colln.) 430–1871.

27. BRONZE; pointed oval bezel engraved with a seated female figure playing at knuckle-bones.
4th Century B.C. *Plate II.*
(Waterton Colln.) 432–1871.
Ironmongers' Hall Exhibition, 1861, ii. 490.

28. GOLD; oval bezel engraved with a figure of Hera (or Persephone).
4th Century B.C. *Plate II.*
(Salting Bequest.) M. 552–1910.

29. GOLD; formed of a beaded hoop with a double twisted wire applied to each edge.
3rd Century B.C.
(Webb Colln.) 8770–1863.

30. SILVER; oval bezel engraved with a woman fastening her sandal.
3rd Century B.C.
(Waterton Colln.) 435–1871.

31. GOLD; oval bezel set with a ribbon-onyx paste intaglio of a female figure.
3rd Century B.C. *Plate II.*
(Webb Colln.) 8781–1863.

32. GOLD; thin circular bezel engraved with a female figure standing at a tripod.
3rd Century B.C. *Plate II.*
(Waterton Colln.) 429–1871.

33. SILVER; thin circular bezel engraved with a galley between two dolphins.
3rd Century B.C.
(Waterton Colln.) 458–1871.

34. BRONZE; tapering hoop flattened to form the bezel, which is engraved with a pigeon, a panther and a doe (Bacchic emblems).
3rd or 2nd Century B.C. *Plate II.*
(Waterton Colln.) 433–1871.

35. IRON; large circular bezel engraved with a Victory crowning a warrior.
3rd or 2nd Century B.C.
(Waterton Colln.) 427–1871.

35*a*. BRONZE; large almost circular bezel engraved with a Cupid holding out a wand; traces of gilding inside.
3rd or 2nd Century B.C.
Given by Dr. W. L. Hildburgh, F.S.A.
M. 154–1929.

36. BRONZE; large circular bezel engraved with a female figure seated on a throne with the arms in the form of lions.
3rd or 2nd Century B.C.
(Waterton Colln.) 428–1871.

37. GOLD; oval bezel set with a paste intaglio of a male head in profile.
2nd Century B.C.
Given by Mr. Walter Child, A.R.S.M.
M. 151–1909.
From a tomb at Ephesus.

C. *ETRUSCAN*

38. GOLD; oblong bezel with rounded ends, engraved with a Siren, Oedipus with the Sphinx, and a winged star (?).
6th Century B.C. *Plate III.*
(Webb Colln.) 8779–1863.

39. GOLD; oblong bezel with rounded ends, embossed (stamped?) with a winged man between a sphinx and a panther.
Early Ionic work, probably from Etruria, first half of 6th Century B.C. *Plate III.*
(Webb Colln.) 8775–1863.

Other examples of this design are in the British Museum (Marshall, 209) and the Bibliothèque Nationale, Paris (No. 485).

40. GOLD; oblong bezel with rounded ends, embossed (stamped?) with two lions led by two men; the hoop of plated white metal.
Ionic-Etruscan, 6th Century B.C.
Plate III.
(Webb Colln.) 8774–1863.

41. WHITE METAL plated with gold; oblong bezel with rounded ends, engraved with a deer, a lion and a scarab (?).
Ionic-Etruscan, 6th or 5th Century B.C.
(Waterton Colln.) 437–1871.

42. GOLD; oval bezel with an empty setting surrounded by filigree scrollwork.
5th Century B.C. *Plate III.*
(Webb Colln.) 8768–1863.

43. GOLD; a plain thin band widening to form the bezel.
5th Century B.C.
(Waterton Colln.) 442–1871.

44. GOLD; a plain thin band of curved section.
5th or 4th Century B.C.
(Waterton Colln.) 443–1871.

Compare No. 64.

45. GOLD; large flat pointed oval bezel of sheet-metal; hollow hoop of the same.
5th or 4th Century B.C.
(Waterton Colln.) 444–1871.

Compare No. 62.

46. BRONZE; pointed oval bezel engraved with a man carrying fishes (?).
5th or 4th Century B.C.
(Waterton Colln.) 441–1871.

47. GOLD; bezel set with a composition scarab; the shoulders chased with the figures of Hercules and Juno Lanuvina (Sospita).
4th Century B.C. *Plate III.*
(Waterton Colln.)
445–1871.

Found in the Maremma, 1856.

Father Garrucci, S.J., in a note to Waterton, gives the following grounds for this identification:—One of the figures is clearly that of a male; it is dressed in a stole and wears the spoils of a lion on its head. In its right hand is a club. The female figure is dressed in a tunic and wears the spoils of a goat on its head. In one hand is a girdle. He thought that this was a marriage ring, as Juno is carrying the girdle or *Nodus Herculeus* which a betrothed woman wore until released by her husband on the day of marriage. Waterton MS., pp. 41-2.

Ironmongers' Hall Exhibition, 1861, ii. 490-1.

Bullettino dell' Instituto di Corrispondenza Archeologica, 1858, pp. 49-50.

48. BRONZE plated with gold; the hoop flattened to form an oval bezel stamped with a boar in intaglio.
4th Century B.C. *Plate III.*
(Waterton Colln.) 446–1871.

49. WHITE METAL plated with gold; large flat circular bezel.
4th Century B.C.
(Waterton Colln.) 447–1871.
Compare a ring of similar form in the British Museum (Marshall, 912).

50. GOLD; set with a revolving cornelian scarab engraved with a doe; the shoulders bound with wire.
About 4th Century B.C.
(Webb Colln.) 8769–1863.

51. GOLD; set with a revolving onyx scarab engraved with a man seated and holding a bowl; the shoulders chased to imitate wire binding.
About 4th Century B.C. *Plate III.*
(Webb Colln.) 8777–1863.

52. GOLD; oblong bezel with rounded ends, engraved with an ibis and a sphinx; the shoulders lightly chased.
Ionic-Etruscan; 4th Century B.C.
(Waterton Colln.) 438–1871.
Presented to Waterton by Cardinal Antonelli, 1857. Waterton MS., p. 44.

53. GOLD; wide oval bezel set with a garnet intaglio of a dolphin.
5th or 4th Century B.C. *Plate III.*
(Waterton Colln.) 449–187 .

54. GOLD; oval bezel, with filigree border, set with a cabochon crystal over red foil.
4th or 3rd Century B.C. 817–1902.

55. BRONZE; the hoop widening to form the bezel, which is engraved with a warrior.
4th or 3rd Century B.C.
(Waterton Colln.) 440–1871.
Found near Rome, 1857. Waterton MS., p. 46.

55*a*. BRONZE; oblong bezel engraved with a bull charging to right.
4th or 3rd Century B.C.
Given by Dr. W. L. Hildburgh, F.S.A.
M. 153–1929.

56. BRONZE; hoop flattened to form the bezel, which is inscribed (unread).
4th or 3rd Century B.C.
(Waterton Colln.) 440*–1871.

57. SILVER; circular bezel set with a sardonyx paste in imitation of an eye.
3rd Century B.C. *Plate III.*
(Waterton Colln.) 450–1871.
Found at Volterra, 1857.

57*a*. BRONZE plated with silver; circular bezel set with a brown paste intaglio, in gold collet, of a man holding a branch and leaning against a column.
3rd Century B.C.
Given by Dr. W. L. Hildburgh, F.S.A.
M. 158–1929.

58. GOLD; large, flat, almost circular bezel, set with a cabochon garnet surrounded by small sun-rays engraved.
3rd Century B.C. *Plate III.*
(Waterton Colln.) 448–1871.

59. GOLD; pointed oval bezel engraved with a female figure holding a palm-branch.
3rd Century B.C.
(Webb Colln.) 8767–1863.

60. GOLD; oval bezel set with a garnet intaglio of a shoe.
3rd Century B.C. *Plate III.*
(Waterton Colln.) 454–1871.
It has been suggested that this is a comedian's *soccus*, and that the ring therefore belonged to an actor. Waterton MS., p. 72.
Ironmongers' Hall Exhibition, 1861, ii. 492.

61. GOLD, hollow; long oval bezel, the stone missing.
3rd Century B.C.
(Waterton Colln.) 452–1871.

Perhaps found in the Necropolis de' Marmini, Volterra. Waterton MS., p. 44.

62. GOLD FOIL; very large, flat, transverse oval bezel.
3rd Century B.C.
(Webb Colln.) 8782–1863.

Compare No. 45.

63. BRONZE plated with gold; large, long oval bezel, set with a brown paste intaglio of Bacchus and Ampelus.
3rd Century B.C.
(Waterton Colln.) 451–1871.

Found at Chiusi, on the index finger of the left hand of the skeleton of a man. Waterton M.S., p. 45.

Ironmongers' Hall Exhibition, 1861, ii. 491.

64. GOLD; a plain thin band of curved section.
3rd or 2nd Century B.C. (?).
(Webb Colln.) 8772–1863.

Compare No. 44.

65. Number cancelled.

66. GOLD; oval bezel, the stone missing; the hoop hollow.
3rd or 2nd Century B.C.
(Waterton Colln.) 453–1871.

67. GOLD; projecting oval bezel set with a paste amethyst intaglio.
2nd Century B.C.
(Waterton Colln.) 456–1871.

68. GOLD; oval bezel set with a garnet intaglio (head of Mercury to left).
2nd Century B.C.
(Waterton Colln.) 455–1871.

69. GOLD; a six-fold coil of double wire.
Etruscan (?).
(Waterton Colln.) 436–1871.

D. *ROMAN*

(1) 2ND CENTURY B.C. TO 2ND CENTURY A.D.

70. BRONZE; almost circular bezel engraved with a harpy.
2nd or 1st Century B.C.
Given by Mrs. Hamilton Evans.
M. 107–1913.

70*a*. BRONZE; oval bezel set with a paste ribbon-onyx intaglio of a man with two oxen.
2nd or 1st Century B.C.
Given by Dr. W. L. Hildburgh, F.S.A.
M. 156–1929.

71. GOLD; oval bezel with corded edge, set with a cornelian intaglio of two horses.
1st Century B.C. *Plate IV.*
(Waterton Colln.) 575–1871.

Presented to Waterton by Cardinal Antonelli, Rome, 1856. Waterton MS., p. 65.

72. BRONZE; oval bezel engraved with Hercules crowned by Victory.
3rd or 2nd Century B.C.
(Waterton Colln.) 459–1871.

The greater part of the hoop wanting.

PLATE V

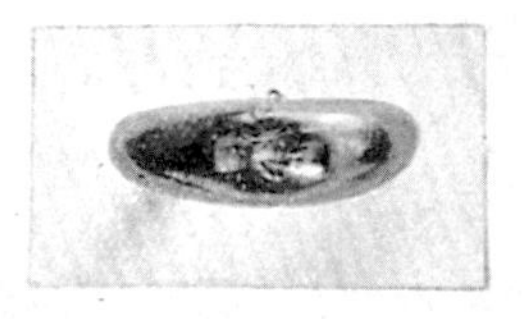

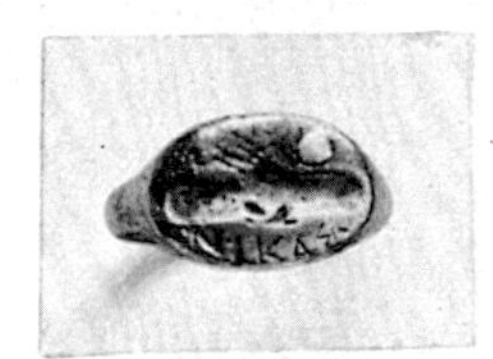

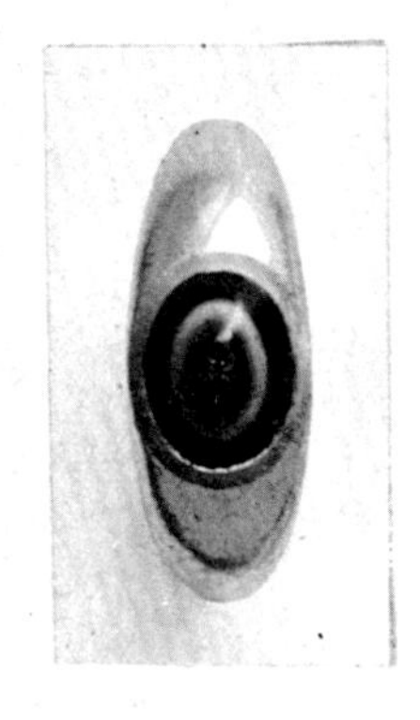

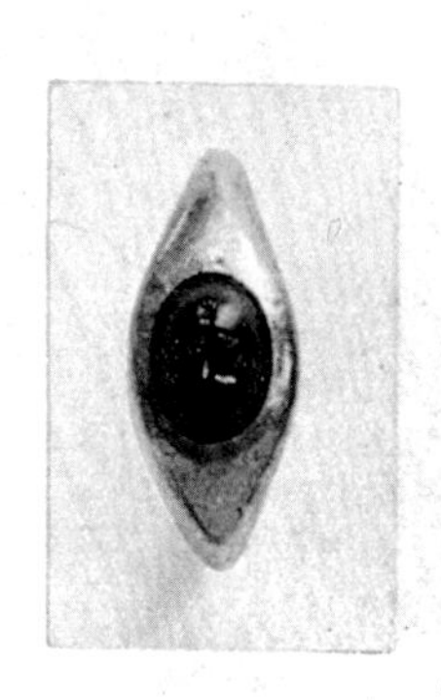

ANCIENT ROMAN RINGS

127		137		128
125	110		118	131
146		126		147
113		119		111

PLATE VI

ANCIENT ROMAN RINGS

149		163		161
	156		155	
140		142		154
	145		150	
166		174		172

EARLY CHRISTIAN AND BYZANTINE RINGS

199

200 205 206

204 *204a* 203

207 210 208

211 212 217

PLATE VIII

BYZANTINE RINGS

214 216 213
221 220 224
215 220 215
222 218 223

73. GILT BRONZE; oval bezel with a bust in relief.
2nd Century B.C.
(Waterton Colln.) 535–1871.

74. SILVER; lozenge-shaped bezel engraved with a figure of Hercules.
2nd Century B.C.
(Waterton Colln.) 457–1871.

75. LAPIS-LAZULI; bezel in form of a male head in full relief; the greater part of the hoop restored in gold.
1st Century B.C.
(Waterton Colln.) 567–1871.

Found near Rome, 1857. Waterton MS., p. 76.

Ironmongers' Hall Exhibition, 1861, ii. 493.

76. GOLD; widening towards the bezel, to which is applied a comic mask in full relief.
1st Century B.C. or 1st Century A.D.
Plate IV.
(Webb Colln.) 8780–1863.

77. GOLD; widening towards the bezel, to which is applied a comic mask; ribbed hoop; each shoulder engraved with a rosette.
1st Century B.C. or 1st Century A.D.
Plate IV.
(Waterton Colln.) 463–1871.

78. BRONZE; hoop formed by seven coils of flattened tapering wire.
1st Century B.C. to 2nd Century A.D.
(Waterton Colln.) 552–1871.

79. GOLD; hoop widening to form the bezel, which is engraved with a phallus.
1st Century B.C. to 2nd Century A.D.
(Waterton Colln.) 464–1871.

80. GOLD; flat octagonal hoop widening to the bezel, which is set with a phallus in relief.
1st Century B.C. to 2nd Century A.D.
Plate IV.
(Waterton Colln.) 465–1871.

81. GOLD; oval bezel engraved with a caduceus within a laurel wreath.
1st Century B.C. to 2nd Century A.D.
(Webb Colln.) 8771–1863.

82. GOLD; oval bezel set with an onyx cameo (of two strata) of a child's head.
1st Century B.C. to 2nd Century A.D.
Plate IV.
(Webb Colln.) 8778–1863.

83. BRONZE; penannular hoop ending in two serpents' heads.
1st Century B.C. to 2nd Century A.D.
(Waterton Colln.) 479–1871.

Compare No. 84.

83*a*. A duplicate of the last.
Given by Dr. W. L. Hildburgh, F.S.A.
M. 155–1929.

84. SILVER; penannular, in the form of a serpent with two heads; the eyes formerly set with stones.
1st Century B.C. to 2nd Century A.D.
Plate IV.
(Waterton Colln.) 478–1871.

Compare British Museum (Marshall, 1135–1141), and two rings (337, 338) illustrated by Henkel, *Die römischen fingerringe der Rheinlande*, Berlin, 1913.

85. SILVER; four coils of plain wire ending in serpents' heads.
1st Century B.C. to 2nd Century A.D.
Plate IV.
(Waterton Colln.) 477–1871.

Compare a similar ring in the British Museum (Marshall, 938).

86. AMBER; the hoop spirally grooved, the bezel set with a paste (head of Jupiter Ammon).
1st Century A.D.
(Waterton Colln.) 509–1871.

Found at Rome, in 1860, during excavations made in connection with the railway. The workman unfortunately broke the ring in order to extract the intaglio with which it was set. The present paste was substituted when the ring was mended. A similar ring found at the same time was treated in the same way. Waterton MS., p. 77.

87. GOLD ; in the form of a serpent, the bezel formed by the head and coiled tail ; the eyes formerly set with stones.
1st Century A.D. *Plate IV.*
(Waterton Colln.) 476–1871.

For a similar ring, compare Musée du Louvre, *Catalogue Sommaire des bijoux antiques*, 1141.

88. GOLD ; oval bezel inlaid with a small cornelian intaglio of Augustus, cut to the shape of the head.
1st Century A.D. *Plate IV.*
(Waterton Colln.) 461–1871.

Found near Rome, 1857. Waterton MS., p. 74.

Ironmongers' Hall Exhibition, 1861, ii. 493.

89. GOLD ; the hoop slit from the shoulders and flattened to form two bezels each engraved with a palm branch.
1st Century A.D. *Plate IV.*
(Waterton Colln.) 473–1871.

Ironmongers' Hall Exhibition, 1861, ii. p. 493.

For a similar ring, compare Musée du Louvre, *Catalogue Sommaire des bijoux antiques*, 1029.

90. GOLD ; the hoop slit from the shoulders and flattened to form two bezels inscribed with πωπολ and APE.
1st Century A.D.
(Waterton Colln.) 474–1871.

Found near Rome, 1856. Waterton MS., p. 68.

91. BRONZE ; projecting circular bezel engraved with a monster.
1st Century A.D.
(Waterton Colln.) 539–1871.

92. RED EARTHENWARE ; a plain hoop.
1st Century A.D.
(Waterton Colln.) 555–1871.

93. BROWN GLASS with white twists ; hoop flattened to form a bezel and set with a mask in blue.
1st or 2nd Century A.D.
(Fould and Waterton Collns.) 559–1871.

Waterton MS., p. 76.

94. BRONZE ; plain flat hoop set with a comic mask.
1st or 2nd Century A.D. *Plate IV.*
Presented by Mr. Harold Wallis.
M. 76–1917.

From the Henry Wallis Collection.

Compare similar rings in the British Museum (Marshall, 226 and 1328–30).

95. WHITE CORNELIAN ; plain hoop, ground to form an oval bezel on which is engraved a standing figure of Æsculapius.
1st or 2nd Century A.D.
(Waterton Colln.) 566–1871.

96. PLASMA ; bezel in form of a head in full relief.
1st or 2nd Century A.D.
(Waterton Colln.) 568–1871

Acquired at Rome, 1858. Waterton MS., p. 76.

The hoop restored in gold.

97. LEAD ; hoop widening to form the large oval bezel, which is set transversely with an oval onyx intaglio of a woman bathing.
1st or 2nd Century A.D.
(Waterton Colln.) 492–1871.

Clement of Alexandria, in his *Paedagogus Christianus* (ii. 11), specially condemns the use of subjects like this by Christians on their rings and enumerates what he considers to be more suitable. (Quoted in C. W. King, *Antique Gems*, i. 329.)

98. IRON ; large transverse oval bezel with setting for a stone ; the shoulders overlaid with the letters C and S in gold foil.
1st or 2nd Century A.D.
(Waterton Colln.) 990–1871.

99. GOLD, hollow; ridged hoop with swelling shoulders; small oval bezel set with a sard intaglio (winged human figure).
2nd Century A.D.
Presented by Mr. Walter Child, A.R.S.M. M. 149–1909.

From a tomb at Ephesus.

100. IRON; set with an intaglio on nicolo onyx of Apollo Delphicus within a collet of gold; the hoop with remains of silver plating.
2nd Century A.D.
(Waterton Colln.) 483–1871.

101. GOLD; oval bezel inscribed in stippled characters.
2nd Century A.D.
(Waterton Colln.) 466–1871.

102. GOLD; signet; applied oval bezel inscribed ITERE FELIX.
2nd Century A.D. *Plate IV.*
(Waterton Colln.) 502–1871.

Ironmongers' Hall Exhibition, 1861, ii. 494.

103. GOLD; signet; oval bezel inscribed ΑΛΗΘΙ ΖΗCΑΙC within a grooved border; the shoulders chased with acanthus leaves.
2nd Century A.D. *Plate IV.*
(Waterton Colln.) 503–1871.

Ironmongers' Hall Exhibition, 1861, ii. 494.

104. GOLD; five thin wire hoops joined together, flattened and separated at the shoulders, and reunited at the bezel, where each is set with a garnet or a sapphire; one of the two sapphires is inscribed EVME in reverse.
2nd Century A.D. *Plate IV.*
(Waterton Colln.) 475–1871.

Ironmongers' Hall Exhibition, 1861, ii. 492.

105. GILT BRONZE; oval bezel with a bust of Serapis wearing a modius, in full relief.
2nd Century A.D. *Plate IV.*
(Waterton Colln.) 534–1871.

Compare similar rings in the British Museum (Marshall, 1122 and 1302).

106. IRON; oval bezel engraved with a bust of Serapis above a griffin.
2nd Century A.D.
(Waterton Colln.) 489–1871.

The presence of the griffin, the peculiar attribute of Phoebus, shows that Serapis is here considered as the Solar God. C. W. King, *The Gnostics and their Remains*, pp. 70, 235.

107. GOLD; widening towards the bezel, which is rudely engraved with a palm branch.
2nd Century A.D.
(Waterton Colln.) 467–1871.

108. BRONZE; circular bezel with an empty setting.
2nd Century A.D.
(Waterton Colln.) 599–1871.

Made for a colossal statue. Waterton (MS., p. 78) states that he had then in his possession the finger of a colossal bronze statue with a ring on the second joint. It had been presented to him by Signor Luigi Saulini at Rome in 1860. Perhaps it is identical with the ring described above.

(2) About 3rd Century to 5th Century A.D.

109. GOLD; the hoop widening to form the bezel, which is engraved with a Victory.
2nd or 3rd Century A.D.
(Waterton Colln.) 470–1871.

Found at Rieti, in 1856, with No. 118. Waterton MS., p. 57.

110. GOLD; pointed oval bezel engraved with the head of Cybele and the letters G (or C) R F.
2nd or 3rd Century A.D. *Plate V.*
(Waterton Colln.) 471–1871.

111. GOLD; swelling shoulders; bezel set with an oval intaglio in oriental onyx of a dancing girl.
2nd or 3rd Century A.D. *Plate V.*
(Waterton Colln.) 488–1871.

112. GOLD; swelling shoulders, bezel set with an oval nicolo onyx intaglio of a woman standing before a trophy of arms.
2nd or 3rd Century A.D.
Bequeathed by the Rev. Chauncy Hare Townshend. 1817–1869.

113. GOLD; massive; swelling shoulders; flattened oval bezel set with a projecting oval intaglio in oriental onyx of an ant.
2nd or 3rd Century A.D. *Plate V.*
(Waterton Colln.) 487–1871.

114. GILT BRONZE; massive; swelling shoulders; bezel with oval setting for a stone.
2nd or 3rd Century A.D.
(Waterton Colln.) 491–1871.

115. BLUE GLASS; plain thin hoop flattened to form a small plain oval bezel.
2nd or 3rd Century A.D.
(Waterton Colln.) 557–1871.

116. PURPLE GLASS with three white twists; hoop flattened to form bezel, which is set with an eye of brown glass surrounded by opaque yellow.
2nd or 3rd Century A.D.
(Waterton Colln.) 560–1871.

Fairholt (*Rambles of an Archaeologist*, p. 93) considered rings of this sort to be intended only as mortuary rings. This example appears to be illustrated in Jones, *Finger-ring Lore*, 1877, p. 48.

117. GOLD; plain, with central ridge and small circular setting for a stone.
2nd or 3rd Century A.D.
(Webb Colln.) 8766–1863.

118. GOLD; a flat strip widening to form a bezel, which is engraved with the Genius of Death.
2nd or 3rd Century A.D. *Plate V.*
(Waterton Colln.) 468–1871.

Found at Rieti, in 1856, with No. 109. Waterton MS., p. 57.

119. GOLD; projecting circular bezel with a burnt sardonyx engraved with a figure of Abundantia with cornucopia, and an eagle holding a wreath.
2nd or 3rd Century A.D. *Plate V.*
(Waterton Colln.) 460–1871.

120. IRON; bezel set with a projecting oval onyx of four strata engraved with two goats.
2nd or 3rd Century A.D.
(Waterton Colln.) 482–1871.

121. IRON; projecting bezel set with an oval paste intaglio of Cupid.
2nd or 3rd Century A.D.
(Waterton Colln.) 508–1871.

122. IRON; bezel set with an oval nicolo onyx intaglio of Rome holding a Victory.
2nd or 3rd Century A.D.
(Waterton Colln.) 496–1871.

The hoop wanting.

123. GLASS PASTE ; brown, with traces of a black surface ; the hoop flattened to form the bezel, the shoulders each with two transverse grooves.
2nd or 3rd Century A.D.
(Waterton Colln.) 553–1871.

124. LEAD ; oval bezel inlaid with a cornelian intaglio of two conjoined masks.
2nd or 3rd Century A.D.
(Waterton Colln.) 541–1871.

125. GOLD ; the hoop flattened to form the bezel, which is roughly engraved with clasped hands.
2nd or 3rd Century A.D. *Plate V.*
(Waterton Colln.) 829–1871.

Bought at Florence, 1858. Waterton MS., p. 109.

Ironmongers' Hall Exhibition, 1861, ii. 493.

126. GOLD ; octagonal openwork hoop, the bezel inlaid with a garnet intaglio of the Genius of Death.
3rd Century A.D. *Plate V.*
(Waterton Colln.) 469–1871.

Given to Waterton in 1857 by Father Marchi, S.J. Waterton MS., p. 72.

Compare a ring (89) illustrated by Henkel, *Die römischen Fingerringe der Rheinlande*, Berlin, 1913.

127. GOLD ; ridged hoop dividing at the shoulders to form four supports for the bezel, which is set with a heart-shaped blue paste.
3rd Century A.D. *Plate V.*
(Waterton Colln.) 500–1871.

Acquired at Rome, 1858. Waterton (MS., p. 75) does not seem to have considered the stone a paste. For a similar ring, compare an example set with a sapphire in the Don de Luynes at the Bibliothèque Nationale, Paris.

128. GOLD ; oblong bezel set with a cabochon sapphire and chrysoprase, the sides pierced with leaves and scrolls ; the hoop chased with leaves.
3rd Century A.D. *Plate V.*
(Fould and Waterton Collns.) 501–1871.

For a similar ring, compare an example set with an emerald and two sapphires in the Bibliothèque Nationale, Paris (472).

129. BRONZE ; swelling shoulders and large oval bezel engraved with a figure pouring a libation on an altar.
3rd Century A.D.
(Waterton Colln.) 490–1871.

130. GLASS PASTE ; brown, with traces of a black surface ; bezel with plain projecting disk ; the shoulders each with two transverse grooves.
3rd Century A.D.
(Waterton Colln.) 554–1871.

Compare a ring, dug up in Smithfield, now in the London Museum (A 1267).

131. SILVER ; oval bezel engraved with two clasped hands ; with the inscription ΝΙΚΑΣ below and Ω above. A hole has been pierced and plugged with gold near the wrist of one of the hands.
3rd Century A.D. *Plate V.*
(Waterton Colln.) 824–1871.

Ironmongers' Hall Exhibition, 1861, ii. 493.

132. SILVER ; signet ; circular bezel inscribed LIBERI VIVAS.
3rd Century A.D.
(Waterton Colln.) 505–1871.

133. SILVER ; signet ; square bezel inscribed APOLLINARES.
3rd Century A.D.
(Waterton Colln.) 504–1871.

134. GOLD ; hollow ; oval bezel set with an intaglio on oriental onyx of a male head to left with a wing behind the neck.
3rd Century A.D.
(Waterton Colln.) 486–1871.

135. WHITE CORNELIAN; the hoop spirally grooved; oval setting for a gem.
3rd Century A.D.
(Waterton Colln.) 565–1871.

136. WHITE METAL; oval bezel engraved with a female head to right.
3rd Century A.D.
(Waterton Colln.) 542–1871.

137. BRONZE; signet; projecting oval bezel engraved with a two-horse chariot with three figures and inscribed OSIMIVS BARBARVS; each shoulder has two knobs.
3rd Century A.D. *Plate V.*
(Waterton Colln.) 595–1871.

137*a*. BRONZE; circular bezel engraved with a comic mask.
3rd Century A.D.
Given by Dr. W. L. Hildburgh, F.S.A. M. 152–1929.

138. BRONZE; circular bezel with a wheel pattern in red and green champlevé enamel.
3rd Century A.D.
(Waterton Colln.) 630–1871.

The hoop wanting. Compare British Museum (Marshall, 1452).

Ironmongers' Hall Exhibition, 1861, ii. 492.

139. GOLD; square bezel engraved and nielloed with a dolphin; the hoop flattened and shoulders grooved.
3rd Century A.D.
(Waterton Colln.) 499–1871.

140. GOLD; oblong bezel inlaid with an onyx of two strata engraved with lettering.
3rd Century A.D. *Plate VI.*
(Waterton Colln.) 485–1871.

141. BRONZE; octagonal hoop engraved with eight signs of the Zodiac.
3rd Century A.D.
(Waterton Colln.) 543–1871.

142. BRONZE; bezel in the form of a shoe-sole inscribed FELIX.
3rd Century A.D. *Plate VI*
(Waterton Colln.) 544–1871.

Part of hoop wanting. Compare British Museum (Marshall, 1390–1).

143. GOLD; plain wire hoop threaded with a faceted blue-paste bead.
3rd Century A.D.
6580–1855.

144. IRON; the bezel set with an oval intaglio in jasper.
3rd Century A.D.
(Waterton Colln.) 484–1871.

More than half the hoop wanting.

145. BRONZE; oval bezel engraved with two male busts face to face; cusped shoulders.
3rd or 4th Century A.D. *Plate VI.*
(Waterton Colln.) 827–1871.

146. SILVER; bezel set with an oval bloodstone intaglio of Abraxas, jackal-headed; the hoop with angular shoulders.
Gnostic, 3rd or 4th Century A.D.
Plate V.
(Waterton Colln.) 608–1871.

Jones, *Finger-ring Lore*, pp. 107-8.

C. W. King, *Handbook of Engraved Gems*, pp. 97, 378, illus.

147. BRONZE; square bezel engraved with a figure of Abraxas.
Gnostic, 3rd or 4th Century A.D.
Plate V.
(Waterton Colln.) 609–1871.

148. LEAD, with traces of gold plating; set with a cornelian intaglio of clasped hands.
3rd or 4th Century A.D.
(Waterton Colln.) 826–1871.

Part of the hoop wanting.

149. GOLD ; transverse raised bezel set with a ruby and a carbuncle ; a rose applied to each shoulder.
4th Century A.D.
Given by Mr. Walter Child, A.R.S.M.
M. 150–1909.
From a tomb at Ephesus.

150. JET ; projecting oval bezel, the shoulders notched.
4th Century A.D. *Plate VI.*
(Waterton Colln.) 564–1871.
A number of other rings of this type have been found in connection with coins of Valentinian and Valens, in the neighbourhood of Bonn. *Bonner Jahrbuch*, cx. 1903, Pl. VIII.

150*a*. BRONZE ; raised circular bezel set with a cornelian intaglio of a man reaping corn.
4th Century A.D.
Given by Dr. W. L. Hildburgh, F.S.A.
M. 157–1929.

151. BRONZE ; projecting circular bezel engraved with a head ; elliptical hoop ; angular shoulders.
4th or 5th Century A.D.
(Waterton Colln.) 497–1871.

152. BRONZE ; large oval setting for a stone ; elliptical hoop ; wide angular shoulders, deeply grooved.
4th or 5th Century A.D.
(Waterton Colln.) 494–1871.

153. GILT BRONZE ; square bezel set with an oval oriental onyx (restored ?) ; elliptical hoop ; wide angular shoulders, deeply grooved.
4th or 5th Century A.D.
(Waterton Colln.) 495–1871.
Part of the hoop wanting.

154. GOLD ; bezel set with a cabochon sapphire ; elliptical hoop ; angular shoulders decorated with niello and openwork.
4th or 5th Century A.D. *Plate VI.*
(Waterton Colln.) 498–1871.
Ironmongers' Hall Exhibition, 1861, ii. 495.

155. SILVER ; octagonal bezel with nielloed inscription FAVS TINVS NICHA FRA ; elliptical hoop ; wide angular shoulders with nielloed foliations ; bezel laterally pierced.
4th or 5th Century A.D. *Plate VI.*
(Waterton Colln.) 825–1871.

156. SILVER ; circular bezel with nielloed inscription AVE DAX ; elliptical hoop of triangular section ; wide triangular shoulders with radiating grooves.
4th or 5th Century A.D. *Plate VI.*
(Senckler and Waterton Collns.)
601–1871.
The inscription means 'Hail, the Dacian !', but it may be intended for *Ave Pax*.
Found at Cologne.
Henkel, *Die römischen Fingerringe der Rheinlande*, Berlin, 1913, No. 395.

157. BRONZE ; slender hoop, widening towards the bezel, which has an oval open setting for a stone.
Romano-Egyptian, 4th or 5th Century.
Given by the Egypt Exploration Fund.
1894*e*–1897.
From Behnesa (Oxyrhynchus), 1896-1897.

158. GILT BRONZE ; hoop widening to form the broad bezel, which has an oval setting for a stone.
5th Century A.D.
(Waterton Colln.) 493–1871.

159. IRON ; signet ; the hoop flattened to form an oval bezel engraved with a head in profile and the letters ΘΑΩΤΘ (?).
Romano-Egyptian, 4th or 5th Century A.D.
(Waterton Colln.) 594–1871.

160. BRONZE ; square bezel engraved with a male and a female bust face to face ; above them BENERAN DUS BARUL I A.
4th or 5th Century A.D.
(Waterton Colln.) 828–1871.

161. GOLD; hexagonal bezel set with a nicolo onyx intaglio of a female head; two large pellets at each shoulder.
5th Century. *Plate VI.*
(Waterton Colln.) 614–1871.

162. BRONZE; projecting hexagonal bezel set with a paste; angular shoulders simply grooved.
5th Century A.D.
(Waterton Colln.) 993–1871.

163. GOLD; bezel a hollow bead, the hoop hollow with a notch at the back for use as a whistle. *Plate VI.*
(Waterton Colln.) 93–1899.

Found on the Aventine Hill, Rome. Waterton MS., p. 72.

Ironmongers' Hall Exhibition, 1861, ii. 492.

164. GOLD; a miniature ring; oval bezel set with an onyx cameo.
(Waterton Colln.) 472–1871.

Perhaps a ring for the finger of a small statuette of a god. Waterton MS., p. 68.

Ironmongers' Hall Exhibition, 1861, ii. 492.

165. BRONZE; oval bezel with setting for a stone (wanting).
Given by the Egypt Exploration Fund.
1894*c*–1897.

From Behnesa (Oxyrhynchus), 1896-1897.

166. BRONZE; a key-ring; hollow stem and elaborate wards.
Plate VI.
(Waterton Colln.) 545–1871.

Five key-rings are listed in the Waterton MS. (p. 77), of which three were acquired in Rome, one was found in London and one in the Thames.

167. BRONZE; a key-ring; hollow stem externally grooved.
(Waterton Colln.) 546–1871.

168. BRONZE; a key-ring; hollow stem and two wards.
(Waterton Colln.) 547–1871.

168*a*. Similar to the last.
Given by Dr. W. L. Hildburgh, F.S.A.
M. 148–1929.

168*b*. BRONZE; a key-ring, three wards.
Given by Dr. W. L. Hildburgh, F.S.A.
M. 149–1929.

168*c*. BRONZE; a key-ring; curved bit with five wards.
Given by Dr. W. L. Hildburgh, F.S.A.
M. 150–1929.

169. BRONZE; a key-ring; solid ward and hollow stem riveted to hoop.
(Waterton Colln.) 548–1871.

170. BRONZE; a key-ring; the wards on the hoop.
(Waterton Colln.) 549–1871.

171. BRONZE; a key-ring; the bit with voided oblong.
(Waterton Colln.) 550–1871.

171*a*. Almost a duplicate of the last.
Given by Dr. W. L. Hildburgh, F.S.A.
M. 145–1929.

171*b*. Similar to the last.
Given by Dr. W. L. Hildburgh, F.S.A.
M. 146–1929.

171*c*. Almost a duplicate of the last.
Given by Dr. W. L. Hildburgh, F.S.A.
M. 147–1929.

172. BRONZE; a key-ring; circular bit pierced with seven holes.
Plate VI.
(Waterton Colln.) 551–1871.

172*a*. BRONZE; a key-ring; circular bit pierced with a mask.
Given by Dr. W. L. Hildburgh, F.S.A.
M. 151–1929.

The following group of bronze rings bearing numbers, sometimes accompanied by letters and signs, may be dated to about the 3rd century A.D. All appear to be of Roman or Italian provenance, but their purpose is quite unknown. Their suggested connection with the Roman legions, or with other corps, is entirely conjectural. (All are from the Waterton Collection.)

173. Elliptical hoop, flattened oval bezel engraved with I.
510–1871.

174. Oblong flattened bezel engraved with VI, the shoulders with R and N (?).
Plate VI.
511–1871.

175. Flattened oval bezel engraved with VIII.
512–1871.

176. Flattened oval bezel engraved with VIIII.
513–1871.

177. Elliptical hoop, flattened oval bezel engraved with X.
514–1871.

178. Flattened oval bezel engraved with XI.
515–1871.

179. Flattened oblong bezel engraved with XII, the shoulders with T and L.
516–1871.

180. Flattened oblong bezel engraved with XIV. 517–1871.

181. Flattened oval bezel engraved with XIIX.
518–1871.

182. Flattened oval bezel inscribed with XIX between a double-barbed arrow-head and Greek minuscule "a."
519–1871.

183. Flattened oval bezel inscribed XXI.
520–1871.

184. Flattened oval bezel inscribed XXII.
521–1871.

185. Elliptical hoop, flattened oblong bezel inscribed XXII, the shoulders with P and R. 522–1871.

186. Elliptical hoop, flattened oblong bezel inscribed XXIII. 523–1871.

187. Elliptical hoop, oblong flattened bezel inscribed XXV, the shoulders with ꟲ and ⩓. 97–1899.

188. Flattened oblong bezel inscribed XXVII; on the shoulders G and D (?).
524–1871.

189. Oblong flattened bezel inscribed with XXIIX; on the shoulders E and L.
525–1871.

190. Oblong flattened bezel inscribed XXXVI; on the shoulders M and T.
526–1871.

191. Elliptical hoop; oblong flattened bezel inscribed XXXIX; one shoulder with a letter (?). 527–1871.

192. Elliptical hoop, oblong flattened bezel inscribed XLIII; on the shoulders C C and NB. 528–1871

193. Elliptical hoop; oblong flattened bezel inscribed LXII; on one shoulder a star; on the other, ↑. 529–1871.

194. Elliptical hoop, oblong flattened bezel inscribed XCIII; on one shoulder a star.
530–1871.

195. Oval hoop, with oblong flattened bezel inscribed XCIIX; one of the shoulders pierced. 532–1871.

196. Elliptical hoop; oblong flattened bezel inscribed C. 533–1871.

197. Oval hoop; oblong flattened bezel inscribed XX CO IV; on one shoulder the letter A. 98–1899.
Jones, *Finger-ring Lore*, p. 98, illus.

198. Oblong bezel inscribed XXCVI.
531–1871.

PART II.—EARLY CHRISTIAN AND POST-CLASSICAL RINGS

A. *THE PERIOD BEFORE A.D. 1000*

(1) EARLY CHRISTIAN

199. BRONZE ; signet ; oblong bezel engraved VIVAS IN DIO ; line ornament on shoulders.
Italy or Gaul. 4th Century. *Plate VII.*
(Waterton Colln.) 603–1871.

Compare rings with the same inscription in the British Museum (Dalton, 8) and the Vatican Museum. *Arch. Journal*, xxviii. 266 *f*.

200. BRONZE ; signet ; circular bezel engraved with monogram of VIVAS IN DEO.
Italy or Gaul. 4th Century. *Plate VII.*
(Waterton Colln.) 591–1871.

For the monogram, compare No. 372 in the Fortnum Collection, Ashmolean Museum, and note in *Arch. Journal*, xxvi. 144.

201. BRONZE ; signet ; square bezel engraved with monogram of VIVAS IN DEO.
Italy or Gaul. 4th Century.
(Waterton Colln.) 587–1871.

About half the hoop wanting.

202. SILVER ; oval bezel lightly engraved with a monogram perhaps intended for VIVAS IN DEO.
Italy or Gaul. 4th Century.
(Waterton Colln.) 590–1871.

203. BRONZE ; signet ; oval bezel engraved with a lamb and two branches ; the hoop chased in the form of a wreath of palms.
Italy. 4th Century. *Plate VII.*
(Waterton Colln.) 604–1871.

Figured in Smith & Cheetham, *Dictionary of Christian Antiquities*, ii. 1799.

204. BRONZE ; signet ; projecting octagonal bezel engraved with a dove, a branch, and a star ; the hoop with knops perhaps intended to represent a wreath.
Italy. 4th Century. *Plate VII.*
605–1871.

Arch. Journal, xxviii. 273.

204*a*. BRONZE ; raised circular bezel set with a silver intaglio ; the latter is engraved with a vase, at either side of which is perched a dove with an olive branch between ; below are two indeterminate objects.
Italy. 4th Century. *Plate VII.*
Given by Dr. W. L. Hildburgh, F.S.A.
M. 159–1929.

205. BRONZE ; signet ; oval bezel engraved with a ship bearing on the sail the XP monogram and surrounded by the inscription STEPANVS HELENAE.
Italy. 5th Century. *Plate VII.*
(Waterton Colln.) 95–1899.

206. BRONZE ; signet ; circular bezel engraved with a cross monogram, the hoop with vertical and horizontal grooves.
Italy. 5th Century.
(Waterton Colln.) 589–1871.

207. SILVER ; circular signet bezel engraved with a palm-tree, above which, within a nimbus, is a lamb with the XP monogram. Flanking the tree are two deer (?), two flying doves, and the inscription IANVARI VIVAS. Mounted in a modern gold setting.
Italy. 5th or 6th Century. *Plate VII.*
(Waterton Colln.) 92–1899.

Ironmongers' Hall Exhibition, 1861, ii. 495.

This appears to be identical with an "annular engraved stone" figured in Smith and Cheetham, i. 718, together with the explanation of its iconography as interpreted by Father Garrucci, S.J. According to this, the Lamb of God is represented in a nimbus with the Chrisma, and is standing on a column, the symbol of the church; twelve gems on it (Rev. xxi.) represent the twelve apostles; at the base are two lambs, the Jewish and Gentile believers.

208. GOLD; signet; circular bezel engraved with an eagle, whose raised wings enclose a cross monogram of the letters Ω, M, A and K.
Egypt. 5th Century. *Plate VII.*
(Waterton Colln.) 621–1871.

Smith and Cheetham, ii. 1798. A very similar ring with a design of a like description from Akhmîm (Egypt) is illustrated by Claudius Côte, *Collection de Bagues*, 1906, p. 16.

209. BRONZE; roughly circular bezel, engraved with a cross motive within a circle.
Egypt. 5th or 6th Century.
Given by the Egypt Exploration Fund.
1894-1897.

Found at Behnesa (Oxyrhynchus), 1896-97.

210. BRONZE; signet; projecting oval bezel engraved with two nimbed figures (the Annunciation or the Visitation ?).
Palestine. 5th or 6th Century.
Plate VII.
1377–1904.

From Jerusalem.

211. IRON; signet; circular bezel engraved with a monogram and a cross.
Egypt. 6th Century. *Plate VII.*
Given by the Egypt Exploration Fund.
1894*a*–1897.

Found at Behnesa (Oxyrhynchus), 1896-97.

212. BRONZE with traces of silvering; an octagonal hoop, engraved with a lion and the remains of an inscription filled in with black lac.
6th or 7th Century. *Plate VII.*
M. 1142–1926.

Said to have come from Mount Carmel.

(2) Byzantine

213. GOLD; signet; circular bezel engraved with a cross monogram including the letters SIONA; wire hoop.
6th or 7th Century. *Plate VIII.*
(Fould and Waterton Collns.)
622–1871.

214. GOLD; circular bezel engraved with a monogram; wire hoop.
6th or 7th Century. *Plate VIII.*
(Waterton Colln.) 623-1871.

215. GOLD; bezel formed by a solidus of Constans II (641-668), of the type issued about 641-6, within a beaded border, the hoop faceted and inscribed +BARINOTA.
7th Century. *Plate VIII.*
(Waterton Colln.) 617–1871.

It has been suggested that Bari may have been the name of the imperial notary (*Arch. Journal*, xvi. 1859, p. 194).

Ironmongers' Hall Exhibition, 1861, ii. 495.

216. GOLD; circular bezel with bust of the Virgin Mary between the letters M and A, on a nielloed ground; wide hoop.
6th to 8th Century. *Plate VIII.*
(Waterton Colln.) 618–1871.

Smith and Cheetham, ii. 1299.

217. BRONZE; curved circular bezel engraved with the bust of a saint.
6th to 8th Century. *Plate VII.*
(Waterton Colln.) 619–1871.

218. BRONZE; signet; large circular bezel engraved with the figure of an orante; on the opposite side of the hoop is a smaller bezel engraved with a cross.
6th to 8th Century. *Plate VIII.*
(Waterton Colln.) 606–1871.

219. BRONZE; signet; oval bezel inscribed + πετρου.
6th to 8th Century.
(Waterton Colln.) 507–1871.

220. GOLD; chased in the form of two peacocks *affrontés*, their heads raised to form the bezel.
6th to 11th Century. *Plate VIII.*
(Waterton Colln.) 615–1871.

Ironmongers' Hall Exhibition, 1861, ii. 496.

221. BRONZE; circular bezel engraved with a cross monogram.
10th or 11th Century. *Plate VIII.*
(Waterton Colln.) 588–1871.

221*a*. BRONZE; oval bezel engraved with a cross monogram.
Byzantine. 10th or 11th Century.
Given by Sir Otto Beit, Bart., K.C.M.G.
Acquired in Sicily. M. 251–1929.

222. SILVER; circular bezel inscribed κεβ τον φο (κύριε βοήθει τὸν φοροῦντα, "O Lord, help the wearer"), the hoop engraved with linear foliations.
10th or 11th Century. *Plate VIII.*
(Waterton Colln.) 506–1871.

223. GOLD; the shoulders and circular bezel with applied filigree framing a medallion of cloisonné enamel (triangular device).
10th to 12th Century. *Plate VIII.*
4917–1901.

Transferred from the Museum of Practical Geology, Jermyn Street.

Found in Ireland. *Arch. Journal*, xix. p. 182.

224. GOLD; transverse oval bezel with engraved border of semicircles, set with a bloodstone intaglio of St. John the Evangelist, inscribed, in contracted form, ὁ ἅγιος θεόλογος; plain wire hoop.
11th Century. *Plate VIII.*
(Waterton Colln.) 616–1871.

Ironmongers' Hall Exhibition, 1861, ii. 496.

(3) Early Teutonic Rings

(*a*) *Anglo-Saxon and Viking*

224*a*. BRONZE WIRE; the ends tapered and twisted to form the bezel.
5th to 7th Century. *Frontispiece.*
(Waterton Colln.) 598–1871.

224*b*. BRONZE WIRE; the ends twisted together to form the bezel.
5th to 7th Century.
(Waterton Colln.) 596–1871.

224*c*. A duplicate of the last.
Frontispiece.
(Waterton Colln.) 597–1871.

225. SILVER-GILT; oval bezel, with central dragon medallion flanked by four animal heads.
Anglo-Saxon. Late 8th or Early 9th Century. *Frontispiece.*
(Waterton Colln.) 628–1871.

Found in the Thames at Chelsea, 1856.

Dr. Brønsted (*Early English Ornament*, p. 155) pronounces this ring to be of South English workmanship and points to the resemblance to the interlaced work on the bowl found at Fejo, Denmark, and the book-cover from Lindau in the Pierpont Morgan Collection.

Mr. R. A. Smith (*Archaeologia*, lxxiv. 1923, p. 247) considers this ring to be of very similar workmanship to the pins discovered in the River at Witham and at Ixworth.

Fairholt (*Rambles of an Archaeologist*, p. 101) supposed that the ground had originally been nielloed, but this is certainly not the case.

Jones (*Finger-ring Lore*, 1877, p. 60) illustrates the ring and calls it South Saxon.

Rohault de Fleury, *La Messe*, viii. 260, Pl. DCLXXX; Ironmongers' Hall Exhibition, 1861, ii. 496.

See p. 137 for additional note.

226. GOLD; stirrup-shaped hoop, the shoulders with filigree and granular decoration in the form of dragon-heads, the bezel a plain ball of gold.
Anglo-Saxon. 9th Century (?).
Frontispiece.
M. 277–1920.

Found in the moat at Meaux Abbey, Yorks., 1867.

came to England from the Caspian during the Viking period, but the ornamentation was quite different.

227. GOLD; massive, formed of eight members alternately circular and lozenge-shaped, nielloed and chased with leaf borders; in the lozenges are conventional animals, in the roundels is the name +ALHSTAN.
Anglo-Saxon. 9th Century. *Frontispiece.*
(Waterton Colln.) 627–1871.

Found at Llysfaen in N.E. Carnarvonshire, previous to December 1773.

The ring is thought to have belonged to Alhstan, Bishop of Sherborne, from 817 to 867. From its artistic merit it must clearly have been owned by some important person, and it is thought that

No. 227.

Proc. Soc. Ant., 2nd Series, vol. xxxii. 1919-20, pp. 112-114. For a similar use of granular ornament, compare the Ethelswith ring in the British Museum (Dalton, 180) and the Anglo-Saxon ring found at Oxford (*Proc. Soc. Ant.*, 2nd Series, vol. xxix. 1916-17, p. 123). Boars' heads may be seen on the Berkeley Castle ring (Clifford Smith, *Jewellery*, Pl. XIII, Fig. 10).

When this ring was exhibited to the Society of Antiquaries, Mr. Reginald Smith pointed to a resemblance to certain bracelets in the Oxus Treasure of the 4th Century B.C. (Dalton, *Treasure of the Oxus*, Nos. 118, 129, 132 and 133), which had a similar double row of cells behind the animals' heads. Much silver and some gold

Alhstan, who certainly took part in two other campaigns, may have accompanied King Egbert's invasion of North Wales in the year 828. For this reason the Bishop of Sherborne seems a more probable candidate for the ownership of the ring than others who have been suggested, though the fact that there are fifteen ways of spelling this name used in reference to this person must inevitably leave a rather wide field for alternatives.

The Ethelwulf and Ethelswith rings in the British Museum both belong to this same period and are ornamented with a similar niello. A marked Merovingian influence is visible in all these rings in the treatment of the animals.

Archaeologia, vol. iv. 1786, p. 47;

Brønsted, *Early English Ornament*, pp. 133-4; *Gentleman's Magazine*, xciii. 1823, p. 483; Smith and Cheetham, ii. 1804 *n.*; Waterton MS., pp. 163-174; Fairholt, *Rambles of an Archaeologist*, p. 102; C. J. Jackson, *History of English Plate*, p. 55; Ironmongers' Hall Exhibition, 1861, ii. 496.

228. GOLD; signet; circular bezel engraved with the full-face bust of a bearded man dividing the inscription +AVF RET. Both the shoulders have a flattened pellet on either side of the hoop.
Anglo-Saxon. 9th Century. *Frontispiece.*
(Waterton Colln.) 629–1871.

Said to have been found at Rome in conjunction with coins of Alfred the Great (*Arch. Journal*, xvi. 1859, 194).

Ironmongers' Hall Exhibition, 1861, ii. 496.

A ring very similar in form and workmanship, found at Benevento in 1864 and inscribed MAVRICI, is in the Ashmolean Museum (Fortnum Colln., 341), whilst another, inscribed CHARI (?), in the possession of M. Claudius Côte, is illustrated in the *Revue Archéologique*, 4e série, v. 1905, pp. 195, 199. In the Bargello Museum, Florence, is another gold ring (No. 319), of similar design but poor workmanship, with inscription FAOLFVS.

A ring of similar form, but crude like the last, was found at Wittislingen, Bavaria, in 1881, and is in the National Museum, Munich (No. 235), being illustrated in Deloche, *Anneaux Sigillaires*, p. 344.

229. GOLD; a hoop of two wires twisted together, diminishing towards the back, where it is beaten flat with four incuse dots.
Viking. 9th to 11th Century.
Frontispiece.
(Waterton Colln.) 631–1871.

Compare a ring in the British Museum (Dalton, 215*c*).

230. GOLD; hoop of plaited wires, diminishing towards the back, where it is beaten flat.
Viking. 9th to 11th Century.
Frontispiece.
(Waterton Colln.) 632–1871.

Compare examples in the British Museum (Dalton, 213, 214, 215, 215*a*) and the National Museum of Antiquities of Scotland (*Catalogue*, pp. 210-212, Nos. F. E. 17-22, 28-31, 40).

(*b*) *Continental*

231. BRONZE; signet (?); narrow hoop expanding to form a bezel, which is engraved with . . . H C (?).
Merovingian (?). 6th Century.
(Waterton Colln.) 586–1871.

Not unlike the ring from the cemetery of Herpes (Charente) figured in Deloche, *Anneaux Sigillaires*, pp. 256-7.

232. BRONZE; signet; thin hoop flattened to form an oblong bezel engraved with a monogram; the shoulders chased with foliated scrolls.
Merovingian. 6th or 7th Century.
Plate IX.
(Waterton Colln.) 730–1871.

The form of the hoop and decoration are very similar to one from Armentières (Aisne) figured in Deloche, *Anneaux Sigillaires*, p. 132.

233. BRONZE; signet; small projecting square bezel engraved with a monogram; the hoop engraved with scales filled in with silver.
Merovingian. 6th or 7th Century.
Plate IX.
(Waterton Colln.) 592–1871.

For the use of damascening and incrustation by the Franks, see Barrière-Flavy, *Les Arts Industriels des Peuples Barbares de la Gaule*, i. 180-182. Deloche, *Anneaux Sigillaires*, p. xxi. Compare also a ring at Lyons (*ibid.*, p. 320).

234. BRONZE ; signet ; projecting square bezel engraved with a monogram.
Merovingian. 6th or 7th Century.
Plate IX.
(Waterton Colln.) 593–1871.

For a ring of this form, see one from Wallers (Nord) in Deloche, *Anneaux Sigillaires*, p. 184.

235. SILVER ; circular bezel composed of seven arches supporting a gallery with setting for a central stone.
Merovingian or Lombard. 6th or 7th Century. *Plate IX.*
(Waterton Colln.) 952–1871.

For rings with bezels of "architectural" form, see Deloche, *Anneaux Sigillaires*, p. 4, illustrating an example from Garde (Loire) ; one in the Collection of M. Claudius Côte from Beauvais, see *Revue Archéologique*, 4e série, pp. 195, 199 ; and another in the Museum of Cividale del Friuli (723), see Gino Fogolari, *Cividale del Friuli*, p. 29. Compare also one in the British Museum (Dalton, 175). In the Carrand Collection in the Bargello, Florence, is another Frankish ring (No. 968) having a hoop with filigree decoration and a domed bezel set with a small flat garnet supported by an open arcade. There is also a pin (No. 960) of a similar design.

235*a*. [See p. 137.]

236. GOLD ; transverse oval bezel with an antique onyx intaglio of Bonus Eventus (?) in a beaded setting ; the shoulders each with three pellets and attached to the back of the bezel by volutes.
Merovingian. 6th or 7th Century.
Plate IX.
(Waterton Colln.) 620–1871.

The volutes appear to be very characteristic of Merovingian work ; see Deloche, *Anneaux Sigillaires*, ring from Mâcon, p. 25, from Jumelle, p. 103, from Amiens, p. 197, and three in the Cabinet des Médailles at the Bibliothèque Nationale, *ibid.*, pp. 293-296.

237. GOLD ; circular bezel with corded edge, set with four slices of garnet surrounding a central setting (now empty).
Merovingian. 6th or 7th Century.
Plate IX.
(Waterton Colln.) 626–1871.

Ironmongers' Hall Exhibition, 1861, ii. 496.

Compare the next, and one in the British Museum (Dalton, 170) ; also Deloche, *Anneaux Sigillaires*, p. 122, for a ring from Samson, near Namur, and another (p. 185) from Artres (Nord).

238. GOLD ; circular bezel with corded edge, the central setting (now containing a garnet bead) surrounded by four slices of garnet with a border of eleven beads (six missing) ; hoop with raised edges.
Merovingian. 6th or 7th Century.
Plate IX.
(Waterton Colln.) 625–1871.

Compare the last.

239. GOLD ; the hoop with edge and cross-divisions of beaded wire, pierced with five lozenge-shaped holes ; pierced beaker-shaped bezel rising from two groups of three pellets and set with a cabochon sapphire within beaded wire borders. On one side of the bezel is fixed a tube with a setting for a gem.
Merovingian. 6th or 7th Century.
Plate IX.
(Waterton Colln.) 624–1871.

For a similar ring, but without the side tube, see No. 187 in the Fortnum Collection, Ashmolean Museum. For other rings with pierced hoops, see British Museum (Dalton, 176), and a ring from Spontin, near Namur, in Deloche, *Anneaux Sigillaires*, p. 119.

A ring in the Cinquantenaire Museum at Brussels, found at Lede (E. Brabant), has an inverted pyramidal bezel, and at one side a horn-shaped tube and some scrollwork. In the Kunstgewerbe

Museum at Cologne is a ring with a beaker-shaped bezel of lozenge section set with a green stone and having a grooved border; at the side is a small ruby set in an openwork horn-shaped setting. Its decoration is not, however, very similar, and it is attributed by the authorities to the end of the 13th century. E. Moses, *Der Schmuck der Sammlung Clemens*, p. 21.

240. SILVER-GILT; fluted hoop; boldly projecting beaker-shaped bezel set with an oval red-and-blue glass mosaic (quatrefoil design).
Carolingian. 9th Century. *Plate IX.*
Given by Sir James Hudson, K.C.B.
7442–1860.

Found in Lombardy.

Compare a ring in the British Museum (Dalton, 176).

B. *DECORATIVE RINGS* [1]

(1) 12TH TO END OF 15TH CENTURY

241. SILVER-GILT; pyramidal bezel (imitating a diamond), the shoulders chased in the form of monsters' heads.
12th Century. *Plate X.*
(Waterton Colln.) 937–1871.

Compare an almost identical ring in the Museum at Tournai.

242. GOLD; long oval bezel inscribed MAȜNE; the flattened shoulders enriched with cloisonné niello in a simple scroll pattern.
12th Century (?). *Plate X.*
525–1868.

243. GILT BRONZE; transverse oblong bezel with four claws holding a blue paste; wire hoop.
12th Century. *Plate X.*
(Waterton Colln.) 648–1871.

Compare the ring found near the tomb of William Rufus in Winchester Cathedral (South Kensington Museum, *Catalogue of the Special Exhibition*, 1862, p. 637), and others in the British Museum (Dalton, 1743-8).

[1] Other rings to which this description might be applied will be found in the following sections:—
Early Christian, Nos. 202, 212.
Byzantine, Nos. 215-17, 220, 223.
Early Teutonic—Anglo-Saxon, Nos. 224*a*-7, 229, 230.
Early Teutonic—Continental, Nos. 235, 237, 240.

244. GOLD; the bezel set with an uncut oriental sapphire held by four claws; wire hoop.
12th Century. *Plate X.*
(Waterton Colln.) 644–1871.

245. GOLD; moulded shoulders; forked supports for the cup-shaped bezel, the latter set with an uncut sapphire held by four claws.
13th Century. *Plate X.*
(Waterton Colln.) 645–1871.

246. GOLD; oblong bezel with a lion passant in relief; the shoulders engraved with reticulated ornament.
Italian (Venetian). 13th Century.
Plate X.
26–1894.

247. GOLD; shaped tranverse bezel set with a female bust in full relief in plasma, held by four claws; wire hoop.
English. 13th Century. (The gem Ancient Roman.) *Plate X.*
(Waterton Colln.) 646–1871.

Found at Canmore Place, near Witney, in 1856.

Ironmongers' Hall Exhibition, 1861, ii. 499.

Rohault de Fleury, *La Messe*, viii. 264, Pl. DCLXXX.

EARLY TEUTONIC RINGS (CONTINENTAL)

233		232		234
	236		236	
238		235		237
	239		240	

PLATE X

DECORATIVE RINGS: 12TH TO 14TH CENTURY

	242	
241	246	243
245	249	244
251	248	253

DECORATIVE RINGS: 13TH TO 15TH CENTURY

	263	
247	263	258
255	256	257
259	261	260

DECORATIVE RINGS: 15TH CENTURY

269	266	268
	265	
270	264	271
273	275	274

248. GOLD ; the bezel set with a cabochon sapphire held by four claws alternating with four small amethysts in detached collets ; thin hoop.
English. 13th Century. *Plate X.*
(Harman Oates Colln.) M. 7–1929.

Found at Epsom.

Compare the ring found in the grave of an unknown Bishop of Chichester, illustrated in *Arch. Journal*, xx. 1863, p. 235, Fig. 8.

249. GOLD ; thin stirrup-shaped hoop with flattened sides swelling towards the shoulders ; cup-shaped bezel with four claws holding a cabochon oriental carbuncle.
13th Century. *Plate X.*
(Waterton Colln.) 650–1871.

250. GOLD ; stirrup-shaped ; set with a small cabochon sapphire.
13th Century.
(Waterton Colln.) 633–1871.

251. GOLD ; stirrup-shaped ; set with a small uncut sapphire.
English. 13th Century. *Plate X.*
Given by Dr. Harcourt. 65–1871.

Found in the vicinity of the Chapel Royal, Windsor, about 1835.

251*a*. GOLD ; stirrup-shaped ; set with a small uncut sapphire.
13th Century.
(Waterton Colln.) 634–1871.

252. GILT BRONZE ; stirrup-shaped ; set with a small hexagonal sapphire ; the shoulders nielloed in foliations.
Italian. 14th Century.
(Waterton Colln.) 636–1871.

253. SILVER-GILT ; stirrup-shaped ; set with a threaded pearl ; each shoulder and middle of hoop chased with a sexfoil.
Italian (Venetian). 14th Century. *Plate X.*
(Waterton Colln.) 94–1899.

In the Ashmolean Museum is a very similar ring (Fortnum Colln., 376) from Chalcis. Compare also one in the British Museum (Dalton, 1820).

254. GOLD ; slender wire hoop ; small cup-shaped bezel set with a cabochon sapphire.
13th or 14th Century.
(Waterton Colln.) 637–1871.

255. GOLD ; slender wire hoop ; small cup-shaped bezel set with a cabochon emerald.
13th or 14th Century. *Plate XI.*
(Waterton Colln.) 638–1871.

256. GOLD ; slender hoop ; transverse semicircular bezel set with a cabochon garnet.
13th or 14th Century. *Plate XI.*
(Waterton Colln.) 640–1871.

257. GOLD ; slender hoop ; hexagonal bezel set with a cabochon sapphire.
14th Century. *Plate XI.*
(Waterton Colln.) 639–1871.

258. GOLD ; transverse oval bezel set with a cabochon sapphire ; the shoulders chased with bands of leaves at the junction with the bezel.
14th Century. *Plate XI.*
(Waterton Colln.) 641–1871.

259. GOLD ; hoop of triangular section ; the shoulders chased as dragon-heads ; large hexagonal bezel set with a cabochon sapphire.
French. 14th Century. *Plate XI.*
(Waterton Colln.) 642–1871.

From Amiens.

260. GOLD ; hexagonal bezel set with a cabochon sapphire (simply faceted) ; shoulders chased with dragon-heads, the hoop as a chain of quatrefoils.
14th Century. *Plate XI.*
(Waterton Colln.) 647–1871.

261. GOLD ; large flower-shaped bezel engraved with palm-leaf pattern and set with a roughly cut sapphire ; the shoulders with settings for stones, one of which holds a cabochon ruby (the other empty).
French. 14th Century. *Plate XI.*
(Waterton Colln.) 90–1899.

Said to have been found in the tomb of a bishop in France.

Presented to Waterton by the Hon. Robert Curzon. Waterton MS., p. 180.

Compare the ring on the effigy of Bishop William of Wykeham on his tomb in Winchester Cathedral.

262. GOLD ; large transverse oval bezel set with a lump of composition (a precious balsam ?).
14th Century.
(Waterton Colln.) 643–1871.

263. GOLD ; projecting square bezel set with a small emerald ; roped hoop with pearled borders, interrupted by four lozenges filled with quatrefoils in filigree.
Italian (?). 15th Century. *Plate XI.*
(Waterton Colln.) 652–1871.

264. GOLD ; oval bezel with four claws (stone wanting) ; the hoop chased with an oak-leaf pattern and divided into four sections by three conventional knots, each enclosing a star ; each section is divided down the centre and encloses a row of separately made pellets.
15th Century. *Plate XII.*
(Waterton Colln.) 653–1871.

A very similar example from the Chalcis hoard is in the Ashmolean Museum (Fortnum Colln., 386).

265. GOLD ; the hoop set with a pyramidal diamond and two cabochon rubies and engraved with the letters U and R. Inscribed inside FOR A CAUSE.
English. 15th Century. *Plate XII.*
(Ashburnham Colln.) M. 253–1921.

266. GOLD, with traces of enamel ; the hoop spirally fluted and chased with flowers.
English. 15th Century. *Plate XII.*
(Waterton Colln.) 894–1871.

267. SILVER-GILT ; oblong bezel with three transverse grooves engraved with foliage ; the shoulders with central ridge, the hoop spirally fluted.
English. 15th Century.
(Waterton Colln.) 682–1871.

268. SILVER-GILT ; the hoop and oblong bezel centrally ridged, the shoulders engraved with triangles, the bezel with leafy sprays.
English. 15th Century. *Plate XII.*
(Waterton Colln.) 684–1871.

Compare a similar ring in the Taunton Museum.

269. SILVER - GILT ; the bezel formed by two engraved square quatrefoils set at an angle ; ridged and engraved shoulders.
English. 15th Century. *Plate XII.*
6769–1860.

270. SILVER - GILT ; transverse oval bezel with embattled edge, set with a turquoise (added later ?) ; openwork shoulders with grapes and vine-branches ; hoop reinforced by two rings of twisted wire.
German. 15th Century. *Plate XII.*
1205–1903.

271. SILVER-GILT ; the shoulders and bezel in the form of a stag "at speed" amid leafless branches in openwork ; hoop reinforced by two rings of twisted wire.
German. 15th Century. *Plate XII.*
1204-1903.

272. SILVER ; transverse flat oval bezel nielloed with a symmetrical floral design ; shoulders with chequer pattern.
North Italian. 15th Century.
(Waterton Colln.) 885–1871.

273. SILVER; transverse flat oval bezel, nielloed with an eight-petalled flower.
North Italian. 15th Century.
Plate XII.
(Waterton Colln.) 886–1871.

274. SILVER; the flat circular bezel nielloed with a star formed by triangles, inclosing the letters ˥L, the hoop with a lozenge diaper of quatrefoils.
North Italian. 15th Century.
Plate XII.
(Waterton Colln.) 887–1871.

275. SILVER; projecting lozenge-shaped bezel nielloed with a quatrefoil device; graduated border.
15th Century. *Plate XII.*
(Waterton Colln.) 985–1871.

275*a*. GILT BRONZE; massive, the bezel set with a square projecting green paste, its sides chased to represent four drooping petals; hoop with external ridge and cusped shoulders.
Italian. Late 15th Century.
Given by Dr. W. L. Hildburgh, F.S.A.
M. 160–1929.

Three similar rings are in the Museo Correr, Venice.

(2) 16TH TO MIDDLE OF 17TH CENTURY

276. GOLD; the bezel set with a cabochon turquoise, the sides chased to represent four drooping petals.
16th Century. *Plate XIII.*
(Waterton Colln.) 954–1871.

Compare a similar ring in the British Museum (Dalton, 1928).

277. GOLD; sexfoil bezel set with a cabochon turquoise (engraved later with a Gothic F in reverse); the sides chased as drooping leaves each set with a garnet; shoulders chased, with traces of black enamel.
Italian (?). 16th Century. *Plate XIII.*
(Waterton Colln.) 953–1871.

Said to have belonged to Frederick the Great (*Catalogue of the Special Exhibition at South Kensington Museum*, 1862, p. 631).

Ironmongers' Hall Exhibition, 1861, ii. 503.

278. GOLD; quatrefoil bezel set with a red paste; the sides chased as drooping petals, which, like the spreading shoulders, are chased and filled in with green enamel.
16th Century. 597–1892.

279. GOLD; quatrefoil bezel set with a ruby; the sides chased as drooping petals, which, like the scrolled shoulders, are richly enamelled in black and white.
16th Century. *Plate XIII.*
4397–1857.

280. GOLD; quatrefoil bezel set with a small cabochon ruby; the sides chased as drooping petals, which, like the scrolled shoulders, show traces of white enamel.
16th Century. *Plate XIII.*
(Waterton Colln.) 949–1871.

281. GOLD; quatrefoil bezel set with a jacinth; the sides chased as drooping petals, which, like the spreading shoulders, are richly enamelled.
16th Century. *Plate XIII.*
(Waterton Colln.) 948–1871.

282. GOLD; quatrefoil bezel set with a table-cut diamond; the sides chased as drooping petals, which, like the scrolled shoulders, are richly enamelled.
16th Century. *Plate XIII.*
(Salting Bequest.) M. 556–1910.

283. SILVER-GILT; large quatrefoil bezel set with a red paste, the sides representing drooping petals engraved with trellis pattern; the shoulders chased with scrolls.
16th Century. 1206–1903.

284. GOLD; oblong quatrefoil bezel set with a sapphire; the sides chased as drooping petals, which, like the scrolled shoulders, show traces of green, white and red enamel.
16th Century. *Plate XIII.*
201–1906.

285. SILVER-GILT; square box-shaped bezel set with an almandine; the shoulders chased in open scrolls.
16th Century. 189–1872.

286. GOLD; square box-shaped bezel set with a paste, foiled white; the shoulders chased with scrolls and enamelled.
16th Century.
(Waterton Colln.) 947–1871.

287. GOLD; square box-shaped bezel set with an emerald; the shoulders chased in low scrolls.
16th Century. 193–1864.

288. GOLD; oblong box-shaped bezel set with an emerald; its lower part and the shoulders chased with cartouche-work richly enamelled.
16th Century. *Plate XIII.*
65–1896.

289. GOLD; oblong box-shaped bezel set with a ruby; its lower part and the shoulders chased and enamelled.
16th Century. 731–1902.

290. GOLD; square box-shaped bezel set with a garnet; its lower part and the shoulders chased and enamelled.
16th Century.
(Waterton Colln.) 946–1871.

291. GOLD; square box-shaped bezel set with a diamond; its lower part and the shoulders chased and enriched with enamel.
16th Century. *Plate XIV.*
746–1893.

292. GOLD; square box-shaped bezel set with a crystal; its projecting base and the shoulders chased and enriched with enamel.
16th Century. *Plate XIV.*
30–1894.

293. GOLD; square box-shaped bezel set with an almandine; its projecting base and the shoulders elaborately chased and enriched with enamel.
16th Century. *Plate XIII.*
456–1873.

294. GOLD; square box-shaped bezel set with a small ruby; its lower part and the shoulders chased and enamelled.
16th Century. 7143–1860.

295. GOLD; lozenge-shaped bezel set with a diamond (re-cut and re-set); its lower part and the shoulders chased and enamelled.
English. 16th Century. *Plate XIV.*
730–1904.

Dug up at Petersham, Surrey.

296. GOLD; small; hexagonal bezel set with a turquoise, and, like the shoulders, chased and showing traces of enamel.
16th Century. *Plate XIV.*
(Waterton Colln.) 955–1871.

297. GOLD; small; hexagonal bezel set with a turquoise, and, like the shoulders, chased and enamelled. Rome hall-mark.
Italian. 16th Century.
(Waterton Colln.) 956–1871.

298. GOLD; small inverted pyramidal bezel set with a pointed diamond; thin wire hoop thickening at the shoulders.
16th Century.
(Waterton Colln.) 936–1871.

299. GOLD; transverse oval bezel chased with a woman's bust, showing traces of enamel; shoulders chased with leaves.
16th Century. *Plate XIV.*
(Waterton Colln.) 939–1871.

DECORATIVE RINGS: 16TH CENTURY

276	277	279
281	277	284
	280	
288	282	293
288	288	293

PLATE XIV

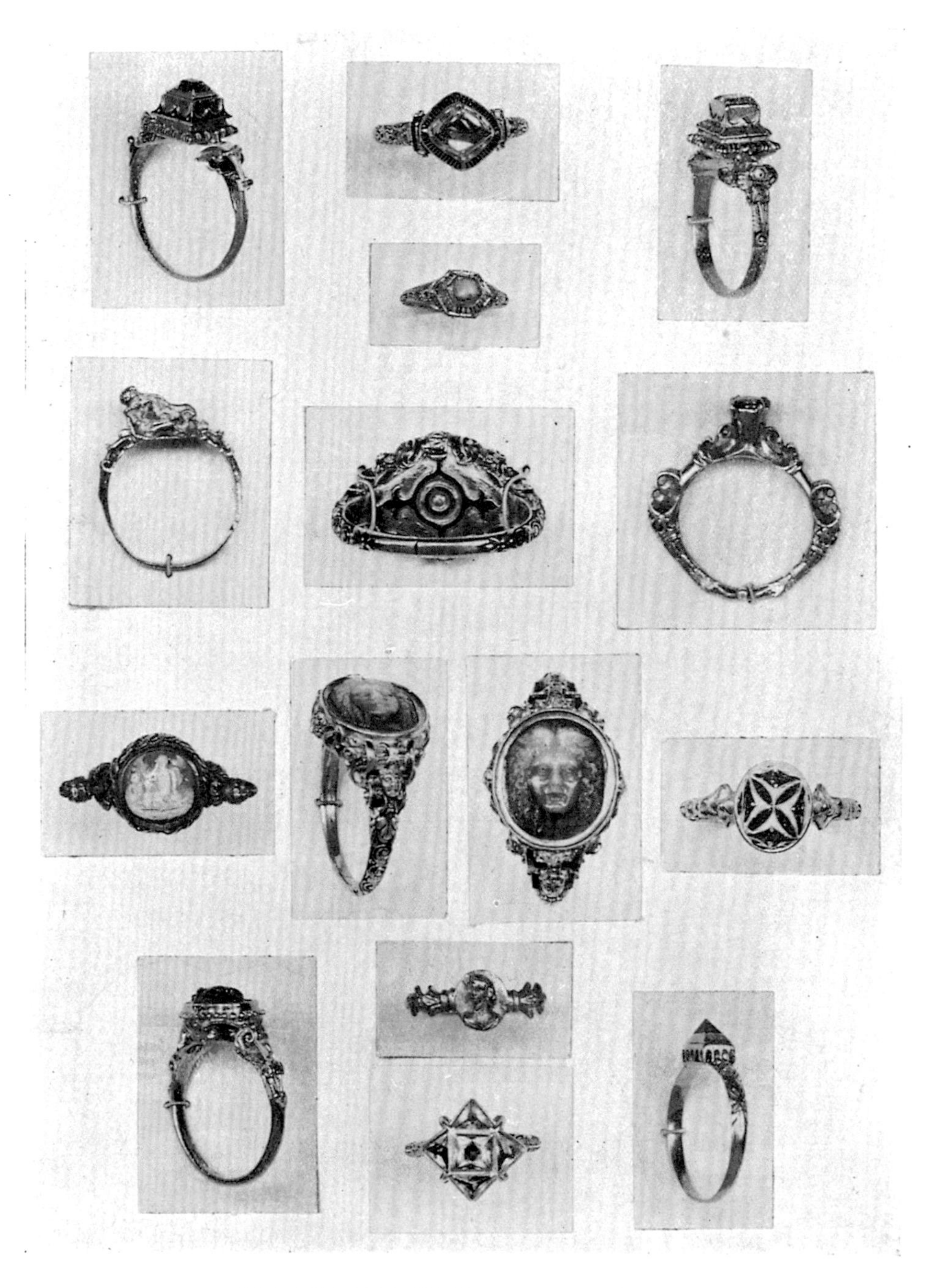

DECORATIVE RINGS: 16TH CENTURY

292		295 296		291
301		305		303
310	305		305	302
307		299 324		307

DECORATIVE RINGS: 16TH AND 17TH CENTURY

315	309	316
319		319*a*
	311	
320	313	317
317	312	317*a*
321		322

DECORATIVE RINGS: 17TH AND 18TH CENTURY

323 327

329 328 318*a*

331 335 337

336

333 338 340

300. GOLD; formerly enamelled; the bezel in the form of a frog, the shoulders chased.
16th Century.
(Waterton Colln.) 938–1871.

301. GOLD; with traces of enamel; the bezel in the form of a man struggling with a unicorn, the shoulders with cartouche-work.
16th Century. *Plate XIV.*
(Waterton Colln.) 963–1871.

302. GOLD; oval bezel enamelled with a cross of St. John in white on black; the shoulders in the form of demi-figures.
Italian. 16th Century. *Plate XIV.*
(Waterton Colln.) 958–1871.
Probably worn by a member of the Order of St. John of Jerusalem.
A similar ring is in the Ashmolean Museum (Fortnum Colln., 372).
Compare later examples, Nos. 370, 371, and others in the British Museum (Dalton, 2138–40).

303. GOLD; the lower part of the hoop formed by two eagles' heads issuing from crowns, the shoulders chased with open scrolls; cup-shaped bezel set with a cabochon sapphire held by four claws.
16th Century. *Plate XIV.*
4377–1857.
A ring formerly in the Collection Tarnóczy (Szendrei, *Catalogue de la Collection de Bagues de Madame Gustave de Tarnóczy*, p. 259) is identical except in being set with a ruby and not having fleurs-de-lys on the pierced openwork volutes of the shoulders. A similar ring in the British Museum (Dalton, 2006) still retains its enamel.

304. GOLD; oval bezel set with an amethyst relief of a cupid's head; the shoulders chased with cartouche-work and enamelled.
Italian. 16th Century. *Plate XIV.*
(Waterton Colln.) 940–1871.
Compare rings in the British Museum (Dalton, 1962–4).

305. GOLD; richly chased and enamelled with cartouche-work, masks and foliage; the bezel set with an onyx cameo head of Medusa.
Italian. 16th Century. *Plate XIV.*
(Salting Bequest.) M. 555–1910.

306. GOLD; enamelled in black and white with arabesques and set with an oval sapphire intaglio of Medusa.
Italian. 16th Century. (The gem Graeco-Roman, 1st Century A.D.)
Plate XXVII.
(Salting Bequest.) M. 553–1910.

307. GOLD; oblong bezel set with a pointed diamond, its lower part and the shoulders chased and showing traces of enamel.
16th Century. *Plate XIV.*
(Waterton Colln.) 935–1871.

308. GOLD; square bezel set with a pointed diamond, its lower part and the shoulders chased and enamelled.
16th Century.
(Waterton Colln.) 934–1871.

309. GILT BRONZE; large; oblong projecting bezel set with a cabochon garnet; the shoulders chased with vine scrolls.
16th Century. *Plate XV.*
(Waterton Colln.) 671–1871.

310. SILVER; circular bezel encased with plaited wire and set with an onyx cameo of a Nereid seated on a dolphin and attended by a Triton; at each shoulder a boldly projecting lion's head.
Italian. 16th Century. *Plate XIV.*
25–1894.

311. ONYX; the oval bezel set with a cameo of a river god in a white stratum, the rest being semi-transparent; the shoulders engraved with terminal figures.
Italian. 16th Century. *Plate XV.*
(Waterton Colln.) 957–1871.

312. GOLD ; inverted pyramidal bezel with setting for a stone, supported at the angles by four claws in openwork ; bezel and shoulders with traces of enamel.
16th or 17th Century. *Plate XV.*
(Waterton Colln.) 944–1871.

Compare rings in the British Museum (Dalton, 1989–91).

313. GOLD ; inverted pyramidal bezel set with a ruby and held at the angles by four adherent birds' claws ; black enamel below bezel, and traces of it on the shoulders.
16th or 17th Century. *Plate XV.*
(Waterton Colln.) 945–1871.

314. GOLD ; inverted pyramidal bezel set with a ruby, and, like the shoulders, enamelled black.
16th or 17th Century. 6826–1860.

315. GOLD ; lozenge-shaped bezel with settings for four foiled crystals and four red pastes (three of the latter wanting).
Spanish (Andalusian). Late 16th or early 17th Century. *Plate XV.*
331–1864.

Found in the bed of the Vega, near Baza, Granada.

316. GOLD ; bezel of a shape based on the cross fitchée, set with crystals.
Spanish (Andalusian, Andujar). Late 16th or early 17th Century. *Plate XV.*
1215–1871.

317. GOLD ; oblong bezel set with a table-cut sapphire with lozenge-shaped facets.
English. Second half of 16th Century.
Plate XV.
(Harman-Oates Colln.) M. 15–1929.

Found in the City of London.

317*a*. GOLD ; long octagonal bezel set with a table-cut white sapphire with lozenge-shaped facets, the hoop and lower part of the bezel enamelled white (decayed).
English. Second half of 16th Century.
Plate XV.
(Harman-Oates Colln.) M. 19–1929.

Found in the City of London.

318. GOLD ; inverted pyramidal bezel set with a jacinth ; the shoulders and lower part of the bezel enamelled green and black.
Late 16th or early 17th Century.
Plate XV.
4398–1857.

318*a*. GOLD ; pyramidal bezel set with diamonds ; the shoulders enamelled with A·I·N· and R·I·C.
Late 16th or early 17th Century.
Plate XVI.
732–1902.

319. GOLD ; octofoil bezel set with eight cabochon emeralds (two wanting) surrounding a larger one ; shoulders and back of bezel enamelled white, the latter with filigree decoration.
English. About 1600. *Plate XV.*
(Harman-Oates Colln.) M. 16–1929.

Found in the City of London.

319*a*. GOLD ; sexfoil bezel set with six garnets surrounding another ; shoulders enamelled white ; back of bezel with a six-petalled flower in blue enamel on white, with filigree outlines.
English. About 1600. *Plate XV.*
(Harman-Oates Colln.) M. 17–1929.

Found in the City of London.

320. GOLD ; large square bezel set with an emerald ; the sides of the bezel and the shoulders enamelled in black and white.
17th Century. *Plate XV.*
194–1864.

321. GOLD ; a thumb ring ; octagonal bezel re-set with a smoked quartz ; the shoulders and the back of the bezel enamelled with conventional ornament in black, white and green.
First half of 17th Century. *Plate XV.*
(Waterton Colln.) 967–1871.

322. GOLD ; oval bezel set with a turquoise, inlaid in gold with a Persian inscription ; the back of the bezel and the shoulders enamelled in black and white conventional patterns.
17th Century. *Plate XV.*
(Waterton Colln.) 965–1871.

323. GOLD ; square bezel set with a foiled almandine garnet.
17th Century. *Plate XVI.*
(Waterton Colln.) 941–1871.

324. GOLD ; bezel in the form of a star of four points alternating with birds' claws, set with four triangular diamonds surrounding a pyramidal one ; shoulders roughened for enamel ; back of bezel decorated with black enamel.
Late 16th or early 17th Century.
Plate XIV.
(Harman-Oates Colln.) M. 20–1929.

324*a*. GOLD ; square bezel set with a foiled crystal.
17th Century.
(Waterton Colln.) 942–1871.

325. GOLD ; small ; oval bezel with eight ribs, set with a turquoise ; the shoulders chased with a central ridge.
17th Century.
(Waterton Colln.) 943–1871.

326. GOLD ; the shoulders chased in broken lines ; square bezel set with a foiled crystal with traces of enamel.
17th Century. 23–1865.

327. GOLD ; square box-shaped bezel with sloping sides, set with a garnet ; the shoulders and lower part of the bezel enamelled in white, black and green. Two marks, unidentified.
17th Century. *Plate XVI.*
(Waterton Colln.) 951–1871.

328. GOLD ; octagonal bezel set with a garnet ; the shoulders and the sides of the hoop chased and enamelled in white and black.
English. 17th Century. *Plate XVI.*
Given by the Rev. R. Brooke.
1112–1864.

329. GOLD ; oblong bezel set with a garnet ; the hoop and the sides of the bezel enamelled in white, black and green.
English. 17th Century. *Plate XVI.*
190–1864.

330. GOLD ; the bezel re-set with a red-foiled crystal, between groups of small diamonds in silver settings ; the shoulders and the sides of the hoop enamelled in white and black.
Italian. 17th Century.
Given by Mr. Walter Child, A.R.S.M.
638–1906.

From Palermo.

331. GOLD ; transverse oval bezel set with a turquoise surrounded by seventeen garnets, with a garnet on each shoulder; the shoulders enamelled black, and the back of the bezel white, in scroll patterns.
17th Century. *Plate XVI.*
(Waterton Colln.) 966–1871.

(3) Middle of 17th to 19th Century

332. GOLD ; pyramidal bezel set with a table-cut diamond, the sides and shoulders enriched with black and white enamel.
Italian. Second half of 17th Century.
(Murray Bequest.) M. 1016–1910.

333. GOLD ; sexfoil bezel set with a garnet surrounded by six turquoises ; the shoulders and back of bezel enamelled in black and white.
Second half of 17th Century.
Plate XVI.
733–1902.

334. GOLD; the bezel set with a rose diamond enclosing plaited hair between groups of three small diamonds in silver collets; the shoulders and back of bezel chased and enamelled in black and white.
English. Late 17th or early 18th Century.
Given by the Rev. R. Brooke.
1115–1864.

335. GOLD; the bezel in the form of three overlapping square settings for seven diamonds; the shoulders and sides of bezel enamelled in black and white.
Italian (?). Late 17th or early 18th Century. *Plate XVI.*
192–1864.

A similar example in the British Museum (Dalton, 2034) has the control mark of the Papal States.

336. GOLD; the bezel set with an oblong jacinth, between two diamonds in silver collets; the shoulders and sides of bezel enamelled in black and white.
English. Late 17th or early 18th Century. *Plate XVI.*
Given by the Rev. R. Brooke.
1113–1864.

337. GOLD; large oval bezel set with a ruby surrounded by ten diamonds in silver collets; the shoulders and back of the bezel enamelled in black and white.
English. Late 17th or early 18th Century. *Plate XVI.*
Given by the Rev. R. Brooke.
1116–1864.

338. GOLD; the bezel formed by a figure 3 in black enamel between three rubies.
Late 17th or early 18th Century.
Plate XVI.
213–1870.

339. GOLD; the bezel set with four rubies and two diamonds and enamelled on the back.
German. Early 18th Century.
171–1872.

340. GOLD; oval bezel set with eight small diamonds surrounding a central one which encloses plaited hair.
English. Early 18th Century.
Plate XVI.
Given by the Rev. R. Brooke.
1117–1864.

341. GOLD; octagonal bezel set with an amethyst.
English. 18th Century.
Given by the Rev. R. Brooke.
1111–1864.

342. GOLD; openwork bezel formed as a spray of three flowers set with diamonds and rubies in silver collets; shoulders spirally gadrooned.
18th Century. *Plate XVII.*
234–1864.
Jones, *Finger-ring Lore*, p. 79, illus.

343. GOLD; openwork bezel formed as a bunch of flowers, set with diamonds in silver collets.
English (?). 18th Century.
214–1870.

344. GOLD; the bezel in the form of a shell filled with Masonic emblems, set with diamonds in silver collets; at each side an emerald.
English. 18th Century. *Plate XVII.*
212–1870.

345. GOLD; openwork bezel in the form of a vase of flowers set with an amethyst, diamonds and rubies in silver collets; the hoop pierced and set with a stone (wanting).
English. Third quarter of 18th Century. 8551–1863.

346. GOLD; openwork bezel in the form of a flower set with a yellow diamond surrounded by rubies, the leaves set with emeralds; the shoulders chased with scrolls in openwork (two outer diamonds in silver collets).
English. Third quarter of 18th Century. *Plate XVII.*
8548–1863.

PLATE XVII

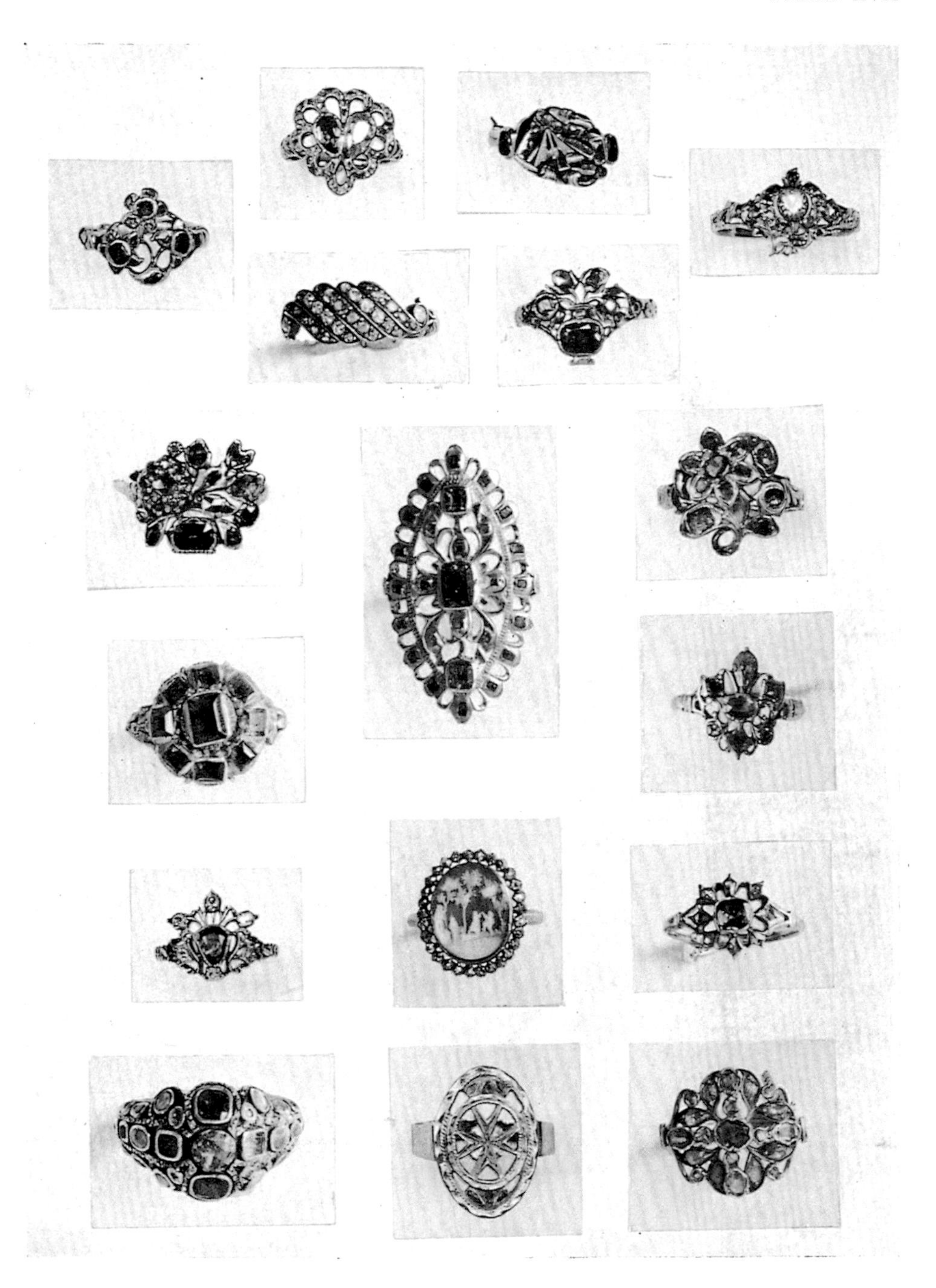

DECORATIVE RINGS: 18TH CENTURY

	347		344	
342	353		348	346
350				351
365		362		354
349		357		355
360		371		369

PEASANT RINGS: FRENCH, ITALIAN, SPANISH

383	396	410
398	431	401
421	412	422
426	433	442

PEASANT RINGS: FROM NORTHERN AND CENTRAL EUROPE

445 462

447 464 463

450 465 456

476 473 480

470 478

PLATE XX

ENGLISH HERALDIC SIGNET RINGS: 16TH CENTURY

484 485

484 484 485 485

486 492 486

488 494 494 493

347. GOLD; openwork bezel in the form of a heart set with a diamond and a ruby surrounded by emeralds in silver collets; shoulders chased with leaves and flowers.
English. Third quarter of 18th Century. 8543–1863.

348. GOLD; openwork bezel formed as a vase of flowers, set with rubies and diamonds; the shoulders chased with flowers and leaves.
English. Third quarter of 18th Century. *Plate XVII.* 8550–1863.

Figured in Fairholt, *Rambles of an Archaeologist*, p. 151, and Jones, *Finger-ring Lore*, p. 79.

349. GOLD; openwork bezel formed as a vase of flowers set with a ruby and diamonds in silver collets; openwork shoulders.
English. Third quarter of 18th Century. *Plate XVII.* 8547–1863.
Fairholt, *Rambles of an Archaeologist*, p. 151, illus.

350. GOLD; openwork bezel formed as a bowl of flowers, set with diamonds, rubies and emeralds in silver collets; the setting of the bezel silver-gilt.
English. Third quarter of 18th Century. *Plate XVII.*
(Waterton Colln.) 970–1871.

351. GOLD; openwork bezel of silver parcel-gilt, formed as a floral spray set with rubies and emeralds.
English. Third quarter of 18th Century. *Plate XVII.* 344–1864.

352. GOLD; circular bezel set with an onyx surrounded by rubies; openwork shoulders.
English. Third quarter of 18th Century. 8546–1863.

353. GOLD; the bezel in the form of five diagonal bands alternately of rubies and diamonds in silver collets; chased shoulders and hoop.
English. Third quarter of 18th Century. *Plate XVII.* 8542–1863.

354. GOLD; openwork bezel of silver parcel-gilt in the form of a fleur-de-lys, set with a diamond, a ruby, emeralds and sapphires.
English. Third quarter of 18th Century. *Plate XVII.* 8549–1863.

355. GOLD; openwork bezel in the form of an eight-petalled flower, set with a ruby and diamonds in silver collets.
English. Third quarter of 18th Century. *Plate XVII.* 8541–1863.

356. GOLD; openwork lozenge-shaped bezel set with six diamonds.
English. Late 18th Century. 8544–1863.

357. GOLD; transverse oval bezel set with a crystal enclosing a pastoral scene carved in ivory; border of jargoons in silver collets.
English. Late 18th Century. *Plate XVII.*
Bequeathed by F. W. Daniels. 21–1883.

358. GOLD; marquise bezel set with a Wedgwood cameo of blue-and-white jasper ware depicting a youth and a maiden; openwork shoulders, each with an applied leaf.
English. Late 18th Century. 621–1894.

358*a*. GOLD; oval bezel set with a Wedgwood cameo of Apollo in blue-and-white jasper ware; the hoop forking at the shoulders.
English. Late 18th Century.
(Schreiber Colln., 1300.)

358*b*. GOLD; octagonal bezel with a bright-cut border set with a Wedgwood cameo in blue-and-white jasper ware of Venus and Cupid with the arms of Mars.
English. Late 18th Century.
(Schreiber Colln., 1301.)

358*c*. SILVER; oblong bezel with a border of steel beads set with a Wedgwood cameo in blue-and-white jasper ware of Venus and Cupid with the arms of Mars.
English. Late 18th Century.
(Schreiber Colln., 1302.)

359. GOLD; set with a square ruby between two crystals, the latter in silver collets; chased shoulders.
Late 18th Century. M. 370–1923.

360. GOLD; the hoop widening into a bezel which is set with a projecting diamond surrounded by two emeralds, two rubies and four diamonds; each shoulder set with a turquoise, two pearls and six garnets.
Hungarian. Early 18th Century.
Plate XVII.
31–1894.

Compare the ring formerly in the possession of Madame de Tarnóczy (Szendrei, *Catalogue de la Collection de Bagues de Madame Gustave de Tarnóczy*, p. 295, No. 10).

361. GOLD; bezel set with a garnet between two diamonds in silver collets; chased hoop.
German (Wurtemberg). 18th Century.
959–1872.

362. GOLD; openwork marquise bezel set with emeralds.
Spanish (Seville). 18th Century.
Plate XVII.
1214–1871.

363. GOLD; openwork marquise bezel set with emeralds.
Spanish. 18th Century.
336–1864.

364. GOLD; circular bezel set with eight emeralds surrounding another; trifid shoulders each set with a fleur-de-lys.
Spanish. 18th Century.
195–1864.

365. GOLD; circular bezel set with eight emeralds surrounding another; trifid shoulders each set with a leaf.
Spanish. 18th Century. *Plate XVII.*
206–1864.

366. GOLD; oval bezel set with eight amethysts surrounding another; the shoulders chased with acanthus foliations.
Spanish. 18th Century.
241–1864.

367. GOLD; circular bezel set with eight emeralds surrounding another; trifid shoulders.
Spanish. Late 18th or early 19th Century. 200–1864.

367*a*. A duplicate of the last.
201–1864.

368. GOLD; square bezel partly of silver set with an emerald; on each shoulder an applied spray of two leaves in silver set with three diamonds.
Spanish. Early 19th Century.
199–1864.

369. GOLD; openwork bezel set with rubies and diamonds in silver settings in a floral design.
Portuguese. 18th Century.
Plate XVII.
M. 86–1913.

370. GOLD; openwork transverse oval bezel in the form of a Maltese cross enamelled white, within a pearled border.
Maltese. Late 18th Century.
Given by the Rev. George Smith.
1060–1905.

Probably worn by members of the Order of St. John of Jerusalem.

Compare 1059–1905 and rings in the British Museum (Dalton, 2138–40).

371. GOLD; openwork transverse oval bezel in the form of a white-enamelled Maltese cross within two wreaths, some of the leaves of which are in green. Marks, a bell, and A.V.
Maltese. Late 18th Century.
Plate XVII.
Given by the Rev. George Smith.
1059–1905.

372. GOLD; spreading bezel set with five rubies in claw-settings, with eight diamond sparks between.
English. 19th Century.
Given by Mr. George A. H. Tucker.
779–1902.

373. GOLD; spreading bezel set with an opal between two rose-cut diamonds in claw settings with diamond sparks between.
English. 19th Century.
Given by Mr. George A. H. Tucker.
778–1902.

374. GOLD; in the form of a snake with tail twisted round its neck. The head set with a diamond, and two ruby sparks as eyes.
English. Middle of 19th Century.
Given by Mr. George A. H. Tucker.
776–1902.

375. GOLD; plain hoop set with a rose-cut diamond.
English. Middle of 19th Century.
Given by Mr. George A. H. Tucker.
777–1902.

376. GOLD; decorated with stars on a ground of blue enamel; the bezel set with an oval onyx cameo of a female head.
Middle of 19th Century. (The gem Italian, 16th Century.)
(Salting Bequest.) M. 557–1910.

377. GOLD; projecting oval bezel set with an amethyst surrounded by diamond sparks, the side enamelled dark blue and white; the wide shoulders chased in openwork with scrolls and palmettes.
Middle of 19th Century.
454–1873.

378. GOLD; large oblong bezel enamelled and set with a violet sapphire, the shoulders chased in openwork with trellis pattern. Made by Giuliano.
Second half of 19th Century.
Given by Mr. Cecil Crofton.
M. 327–1922.

379. GOLD; spreading bezel enamelled and set with five diamonds in the form of a cross, with two on each shoulder.
Second half of 19th Century.
Given by Mr. Cecil Crofton.
M. 328–1922.

C. *PEASANT RINGS*

(1) French

380. BRONZE; the bezel chased in the form of clasped hands.
17th Century.
(Waterton Colln.) 853–1871.

381. BRONZE; lead bezel set with three pastes.
Late 17th Century.
(Waterton Colln.) 992–1871.

382. SILVER; quatrefoil bezel set with two superimposed squares arranged diagonally.
18th Century.
(Waterton Colln.) 1000–1871.

383. SILVER; the bezel formed of two hearts (one gilt) surmounted by a crown set with garnets; the shoulders set with six others.
19th Century. *Plate XVIII.*
(Waterton Colln.) 860–1871.

384. SILVER; bezel in the form of an escutcheon bearing the arms of France in enamel and over them a bend inscribed FRANCE; on the hoop ALSACE and LORRAINE on a blue ground. 1872. From Strasburg.
662–1872.

384*a*. A duplicate of the last.
663–1872.

385. SILVER; bezel in the form of an escutcheon bearing the arms of France in enamel and over them a bend engraved ESPOIR; the hoop engraved ALSACE LORRAINE. 1872. From Strasburg.
664–1872.

386. SILVER; bezel in the form of an escutcheon bearing the arms of France in enamel and over them a bend inscribed ESPOIR; on the hoop ALSACE and LORRAINE on a blue ground. 1872. From Strasburg.
665–1872.

387. GILT METAL; bezel in the form of an escutcheon bearing the arms of France in enamel and over them a bend inscribed ESPOIR; shoulders engraved. 1872.
668–1872.

388. GILT METAL; oval bezel enamelled with two French flags crossed. 1872.
666–1872.

388*a*. A duplicate of the last.
667–1872.

(2) Italian

(*Nos.* 389 *to* 395 *are traditional imitations of a* 16*th-century type; compare Nos.* 285 *to* 294.)

389. GOLD; square box-shaped bezel set with an emerald, the lower part and the shoulders chased and enamelled.
(Murray Bequest.) M. 1008–1910.

390. GOLD; square box-shaped bezel set with a table-cut spinel ruby; its lower part and the shoulders chased.
(Murray Bequest.) M. 1009–1910.

391. GOLD; square box-shaped bezel set with a table-cut crystal over green foil; its lower part and the shoulders chased and enamelled.
(Murray Bequest.) M. 1010-1910.

392. GOLD; square box-shaped bezel re-set with a garnet; the lower part and the shoulders chased and with traces of enamel.
(Murray Bequest.) M. 1011–1910.

393. GOLD; square box-shaped bezel re-set with a brilliant-cut crystal; the lower part of the bezel and the shoulders chased and with traces of enamel.
(Murray Bequest.) M. 1012–1910.

394. GOLD; square box-shaped bezel set with a table-cut crystal; the lower part and the shoulders chased and enamelled.
(Murray Bequest.) M. 1013–1910.

395. GOLD; square box-shaped bezel set with a table-cut emerald; its lower part and the shoulders chased and enamelled.
(Murray Bequest.) M. 1014–1910.

(*Nos.* 396 *and* 397 *are traditional imitations of* 17*th-century types.*)

396. GOLD; square pyramidal bezel set with a paste foiled red; cusped shoulders.
Plate XVIII.
476–1868.

From the Castellani Collection, Paris Exhibition, 1867.
Compare Nos. 323-4.

397. GOLD; raised shaped bezel, set with three rough pearls.
(Waterton Colln.) 969–1871.

(*Nos.* 398 *to* 400 *are traditional imitations of* 17*th to* 18*th-century types.*)

398. GOLD ; rosette-shaped filigree bezel, set with nine rough pearls ; split shoulders, each with an applied flower.
Plate XVIII.
(Waterton Colln.) 1006–1871.

Compare rings in the British Museum (Dalton, 2074-5).

399. GOLD ; raised octofoil bezel, with nine rough pearls in open settings ; cusped shoulders.
482–1868.

From the Castellani Collection, Paris Exhibition, 1867.

400. GOLD ; rosette-shaped bezel set with a rough pearl surrounded by eight others.
Given by the Contessa Gautier.
M. 640–1911.

401. GOLD FILIGREE ; bezel an octofoil rosette ; flat hoop. Marks ; GA, G4A.
18th Century. M. 13–1912.

402. GOLD ; circular silver bezel set with crystals ; the hoop pierced and chased with acanthus leaves.
18th Century. *Plate XVIII.*
428–1868.

From the Castellani Collection, Paris Exhibition, 1867.

(*Nos.* 403 *to* 437 *are* 18*th-century types of contemporary or traditional workmanship.*)

403. GOLD ; circular silver bezel set with a crystal ; a crystal on each shoulder.
457–1868.

From the Castellani Collection, Paris Exhibition, 1867.

404. GOLD ; bezel of silver in the form of an openwork rosette set with diamond sparks.
436–1868.

From the Castellani Collection, Paris Exhibition, 1867.

405. GOLD ; openwork bezel in the form of a rosette of seven rose-cut diamonds in silver settings.
(Murray Bequest.) M. 1017–1910.

406. GOLD ; oval bezel set with a turquoise ; on each shoulder a group of three smaller turquoises.
487–1868.

From the Castellani Collection, Paris Exhibition, 1867.

407. GOLD ; oval silver bezel (the front gilt) set with a topaz ; on each shoulder a group of three garnets in silver collets ; chased hoop.
454–1868.

408. GOLD ; oval bezel set with a red paste ; on each shoulder a group of three white pastes.
427–1868.

From the Castellani Collection, Paris Exhibition, 1867.

409. GOLD ; oval bezel set with a crystal ; on each shoulder a group of three smaller crystals.
488–1868.

From the Castellani Collection, Paris Exhibition, 1867.

410. GOLD ; long oval bezel set with a square red paste between six white ones ; cusped shoulders.
Plate XVIII.
471–1868.

From the Castellani Collection, Paris Exhibition, 1867.

411. GOLD ; the bezel set with an oblong green paste between two small crystals.
449–1868.

From the Castellani Collection, Paris Exhibition, 1867.

412. GOLD ; large octofoil bezel set with radiating red pastes ; cusped shoulders.
Plate XVIII.
441–1868.

From the Castellani Collection, Paris Exhibition, 1867.

413. GOLD ; oval bezel set with a red paste surrounded by crystals, in silver collets ; chased hoop.
461–1868.

From the Castellani Collection, Paris Exhibition, 1867.

414. GOLD ; oval bezel set with a pink topaz surrounded by nine rose-cut diamonds set in silver ; on either shoulder is a ruby in a heart-shaped setting transfixed by an arrow ; the lower part of the bezel and the hoop chased in scrolls.
(Murray Bequest.) M. 1020–1910.

415. GOLD ; bezel in the form of a rosette with an emerald surrounded by a row of diamonds and another of rubies set in silver ; on either side of the shoulders a floral spray.
(Murray Bequest.) M. 1018–1910.

416. GOLD ; oval bezel with a large emerald surrounded by diamonds set in silver.
(Murray Bequest.) M. 1019–1910.

417. GOLD ; circular bezel set with a red paste within a border of crystals and smaller red pastes in silver collets.
462–1868.

From the Castellani Collection, Paris Exhibition, 1867.

418. GOLD ; large polygonal bezel in the form of a rosette of white pastes.
477–1868.

From the Castellani Collection, Paris Exhibition, 1867.

419. GOLD ; large polygonal bezel set with red and white pastes ; shoulders engraved.
465–1868.

From the Castellani Collection, Paris Exhibition, 1867.

420. GOLD ; square bezel arranged diagonally and set with four large white pastes (contiguous).
479–1868.

From the Castellani Collection, Paris Exhibition, 1867.

421. GOLD ; openwork bezel in the form of a vase of flowers set with a crystal, an emerald, garnets and a topaz, in silver collets.
478–1868.

From the Castellani Collection, Paris Exhibition, 1867.

422. GOLD ; bezel in the form of a spray of flowers set with diamonds and red pastes in silver collets.
18th Century. *Plate XVIII.*
455–1868.

From the Castellani Collection, Paris Exhibition, 1867.

423. GOLD ; circular bezel with applied rosette set with garnets, hoop pierced and chased with scrolls.
Maltese.
Given by Mr. Walter Child, A.R.S.M.
M. 131–1909.

424. GOLD ; silver rosette-shaped bezel set with a fresh-water pearl surrounded by two rows of garnets. Rome hall-mark ; maker's mark, P $\overset{\text{I}}{\underset{\text{U}}{}}$ N (?).
Given by the Contessa Gautier.
M. 641–1911.

425. GOLD ; long oval transverse bezel set with a painting under glass of the head and shoulders of a woman in peasant dress.
483–1868.

From the Castellani Collection, Paris Exhibition, 1867.

426. GOLD ; marquise bezel of violet-blue enamel, with applied ornaments and border of diamond sparks in silver collets.

Plate XVIII.
484–1868.

From the Castellani Collection, Paris Exhibition, 1867.

427. SILVER ; marquise bezel with blue-enamelled centre and double openwork border set with diamond sparks.

429–1868.

From the Castellani Collection, Paris Exhibition, 1867.

428. GOLD ; marquise bezel of blue enamel set with three white pastes.

485–1868.

From the Castellani Collection, Paris Exhibition, 1867.

429. GOLD ; openwork marquise bezel with diamonds in silver settings.
(Murray Bequest.) M. 1021–1910.

430. SILVER ; a crucifix, with large titulus, continuous with the hoop.

431–1868.

From the Castellani Collection, Paris Exhibition, 1867.

431. GOLD ; a crucifix, with large titulus, continuous with the hoop.
Maltese. *Plate XVIII.*
1462–1873.

Bought at the Annual International Exhibition, 1872.

432. GOLD ; lozenge-shaped bezel set with nine red pastes ; cusped shoulders.

1000–1903.

433. GOLD ; raised, pointed oval bezel set with turquoises ; cusped shoulders.

Plate XVIII.
440–1868.

From the Castellani Collection, Paris Exhibition, 1867.

434. GOLD ; heart-shaped bezel set with a turquoise ; cusped shoulders.

458–1868.

From the Castellani Collection, Paris Exhibition, 1867.

435. GOLD ; transverse oval bezel set with a baroque pearl ; an oval garnet on each shoulder ; hoop chased with scrolls.

481–1868.

From the Castellani Collection, Paris Exhibition, 1867.

436. GOLD ; five milled wire hoops threaded through a bezel in the form of a key between two hearts.

435–1868.

From the Castellani Collection, Paris Exhibition, 1867.

437. GOLD ; flat hoop in the form of two serpents intertwined.
Maltese. 1460–1873.

Bought at the Annual International Exhibition, 1872.

(3) Spanish

(*Nos.* 438 *to* 443 *are* 18*th-century types of contemporary or traditional workmanship.*)

438. GOLD ; bezel in the form of a sexfoil flower set with crystals.
Valencia. 697–1870.

439. GOLD ; octofoil bezel set with six amethyst pastes surrounding another.
Andujar. 1217–1871.

440. GOLD ; circular bezel set with eight pastes surrounding another, the hoop branching into three at the shoulders.

1216–1871.

441. GOLD ; lozenge - shaped openwork bezel of silver set with diamond sparks and enclosing a small gold figure of the Virgin.

235–1864.

442. GOLD; openwork marquise bezel set with paste diamonds.
Plate XVIII.
204–1864.

443. GOLD; the bezel formed by three emeralds in oblong settings.
197–1864.

(4) German and Austrian

(*Nos.* 444 *to* 449 *are traditional imitations of 15th-century types.*)

444. SILVER-GILT; the shoulders and wide pointed bezel with an openwork representation of a stag "lodged" and foliage.
German. 17th Century. 292–1902.
From Sweden.

445. SILVER-GILT; hoop split to form the bezel with applied openwork of a stag "lodged" and foliage.
German. 17th Century. *Plate XIX.*
28–1894.

446. SILVER-GILT; hoop split to form a wide bezel with applied openwork of foliage and a medallion of the Annunciation.
Tyrolese. 17th Century.
(Waterton Colln.) 973–1871.

447. SILVER-GILT; hoop split to form a wide bezel with applied openwork of foliage and a representation of the Virgin and Child.
Tyrolese. 18th Century. *Plate XIX.*
(Waterton Colln.) 972–1871.

448. SILVER-GILT; hoop split to form a wide bezel with applied openwork of foliage surrounding a flaming heart crowned and winged.
German. 17th Century.
6755–1860.

449. SILVER-GILT; hoop split to form a wide bezel with applied rosette and stamped panels of fleur-de-lys.
German or Scandinavian. 17th or 18th Century. 6754–1860.

450. SILVER-GILT; trefoil bezel set with three garnets; split shoulders with applied sprays.
German. 17th or 18th Century.
Plate XIX.
27–1894.

451. SILVER-GILT; quatrefoil bezel set with four paste garnets and turquoises; split shoulders with applied sprays.
German. 17th or 18th Century.
29–1894.

451*a*. A duplicate of the last.
1207–1903.

452. SILVER-GILT; the bezel set with a garnet and a paste; split shoulders with applied foliage and clasped hands; inscribed within the hoop Q B A M B.
German. 18th Century.
6768–1860.

453. SILVER; quatrefoil bezel set with four garnets; split shoulders with applied acanthus.
German (Bavarian). 18th or 19th Century. 927–1872.

454. SILVER-GILT; square bezel set with a paste; the shoulders chased with flowers partly in openwork.
German (Bavarian). 18th Century.
926–1872.

Traditional imitation of a 16th-17th-century type.

455. GILT BRONZE; projecting quatrefoil bezel set with a white paste; the sides cut to represent four drooping petals and, like the shoulders, chased and enamelled.
German.
(Waterton Colln.) 950–1871.

Traditional imitation of a 16th-century type.

456. SILVER ; spreading square bezel set with a green paste ; the sides and shoulders enamelled white with black dots.
German. 17th Century. *Plate XX.*
457–1873.

457. SILVER ; heavy hoop split at the shoulders, with applied bunches of grapes ; projecting transverse oval bezel with sunk medallion of St. Anthony of Padua and the Infant Christ.
Tyrolese. 17th Century.
Given by Mr. Walter Child, A.R.S.M.
M. 135–1909.

Acquired at Brixen.
Compare No. 952, which is somewhat similar.

458. SILVER PARCEL-GILT ; large curved oval bezel with an openwork representation of St. Michael and the Devil within a garlanded border ; hoop spirally fluted. Maker's marks, I R / V and 13 / W.
German. 18th Century. 46–1872.

459. SILVER-GILT ; hoop and bezel formed of openwork scrolls, the latter set with three garnets.
Tyrolese. 19th Century.
940–1872.

460. SILVER-GILT ; long oval bezel of filigree set with three red pastes.
Tyrolese. Early 19th Century.
939–1872.

Said to be worn by peasants in the Grödener and Eisack valleys.

460*a*. SILVER-GILT ; bezel in the form of a crowned heart (replaced by a shield-shaped bloodstone) held by two hands ; shoulders chased with acanthus foliage.
Tyrolese. 19th Century.
Given by Dr. W. L. Hildburgh, F.S.A.
M. 174–1929.

461. SILVER-GILT ; projecting bezel set with four glass pastes (two wanting).
Upper Bavarian. 17th Century.
925–1872.

(5) SCANDINAVIAN

(*Nos.* 462 *to* 464 *are traditional imitations of* 15*th-century types.*)

462. SILVER-GILT ; hoop split to form a wide bezel with applied openwork of a heart surrounded by foliage.
17th or 18th Century. *Plate XIX.*
949–1902.

From Iceland.

463. SILVER-GILT ; transverse oblong bezel with framed relief of the Virgin and Child ; the shoulders with applied foliage.
18th Century. *Plate XIX.*
Given by Mr. J. H. E. Allen.
398–1896.

Acquired in Norway.

464. SILVER-GILT ; formed of coils of corded and twisted wire ending in dragons' heads. Inscribed within, B M.
17th Century. *Plate XIX.*
(Waterton Colln.) 974–1871.

465. SILVER-GILT ; circular bezel of filigree with ten pendent rosettes ; plain spreading hoop with roped edge.
19th Century. *Plate XIX.*
Given by Mr. J. H. E. Allen.
397–1896.

466. SILVER ; oval incurved bezel surrounded by ten loose rings with filigree rosettes.
19th Century. 1327–1873.

Annual International Exhibition, 1872.

467. SILVER; embossed transverse oval bezel set with small pendent rings.
Swedish. 1357–1873.

Annual International Exhibition, 1872.

At the time of acquisition this type of ring was said to be still used occasionally as a wedding ring in Lapland, but to be giving way to the plain hoop.

468. SILVER-GILT; the bezel in the form of two serpents' heads.
Norwegian. 17th Century.
Given by Mr. Walter Child, A.R.S.M.
M. 446–1910.

Acquired at Molde.

469. SILVER-GILT; the hoop wide and ridged, the bezel formed by an applied rosette between two pairs of clasped hands.
Scandinavian. 18th Century.
904–1904.

(6) Central and Eastern Europe

470. SILVER-GILT; a gimmel fede ring; thin hoop; on each shoulder a quatrefoil set with a garnet.
Bohemian. 17th Century. *Plate XIX*.
(Waterton Colln.) 855–1871.

471. SILVER; transverse oval bezel set with a turquoise; shoulders and hoop chased with shields (?) and other ornament, and enriched with black enamel.
Hungarian. 17th Century.
(Waterton Colln.) 980–1871.

472. SILVER-GILT; oblong bezel set with a red paste; the shoulders with applied foliage and clasped hands.
Hungarian. 18th Century.
(Waterton Colln.) 977–1871.

473. SILVER PARCEL-GILT; cast filigree work; large square projecting bezel set with four groups of four pellets and five tall collets enclosing mother-o'-pearl; flat hoop.
Russian. 18th Century. *Plate XIX*.
114–1866.

Traditional imitation of a mediaeval type.

474. SILVER; cast filigree work; projecting circular bezel set with a red paste; flat hoop.
Russian. 18th Century.
115–1866.

Traditional imitation of a mediaeval type (?).

475. BRASS; oval bezel set with a green satin stone, the hoop and shoulders enamelled.
Russian. 18th Century.
112–1866.

476. SILVER-GILT; filigree; circular cushion-shaped bezel set with a pearl; shoulders with scrolls.
Russian. 18th Century. *Plate XIX*.
116–1866.

477. SILVER; large curved oval bezel set with grouped pellets and five circular projections filled with a moonstone surrounded by two garnets and two corals.
Russian. 18th Century.
113–1866.

478. SILVER; a wire of which the tapered ends, each furnished with a knob, lie side by side to form the bezel, to which is applied a small square plaque; shoulders bound with twisted wire.
Albanian. *Plate XIX*.
(Waterton Colln.) 986–1871.

Traditional imitation of a type of Roman ring.

Compare a Roman example in the British Museum (Marshall, 1129).

479. SILVER; small oval bezel set with a piece of reddish coral; the shoulders enamelled.
Albanian (?).
(Waterton Colln.) 983–1871.

480. SILVER; filigree; enamelled; conical bezel set with a piece of bone or tooth; flat hoop with corded edge.
Albanian. 18th Century. *Plate XIX.*
(Waterton Colln.) 975–1871.

480*a*. GILT BRONZE; stirrup-shaped; bezel stamped with an oval and ΑΘΗ; inscribed inside ΕΤΑΙΡΟΙΣ.
Greek. 19th Century.
(Harman-Oates Colln.) M. 14–1929.

481. GOLD; oval bezel with applied silver shield bearing the crowned arms of Poland and Lithuania with the motto "Usque ad finem"; the shoulders enamelled blue and bearing reserved in the metal a sword and an axe, and a bill and a scythe respectively.
Polish. 19th Century.
Bequeathed by the Rev. Chauncy Hare Townshend. 1831–1869.

D. *SIGNET RINGS*

(1) English Heraldic Signets

482. BRONZE, with traces of gilding; octagonal bezel engraved with a coat of arms.
Late 15th Century.
(Waterton Colln.) 801–1871.

The arms: in chief a demi-lion rampant.

483. GOLD; long hexagonal bezel engraved with a coat of arms, and above on a scroll the letters IVD (?). The hoop with central ridge is engraved externally with SAN TA: ANNA · ORA · PRO · ME, and HELP · SANT · ANNA · SELLEF · OBVR; internally with CASPAR:.: MELCHIAR:.:BALTASAR.
Early 16th Century.
(Waterton Colln.) 702–1871.

The arms (on a fess three boars' heads couped) are those of Lounsdon of Suffolk and Scott of Camberwell.

For the magical use of the names of the Magi, see note to No. 754.

484. GOLD; oval bezel engraved with a castle gateway; inside, the inscription EN BON AN; the shoulders engraved with the Virgin and Child, and St. Christopher.
Early 16th Century. *Plate XX.*
(Waterton Colln.) 695–1871.

This inscription is found inside a number of rings in the British Museum (Dalton, 423, 527, 746, 940, 941) and one in the Ashmolean Museum (Fortnum Colln., 585), as well as the ring of Bishop Stanbery of Hereford (d. 1474) (*Archaeologia*, xxxi. 249). It has been suggested that it may indicate a New Year's gift.

For a note on St. Christopher, see No. 723.

485. GOLD; hexagonal bezel engraved with an eagle displayed; on the under side the letters J and K joined by a true-lover's knot. The shoulders are engraved with the Virgin and Child, and St. John the Divine.
Early 16th Century. *Plate XX.*
(Waterton Colln.) 694–1871.

485*a*. GOLD; octagonal bezel engraved with a pelican in her piety; inside a monogram of T S.
Early 16th Century. *Plate XXI.*
(Waterton Colln.) 792–1871.

An almost identical ring, engraved with the same device, is in the possession of Corpus Christi College, Oxford. It belonged to the founder, Richard Fox, Bishop of Winchester (d. 1528), and is shown in his portrait by Johannes Corvus in the college hall (Mrs. R. L. Poole, *Catalogue of Portraits in the possession of the University . . . of Oxford*, ii., *Frontispiece*).

486. GOLD ; large circular bezel set with a crystal over foil engraved with the arms and crest of Sir Richard Lee, of Sopwell (d. 1575), granted to him in 1554. Inside, the inscription FLAME ET · FAME · and a grasshopper in green enamel.
Between 1554 and 1575. *Plate XX.*
Purchased with the aid of a contribution from Mr. L. C. G. Clarke.
M. 249–1928.

The grasshopper probably denotes some connection with Sir Thomas Gresham, whose badge it was. For other grasshopper rings, see *Antiquaries Journal*, v. 1925, pp. 405-6.

Sir Richard Lee received his grant of arms in recognition of his services as a military engineer at Boulogne.

487. GOLD ; oval bezel engraved with the arms of Baker, co. Devon ; on the reverse the initials C B in monogram ; the shoulders chased in the form of demi-figures.
Late 16th Century. *Plate XXI.*
(Waterton Colln.) 807–1871.

Notes and Queries, 11 July 1925.

488. GOLD ; oval bezel engraved with the arms of Pipart ; above, the initials C P.
Late 16th Century. *Plate XX.*
(Waterton Colln.) 809–1871.

Ironmongers' Hall Exhibition, 1861, ii. 503.

489. GOLD ; oval bezel engraved with a coat of arms.
Late 16th Century. *Plate XXI.*
129–1865.

The arms : a lion rampant, in dexter chief a crescent.

490. GOLD ; octagonal bezel engraved with a coat of arms.
Late 16th Century. *Plate XXI.*
(Waterton Colln.) 812–1871.

The arms : a bend charged with three eagles.

491. GOLD ; oval bezel set with a crystal engraved with an escutcheon, with tinctures beneath.
Late 16th Century.
(Waterton Colln.) 818–1871.

The arms : or, a bend between two crosses crosslet fitchy sable.

492. GOLD ; oval bezel set with a crystal engraved with a warrior's head. Below, red foil for background and gilding for details of helmet.
Late 16th Century. *Plate XX.*
(Waterton Colln.) 737–1871.

493. GILT BRONZE ; oval bezel engraved with a griffin's head erased ducally gorged and the initials I R.
Early 17th Century. *Plate XX.*
Given by Mr. L. A. Lawrence, F.R.C.S.
M. 374–1923.

Among the families using this crest are those of Rackham and Ralphston.

494. GOLD ; oval revolving bezel engraved on one side with the arms of Carew of Beddington, Surrey, and on the other the crest of Throckmorton of Paulers Perry, Northants.
Early 17th Century. *Plate XX.*
(Waterton Colln.) 808–1871.

Sir Nicholas Throckmorton married Anne Carew, who became the heiress of her brother Francis Carew, of Beddington, on his death in 1607. The Throckmortons assumed the name of Carew thereafter.

For the genealogy, see *Surrey Archaeological Collections*, vol. i.

Ironmongers' Hall Exhibition, 1861, ii. 503.

A very similar ring with a revolving bezel is in the Ashmolean Museum (Fortnum Colln., 643).

495. GOLD ; oval bezel engraved with the arms of Willmott.
17th Century. *Plate XXI.*
(Waterton Colln.) 91–1899.

PLATE XXI

ENGLISH HERALDIC SIGNET RINGS: 16TH AND 17TH CENTURY

489		487	497
490		487	498
496	495	499	501
485*a*	500	502	506

PLATE XXII

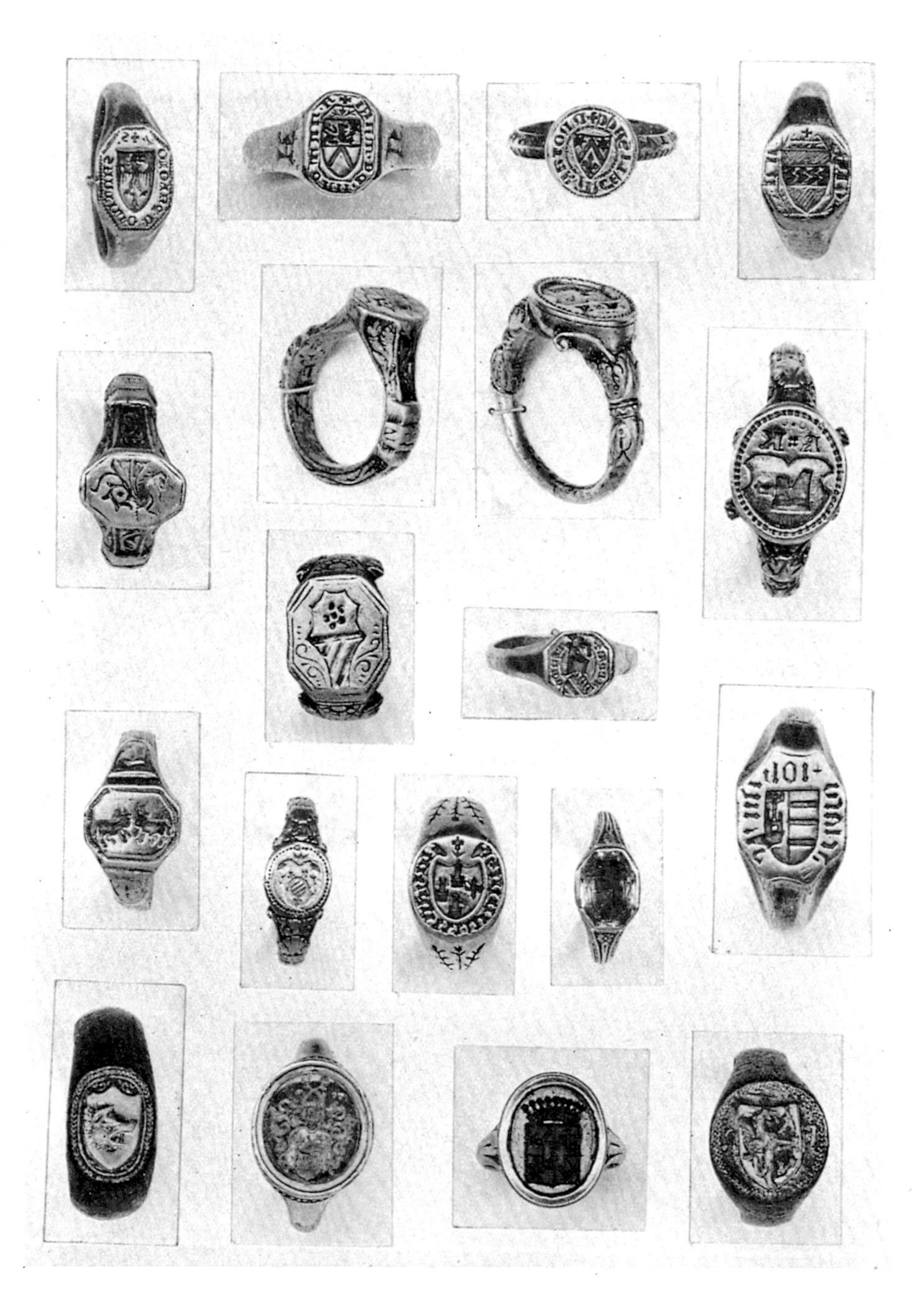

CONTINENTAL HERALDIC SIGNET RINGS: 14TH TO 18TH CENTURY

512	510		511	515
	514		528	
514	516		509	528
513	521	520	532	518
523	527		533	524

ENGLISH MEDIAEVAL SIGNET RINGS ENGRAVED WITH DEVICES

550		534		546
551		535		556
537	535		535	548
545		539		550*a*
547		542		554

PLATE XXIV

ENGLISH SIGNET RINGS ENGRAVED WITH DEVICES:
16TH AND 17TH CENTURY

552	559	559
553	560	572
570		571
566	560	567
557	563	555

496. GOLD ; oval bezel engraved with a coat of arms.
17th Century. *Plate XXI.*
(Waterton Colln.) 810–1871.

Found at Caer Gys, Wales.

Ironmongers' Hall Exhibition, 1861, ii. 503.

South Kensington Museum, Catalogue of the Special Exhibition, 1862, p. 632, No. 112.

Arms : a chevron between three boars' heads couped.

497. GOLD ; oval bezel engraved with the arms of Rolle, co. Devon ; on the reverse the initials G R.
17th Century. *Plate XXI.*
(Waterton Colln.) 811–1871.

The arms are differenced by a mullet.

See *Proc. Soc. Ant.*, ii. 364, where, however, the initials are read as C R. and the ring ascribed to Christopher Rolle, third son of George Rolle, the purchaser of the manor of Stevenstone, about the middle of the 16th century. A number of members of this family bore the initial G about this time, but none of these was a third son, as would seem to be indicated by the mullet. An almost identical ring was in the Harman-Oates Collection (Sotheby's Sale, Feb. 20, 1929, lot 62 ; Burlington Fine Arts Club Exhibition, 1916).

498. GOLD ; octagonal bezel engraved with a coat of arms, Brooke impaling another.
17th Century. *Plate XXI.*
Given by the Rev. R. Brooke.
390–1864.

The arms : Per pale a cross engrailed (Brooke), over all a crescent, impaling a chevron between three stags' heads cabossed.

499. GOLD ; octagonal bezel engraved with a coat of arms ; inside, the initial E.
17th Century. *Plate XXI.*
(Waterton Colln.) 813–1871.

The arms : on a chevron or engrailed between three crosses pattée voided as many fleurs-de-lys.

500. GOLD ; oval bezel engraved with the crest of Toovey and the initials S T ; inside, R. P and the maker's mark I Y.
17th Century. *Plate XXI.*
1583–1902.

Said to have been found in the Thames.

501. GOLD ; oval bezel engraved with the arms and crest of the Norfolk branch of the family of Mortimer.
17th Century. *Plate XXI.*
4–1874.

Given by Mrs. Lucy S. Jarman (*née* Mortimer) as the signet ring of Roger Mortimer, Earl of March (d. 1330).

502. GOLD ; oval bezel engraved with a lion rampant ; above, the initials A H.
17th Century. *Plate XXI.*
(Waterton Colln.) 793–1871.

503. BRONZE ; long octagonal bezel engraved with the letters W H L above a mill-wheel.
English (?). 17th Century.
Given by Dr. W. L. Hildburgh, F.S.A.
M. 163–1929.

504. GOLD ; oval silver-gilt bezel engraved with a coat of arms, the shoulders set with two rose-cut diamonds.
Late 17th Century. 628–1872.

The arms : impaling three boars' heads erased two bars or, the upper charged with a roundel. (The bezel has been adapted to fit the ring.)

505. BRASS ; oval bezel engraved with a lion rampant.
17th Century.
Given by the Rev. R. Brooke.
391–1864.

506. GOLD ; oval bezel set with a cornelian engraved with an escutcheon.
Late 17th Century. *Plate XXI.*
Given by Miss Anna Newton.
1644–1903.

The arms (a bend or between six crosses crosslet) are said to have been those of John Baduley, owner of a bible, inscribed with the date 1675, presented with the ring.

507. GOLD; set with a cornelian engraved with the crest of Townsend of Ellerton Hall, Staffordshire.
Late 18th Century.
Given by Miss Anna Newton.
1636–1903.

508. GOLD; transverse oval bezel engraved with the arms of Henry Charles Howard, 13th Duke of Norfolk (b. 1791, d. 1856; succeeded 1842), impaling those of his wife Charlotte Sophia Leveson-Gower (m. 1814, d. 1870), daughter of George Granville, Marquis of Stafford, afterwards Duke of Sutherland.
19th Century (in the style of the 17th Century). M. 848–1927.

Given by Mr. Mill Stephenson, F.S.A., from the collection of the late Lieut.-Col. G. B. Croft Lyons, F.S.A.

(2) Continental Heraldic Signets[1]

509. GOLD; octagonal bezel engraved with a coat of arms with mantling surrounded by the inscription AR C A M O (?) A BOART:
Italian. 14th Century. *Plate XXII.*
(Waterton Colln.) 798–1871.

The arms: three bars, in chief two pales between three fleurs-de-lys.

510. SILVER; octagonal bezel engraved with a coat of arms surrounded by the inscription +ANNTONII· DE · MARI. On shoulders A N.
Italian. 14th Century. *Plate XXII.*
(Waterton Colln.) 797–1871.

The arms: a chevron, in chief a lion passant, in dexter canton a star.

511. SILVER; circular bezel engraved with a coat of arms and the inscription +N NOTAR ANGELIS ACC. Around the hoop, divided by a central ridge, is +MORTUUS · FUERAM · A · REVIT and +PERIERAM ET INVENTUS SUM.
Italian. 14th Century. *Plate XXII.*
(Waterton Colln.) 805–1871.

Bought in Rome, 1856. Waterton MS., p. 253.

The arms: a chevron, in chief two estoiles and in base a fleur-de-lys.

512. SILVER; octagonal bezel engraved with a coat of arms and the inscription +S · SANTILLO · D · PAHOLO.
Italian. 14th Century. *Plate XXII.*
(Waterton Colln.) 803–1871.

The arms: an eagle displayed.

513. SILVER-GILT; octagonal bezel engraved with a coat of arms; on the shoulders the letters A R; the hoop gilt in a chequy pattern.
Italian. 15th Century. *Plate XXII.*
(Waterton Colln.) 789–1871.

The arms (two oxen affronted) may represent a simplified rendering of those of the Vitelleschi family of Corneto.

514. SILVER; projecting octagonal bezel engraved with a dragon; the shoulders and hoop nielloed.
Italian. 15th Century. *Plate XXII.*
(Waterton Colln.) 785–1871.

515. SILVER; octagonal bezel engraved with a coat of arms surrounded by the inscription +NUCIA (?).
Italian. 15th Century. *Plate XXII.*
Given by Dr. W. L. Hildburgh, F.S.A.
M. 236–1926.

The arms: a fess paly dancetty.

[1] Another ring to which this description might be applied will be found in the section Religious and Magical, No. 771.

515*a*. BRONZE; octagonal bezel engraved with a coat of arms.
15th Century.
Given by Dr. W. L. Hildburgh, F.S.A.
M. 164–1929.

The arms have been purposely obliterated.

516. SILVER; nielloed; octagonal bezel engraved with the arms of Orsini and foliations; on each shoulder a demi-rosette and leaf-ornament.
Italian. 15th Century. *Plate XXII.*
(Waterton Colln.) 799–1871.

Bought in Rome, 1857. Waterton MS., p. 253.

Ironmongers' Hall Exhibition, 1861, ii. 500.

The same arms are also borne, with different tinctures, by the Tibaldeschi family.

517. GILT BRONZE; nielloed; octagonal bezel engraved with a segreant, the hoop with mock inscription.
Italian. 15th Century.
Given by Dr. W. L. Hildburgh, F.S.A.
M. 237–1926.

518. SILVER; octagonal bezel engraved with a coat of arms and IOHANIS DE LASU.
French. 15th Century. *Plate XXII.*
142–1907.

The arms: three barrulets impaling a castle.

519. SILVER; octagonal bezel engraved with an eagle displayed and crowned; on the shoulders the initials A I.
German. 15th Century.
(Waterton Colln.) 786–1871.

519*a*. BRONZE; octagonal bezel engraved with a stag at speed.
15th Century.
Given by Dr. W. L. Hildburgh, F.S.A.
M. 165–1929.

520. GOLD; oval bezel engraved with an inscription (IOHANNI LOUPSHT ?) and a coat of arms surmounted by a fleur-de-lys leaved; the shoulders engraved with thistles.
Hungarian (?). 16th Century.
Plate XXII.
(Waterton Colln.) 804–1871.

The arms: three towers, two in pale, a cross crosslet adextré.

521. GOLD; circular bezel engraved with the arms of Contarini; the shoulders chased with acanthus foliations.
Italian. 16th Century. *Plate XXII.*
(Waterton Colln.) 806–1871.

522. SILVER-GILT; octagonal bezel engraved with a coat of arms.
Italian. 16th Century.
(Waterton Colln.) 800–1871.

The arms: a pale tierced per fess charged with three fleurs-de-lys.

523. GILT BRONZE; oval bezel engraved with a coat of arms.
Italian (?). 16th Century.
Plate XXII.
(Waterton Colln.) 790–1871.

The arms: a boar's head erased.

Compare a ring in the British Museum (Dalton, 517), which has the same shape of shield and decoration.

524. GILT BRONZE; circular bezel engraved with a coat of arms (a segreant), flanked by initials F. R.
Italian (?). 16th Century. *Plate XXII.*
(Waterton Colln.) 791–1871.

524*a*. GILT BRONZE; oval bezel engraved with a coat of arms (a cock).
Italian (?). 16th Century.
Given by Dr. W. L. Hildburgh, F.S.A.
M. 166–1929.

524*b*. GILT BRONZE; oval bezel engraved with a coat of arms (a lion rampant).
Italian (?). 16th Century.
Given by Dr. W. L. Hildburgh, F.S.A.
M. 167–1929.

525. BRONZE; oval bezel engraved with a coat of arms with helm and mantling, surrounded by an inscription.
Swiss (?). 16th Century.
(Waterton Colln.) 802–1871.

The arms: a fess between three roses.

526. GOLD; oval bezel set with a crystal engraved with an escutcheon with tinctures beneath; the shoulders chased in foliations, with traces of enamel.
French (?). Late 16th Century.
(Waterton Colln.) 814–1871.

The arms: azure, a lion rampant or holding in his right paw a flower.

526*a*. BRONZE; octagonal bezel engraved with a lion rampant holding a flower in his right paw, above M K and a quatrefoil.
Late 16th Century.
Given by Dr. W. L. Hildburgh, F.S.A.
M. 168–1929.

527. GOLD; oval bezel set with a crystal engraved with a shield, with helmet, crest and mantling; dated beneath the crystal 1597.
Late 16th Century. *Plate XXII.*
(Waterton Colln.) 817–1871.

The arms: a house between two trees; the crest: two branches crossed in saltire.

528. SILVER-GILT; oval bezel engraved with an implement and the letters R K; the shoulders chased with acanthus ornament.
German. 16th Century. *Plate XXII.*
7753–1863.

529. SILVER; octagonal bezel engraved with an eagle displayed.
German. 17th Century.
(Waterton Colln.) 787–1871

530. BRONZE; square bezel engraved with three fleurs-de-lys and the letters G S.
German (?). 17th Century.
(Waterton Colln.) 731–1871.

531. SILVER; circular bezel engraved with a fleur-de-lys.
Italian (?). 17th Century.
(Waterton Colln.) 748–1871.

A similar example in the Ashmolean Museum (Fortnum Colln.) was acquired at Frankfurt.

532. GOLD; octagonal bezel set with a sapphire engraved with the arms of Pīo di Savoia of Carpi; shoulders and back of bezel chased.
Italian. 17th Century. *Plate XXII.*
(Waterton Colln.) 820–1871.

Ironmongers' Hall Exhibition, 1861, ii. 502.

The arms include the insignia of the Gonfalonier of the Holy Roman Church, which were certainly borne by members of this family as early as the time of Ascanio Pīo (d. 1649).

533. GOLD; oval bezel set with an amethyst, engraved with a coat of arms beneath a coronet.
German (?). 18th Century.
Plate XXII.
(Waterton Colln.) 822–1871.

The arms: quarterly 1. an eagle displayed, 2. a left arm armed and holding a sword, 3. a right arm armed and holding a sword, 4. a lion rampant to sinister, over all an escutcheon of pretence bearing a goose to sinister.

(3) English Signets Engraved with Devices [1]

534. GOLD; oval bezel engraved with the inscription ✱ : TECTA : LEGE : LECTA : TEGE, and set with a sapphire intaglio (head of a monk or of the Virgin?). 13th or 14th Century. *Plate XXIII.* (Waterton Colln.) 89–1899.

Found in a well in Hereford in 1824. *Proc. Soc. Ant.*, 1st Series, iii. 1856, p. 160; 2nd Series, 1861, i. 52. Waterton MS., p. 232. C. W. King, *Handbook of Engraved Gems*, 1st Edition, 1866, p. 130.

Ironmongers' Hall Exhibition, 1861, ii. 501.

The motto is the same as was used by Matthew Paris, historian, monk of St. Albans (born about 1200; d. 1259).

Rohault de Fleury, in *Bulletin Monumental*, xlii. 1876, p. 26, quotes another 13th-century ring with this motto in the Museum at Narbonne.

535. GOLD; circular bezel set with a spinel ruby intaglio of a crowned head; on the setting is engraved *tel il nest* ("there is none like him"); the engraved flowerwork shows traces of enamel.
English (?). 15th Century. (The gem French, second half of 14th Century.) *Plate XXIII.*
(Salting Bequest.) M. 554–1910.

From the Arundel and Marlborough Collections.

This ring and the gem with which it is set have been the subject of much dispute. It was originally identified by Albert Way as a portrait of Henry VI. (*Arch. Journal*, xxi. 1864, 328-9) set in a contemporary ring. In *The Marlborough Gems*, by M. H. N. Story-Maskelyne (1870), the author expresses his thanks to C. W. King for the light thrown on the date of this gem by its identification as a portrait of Charles V. of France (p. ix.), and it is said to accord exactly with the head on that monarch's coins, and with an item in his inventory of the year 1379, "Le signet du Roy qui est de la teste d'un roy sans barbe; et est d'un fin rubis d'Orient, c'est celui de quoi le roy scelle les lettres qu'il escript de sa main" (No. 583, p. 96).

The signet here described is identified by E. Babelon (*Histoire de la Gravure des Gemmes en France*, 1902, p. 101) with another which he illustrates (Pl. VII., 2), but which depicts a bearded king.

The 15th-century date for the ring does not seem improbable, and floral work is characteristic of English rings of this period. It seems likely that the gem, representing so conventional a head, may be of the 14th century (of which the second half is described by Babelon as "l'apogée de la glyptique française"), and in the following century may have been re-set and served as the portrait of another king.

Dalton, in his introduction to the *Catalogue of Engraved Gems of the Post-Classical Periods in the British Museum* (1915), refers to the gem as having "probably belonged to Charles V., whom it has been thought to represent" (p. xxx.).

536. BRONZE; engraved with the letter B. 15th Century. 903–1904.

537. SILVER; octagonal bezel engraved with the letter I between three branches; one shoulder engraved with a star.
15th Century. *Plate XXIII.*
(Croft Lyons Bequest.) M. 819–1926.

The date 1666 is engraved behind the bezel.

[1] Other rings to which this description might be applied will be found in the following sections:—
Anglo-Saxon, No. 228.
Religious and Magical, No. 764.

538. SILVER; octagonal bezel engraved with the letter I surmounted by a crown and flanked by two branches.
15th Century. 1374–1903.

From Chichester (?).

539. SILVER; octagonal bezel engraved with the letter I surmounted by a crown and flanked by two branches; the hoop spirally gadrooned.
15th Century. *Plate XXIII.*
(Waterton Colln.) 771–1871.

Given to Waterton by Major Darell of Cole Hill, in whose family the ring had been preserved as the ring of King John (Waterton MS., p. 242).

540. BRONZE; oblong bezel engraved with the letter M surmounted by a crown.
15th Century.
(Waterton Colln.) 763–1871.

541. BRONZE; oval bezel engraved with the letter N surmounted by a crown and flanked by two branches.
Late 15th Century.
(Waterton Colln.) 769–1871.
Found in the fens near Cambridge (Waterton MS., p. 243).

Very similar to a ring in the London Museum (A 1622), dug up in Blackfriars.

542. SILVER; square bezel engraved with a crowned W and branches; the shoulders with I H S and a T cross.
15th Century. *Plate XXIII.*
(Bernal and Waterton Collns.)
772–1871.

The T cross is found on a number of rings (compare Nos. 547, 592, also British Museum, Dalton, 528, 530, 721, and Ashmolean Museum, Fortnum Colln., 329; see also *Proc. Soc. Ant.*, 2nd Series, vol. vi. 1876, p. 53). It appears to have been early adopted by Eastern Christians as a sacred emblem, afterwards becoming especially associated with St. Anthony, an Egyptian by birth who is reputed to have lived from 251 to 356 A.D. After distributing his goods amongst the poor, he retired into solitude and afterwards founded a religious order. He is said to have acted as a swineherd at some time in his career and is often represented with a pig. In the Middle Ages his intervention was supposed to be particularly efficacious in curing erysipelas ("St. Anthony's fire"), but he was also invoked against the plague. In 1382 Albert II., Duke of Bavaria and Emperor, founded a military order of Knights of St. Anthony on the occasion of his intended crusade against the Turks. The knights wore a collar of gold in the form of a hermit's girdle, from which depended a stick cut like a crutch hung with a small bell. The ring of Bishop Mayo of Hereford (1504-16) (*Archaeologia*, xxxi. 1846, p. 251) is engraved with a bell suspended from a T cross, and it is possible that some of the rings belonged to persons who were connected with the orders under the patronage of St. Anthony or who had visited his shrine at St. Antoine de Viennois, though its amuletic use was probably the most general.

543. SILVER; oblong bezel engraved with the letter W surmounted by a crown.
15th Century.
(Waterton Colln.) 767–1871.

544. BRONZE; rounded oblong bezel engraved with the letter W surmounted by a branch.
15th Century.
(Waterton Colln.) 774–1871.

544*a*. BRONZE; rounded oblong bezel engraved with a crowned W.
15th Century.
(Harman-Oates Colln.) M. 12–1929.

545. SILVER; octagonal bezel engraved with a merchant's mark between the letters I H; on each shoulder a crown in relief.
15th Century. *Plate XXIII.*
783–1877.

546. SILVER-GILT; circular bezel engraved with a merchant's mark; the shoulders each with five rude projections (one wanting); the hoop spirally gadrooned.
15th Century. *Plate XXIII.*
(Waterton Colln.) 756–1871.

547. SILVER; hexagonal bezel engraved with a chalice and wafer between F and O; the shoulders engraved with a T cross and a rose; inside the hoop, +ANA MARIA.
English. Late 15th Century. *Plate XXIII.*
(Harman-Oates Colln.) M. 9–1929.

Found at Stonham Aspall, Suffolk.

For the T cross, compare note to No. 542.

548. SILVER; long octagonal bezel engraved with the letters I B in monogram surmounted by a crown; the hoop spirally gadrooned.
Early 16th Century. *Plate XXIII.*
(Waterton Colln.) 770–1871.

Found at Elmswell, Suffolk. Waterton MS., p. 244.

548*a*. SILVER; long octagonal bezel engraved with the letters I A surmounted by a crown and surrounded by branches.
Early 16th Century.
(Waterton Colln.) 765–1871.

Found at Ashford, Kent. Waterton MS., p. 244.

549. SILVER; long octagonal bezel engraved with a merchant's mark; the hoop spirally fluted.
Early 16th Century.
(Waterton Colln.) 753–1871.

550. SILVER; circular bezel engraved with a device, probably a rebus, containing the letter U; the shoulders fluted, with beaded edges; the hoop spirally gadrooned and beaded.
Early 16th Century. *Plate XXIII.*
(Waterton Colln.) 754–1871.

Found at Coventry, 1856. Waterton MS., p. 259.

Ironmongers' Hall Exhibition, 1861, ii. 508.

Compare a gilt bronze ring in the Cathedral Library, Durham, said to have been found in the tomb of the Venerable Bede. The bezel is engraved with a cinquefoil flower and sprig, but the shoulders and hoop are of very similar design.

550*a*. SILVER; circular bezel engraved with a merchant's mark; hoop spirally fluted, with beaded edges.
Early 16th Century. *Plate XXIII.*
(Laking and Harman-Oates Collns.) M. 11–1929.

Found at Mansfield.

551. GOLD; octagonal bezel engraved with the letter I surmounted by a crown, between two rosettes; the hoop chased in the form of two interlaced ribbons, one with cross-hatching.
Early 16th Century. *Plate XXIII.*
(Waterton Colln.) 773–1871.

Given to Waterton by Lord Herries of Terregles, 1858 (Waterton MS., p. 242).

Ironmongers' Hall Exhibition, 1861, ii. 508.

552. GOLD; circular bezel engraved with a rebus (a tree, perhaps an elm, between W Y and O T with R below, for R. Wylmot?).
First half of 16th Century. *Plate XXIV.*
(Waterton Colln., from the Coleby Hall Sale.) 794–1871.

Waterton MS., p. 245.

Ironmongers' Hall Exhibition, 1861, ii. 508.

553. GOLD; circular bezel engraved with a hound on a leash, couchant beneath a tree, and the letters I L.
16th Century. *Plate XXIV.*
(Waterton Colln.) 795–1871.

554. SILVER; hexagonal bezel engraved with a merchant's mark and foliage; the hoop beaded.
Irish (?) 16th Century. *Plate XXIII.*
(Waterton Colln.) 755–1871.

Found near Cork in 1844 and formerly in the possession of Mr. Edward Hare of that city. Waterton MS., p. 238.

555. BRONZE with traces of gilding; circular bezel engraved with a vine and the letters CENT (probably a rebus for the name Vincent); the shoulders lightly chased with floral ornament.
16th Century. *Plate XXIV.*
(Waterton Colln.) 796–1871.

556. GOLD; oval bezel engraved with a merchant's mark, the shoulders chased with leaves.
16th Century. *Plate XXIII.*
(Waterton Colln.) 759–1871.

557. GOLD; raised circular bezel engraved (in recent times ?) with a merchant's mark and the letters D G A (not in reverse); behind the bezel is the date MDXL; the shoulders are chased with terminal figures.
Dated 1540. *Plate XXIV.*
6807–1860.

558. GOLD; oval bezel set with a crystal engraved with an escutcheon charged with the letters V A in monogram, above which are the initials W G; beneath the crystal is inscribed in gold foil the date 1555.
(Waterton Colln.) 819–1871.

559. GOLD; circular bezel engraved with the letters H M joined, over a true-lover's knot; the shoulders foliated; on the interior of the hoop and the bezel are engraved HENRI. L. DARNLEY. 1565 and a crowned shield of arms (lion rampant).
Scottish. Dated 1565. *Plate XXIV.*
(Waterton Colln.) 841–1871.

This ring is said to have been found near Fotheringay Castle. Formerly in the possession of Colonel Grant, it was exhibited to the Archaeological Institute in 1849, and had passed into Waterton's possession by 1857.

On May 15, 1565, Queen Mary announced her intention of marrying Henry, Lord Darnley. On July 23 she created Darnley Duke of Albany, and on the 28th ordered her heralds to proclaim him King of Scotland in virtue of his marriage, which was solemnised on the following day. There is no sign of the double tressure fleury counter-fleury which would convert the arms on the ring into the royal arms of Scotland, and it has been suggested that either the tressure was omitted for reasons of space, or else that the arms as engraved are those of the ancient Earldom of Fife, which appears to have been used by the later Dukes of Albany and are here allusive to the title conferred on Darnley a few days before the marriage (*Arch. Journal*, xiv. 1857, pp. 297-300).

In the Ashmolean Museum (Fortnum Colln., 597) is a ring very similar in shape with the bezel engraved with H. S. and a true-lover's knot.

Ironmongers' Hall Exhibition, 1861, ii. 502.

560. GOLD; circular bezel engraved with a cradle, the shoulders with flowers and leaves (the ground originally enamelled ?); the hoop spirally gadrooned and beaded. Inscribed inside MY WILLE WERE, with traces of white enamel.
16th Century. *Plate XXIV.*
(Waterton Colln.) 903–1871.

Ironmongers' Hall Exhibition, 1861, ii. 507.

561. SILVER; oval bezel engraved with a shield charged with a merchant's mark; above are the letters G (not in reverse) B; shoulders chased with figures of Adam and Eve.
Second half of 16th Century.
1375–1903.

562. BRONZE, formerly gilt; circular bezel engraved with a merchant's mark; hoop spirally beaded.
16th Century.
(Waterton Colln.) 751–1871.

563. GOLD; oval bezel set with a late Roman sard intaglio of a warrior's head; the shoulders and side of bezel engraved with foliated strapwork formerly enamelled.
Late 16th Century. *Plate XXIV.*
M. 102–1920.

Found in the garden of Llandulas Rectory, North Wales.

564. GOLD; circular bezel set with a white cornelian engraved with a merchant's mark, the monogram E M surmounted by a double cross.
Late 16th Century.
(Waterton Colln.) 761–1871.

Found in Bolford Churchyard, Lincs., in 1849.
Waterton MS., p. 240.

565. BONE; circular bezel engraved with the Sacred Monogram, with an Archbishop's cross below and a crozier above; inside, the initials F. A.
16th Century.
(Waterton Colln.) 698–1871.

Ironmongers' Hall Exhibition, 1861, ii. 439.

566. GOLD; oval bezel engraved with a skull; the reverse inscribed A·B.
Early 17th Century. *Plate XXIV.*
(Waterton Colln.) 921–1871.

Compare a rather similar ring in the British Museum (Dalton, 821).

567. GOLD; octagonal bezel engraved with a skull surrounded by the inscription ·IB·MEMENTO·MORI.
Early 17th Century. *Plate XXIV.*
Given by Mr. T. B. Clarke-Thornhill.
M. 378–1927.

568. GOLD; the bezel set with a cornelian engraved with a merchant's mark.
Early 17th Century.
(Waterton Colln.) 760–1871.

569. GOLD; oval bezel chased with a heart inscribed W R.
17th Century.
(Waterton Colln.) 739–1871.

In *Arch. Journal*, xxii. 164, Waterton is recorded as having exhibited a "gold signet ring, found at Cromer, Norfolk, the device is a heart bearing the initials T W R. Date about 1640."

570. GOLD; oval bezel engraved with a right hand between A R.
17th Century. *Plate XXIV.*
(Waterton Colln.) 738–1871.

571. GOLD; oval bezel engraved with a rose-tree with three flowers between the initials W. C., surrounded by the inscription EX DONO ROBERTI BRADLEY.
17th Century. *Plate XXIV.*
(Waterton Colln.) 740–1871.

572. GOLD; circular bezel inscribed with the letters S G bound by a true-lover's knot, surrounded by ·ELIZABET·EDOLFF.
17th Century. *Plate XXIV.*
(Waterton Colln.) 840–1871.

There was a Kentish family of the name of Edolph in the time of James I. Sir Robert Edolph's daughter Elizabeth married John Angel, of Crowhurst, Surrey, who was provisor or caterer to James I., Charles I., Charles II., and died in 1670. A family of the name of Gaynsford lived at Crowhurst Place, and a Susan Gaynsford (b. 1648, d. 1673) may be the person referred to by the initials on the ring if it was a pledge of friendship from Elizabeth Edolph.

Ironmongers' Hall Exhibition, 1861, ii. 504.

573. BRONZE, formerly gilt; oval bezel inscribed with the letters H B bound by a true-lover's knot.
17th Century.
(Waterton Colln.) 839–1871.

574. GILT BRONZE; circular bezel inscribed with the letters R L surrounded by the inscription +BE·STEDFAST·IN·FAITH.
17th Century.
Presented by Mr. B. L. F. Potts.
507–1894.

575. BRONZE; oval bezel engraved with the letters I S.
17th or 18th Century.
(Waterton Colln.) 784–1871.

(4) Continental Signets Engraved with Devices[1]

576. GOLD; oval bezel inscribed + S.HEMERICI and set with a cornelian intaglio of Ceres.
French. 13th Century. (The gem is Antique Roman.) *Plate XXV.*
(Waterton Colln.) 727–1871.

577. GOLD; oval bezel inscribed +S' CONRADI.DE.COMITE and set with a cornelian intaglio of a janiform helmeted head inscribed M A (in reverse).
Italian. 13th Century. (The gem is Antique Roman.) *Plate XXV.*
(Waterton Colln.) 726–1871.

Arch. Journal, xxii. 121; C. W. King, *Handbook of Engraved Gems*, 1 ed., 1866, p. 143; *Antique Gems and Rings*, vol. ii. p. 63, Pl. XXXIX., 9.

578. GOLD; oval bezel with four claws holding a plasma intaglio of a male figure walking to left.
13th Century. (The gem is Antique Roman.) *Plate XXV.*
(Waterton Colln.) 649–1871.

579. SILVER-GILT; oval bezel inscribed S. F R DE COLUMPNA, set with a red jasper intaglio gryllus composed of two masks, a scorpion, a star and a serpent.
Italian. 13th Century. (The gem is Antique Roman, the hoop modern.)
Plate XXV.
(Waterton Colln.) 725–1871.

This may, perhaps, be attributed to a certain Federigo of the Roman family of Colonna, who was living in Sicily in the middle of the 13th century (Litta, *Famiglie Celebri d'Italia*, III., Tav. II.).

Ironmongers' Hall Exhibition, 1861, ii. 500.

580. SILVER; oval bezel inscribed +S' NOT RICCARDI BUSSONI, set with a red jasper intaglio of a janiform head.
Italian. 14th Century. (The gem is Antique Roman, the hoop modern.)
Plate XXV.
4099–1857.

581. SILVER; oval bezel inscribed +S. ANDREOCTI·D'.S'RA., set with a cornelian intaglio of the heads of Julia, daughter of Augustus, and her two sons Caius and Lucius.
Italian. 14th Century. (The gem is Antique Roman.) *Plate XXV.*
(Waterton Colln.) 723–1871.

Probably once in the possession of a member of the Neapolitan family of Serra. Andreotto is the diminutive of Andrea. Two members of this family bearing this name flourished at this time (Candida-Gonzaga, *Famiglie Nobili delle provincie meridionali d'Italia*).

[1] Other rings to which this description might be applied will be found in the following sections:—
Early Christian, Nos. 199-201, 203-211.
Byzantine, Nos. 213, 214, 218, 219, 221, 222, 224.
Early Teutonic—Continental, Nos. 231-234, 236.
Official, Nos. 781, 782.
Fancy, Nos. 949, 951.

The gem bears strong resemblance to the reverse of a denarius of Augustus issued in 13 B.C. by the moneyer C. Marius Tromentina (Mattingly and Sydenham, No. 116).

See also C. W. King, *Handbook of Engraved Gems*, 1 ed., 1866, p. 143.

582. GOLD ; quadrangular bezel engraved with a merchant's mark and the name +GALGANO D'CICHO ; the hoop inscribed in two lines :

+IESUS·AUTEM·TRANSIENS·
PER·MEDIUM·ILLORUM·IBAT.

Italian. 14th Century. *Plate XXV.*
(Waterton Colln.) 88–1899.

The Christian name of Galgano possibly points to a Sienese origin.

The words *Iesus autem, etc.* (Luke iv. 30) seem to have been used as a charm against sudden danger for travellers, particularly against attack by robbers. Compare " Sir John Mandeville," *Travels*, ch. x. : " and therefore seyen some men when thei dreden them of thefes on any way, or of enemys, Jesus autem, etc., in tokene and mynde that our Lord passed through oute of the Jewes' crueltie and scaped safely fro hem." It was popularly believed by contemporaries (e.g. *Chron. Monast. de Melsa*, Rolls Series, vol. iii. p. xxxii, 45) that Edward III. used this inscription for the noble issued in 1344 in conjunction with the type of the ship to commemorate his escape from perils at sea at the battle of Sluys in 1340. It is, however, doubtful whether the use of the charm had this particular application, as the king had used it on the florin which he issued in 1343 and which can have no possible allusion to Sluys. Further confirmation of its use against thieves may be obtained from Camden's *Remaines concerning Britain*, 1612, p. 206. See *Numismatic Chronicle*, 3rd Series, xii. 1892, 257, xx. 1900, 236 ; *Archaeologia*, xlvii. 1882, p. 140 ; and *Arch. Journal*, xxvi. 1869, p. 231.

It would also seem that these words were used as a charm to procure invisibility when inscribed on rings prepared in a certain manner. See *Secrets of Albertus Parvus*, p. 157, quoted in Waterton MS., p. 307.

Other rings with this inscription are in the British Museum (Dalton, 231, 239, 283, 877-9, 895) and Pichon Collection (*Collections de feu M. Le Baron Jérôme Pichon*, Paris, 1897, Nos. 41, 66).

582*a*. BRONZE ; octagonal bezel engraved with a grotesque monster with a bearded human head wearing a hat.
14th Century. *Plate XXV.*
Given by Dr. W. L. Hildburgh, F.S.A.
M. 169–1929.

583. GOLD ; the shoulders chased as dragons' heads, the double tongues of which act as supports to the cup-shaped bezel set with a cornelian intaglio of Juno (?).
Early 15th Century. (The gem is Antique Roman.) *Plate XXV.*
(Waterton Colln.) 651–1871.

583*a*. BRONZE ; lozenge-shaped bezel with gadrooned edge, set with an antique plasma intaglio of a Victory with a trophy.
15th Century (?).
(Harman-Oates Colln.) M. 13–1929.

584. SILVER ; oval bezel engraved with an inscription (unread), set with a ribbon onyx intaglio of a scorpion.
North Italian. Early 15th Century. (The gem is Antique Roman.)
Plate XXV.
(Waterton Colln.) 724–1871.

It was popularly believed in the Middle Ages that intaglios of scorpions gave protection against fevers : *In quocunque lapide inveneris sigillum sculptum in quo sit cancer et scorpio sive piscis hii frigidi sunt et aquatici et septentrionales et defendunt se ferentes ab ethica et terciana febre atque causon quia hii consecrati sunt perpetua consecratione.* —(B. M. Sloane, 1784, fol. 8, a French 14th-century MS. quoted in Evans,

Magical Jewels, p. 245; similarly in B.M. Harl. 80, fol. 105, 13th Century, printed in *Archaeologia*, xxx. 1844, p. 450.)

585. SILVER; octagonal bezel engraved with a crowned M surrounded by +MARTINNI DT (?).
Italian. Early 15th Century.
(Waterton Colln.) 762–1871.

586. SILVER; oval bezel engraved with an arm holding a sword and the motto PER·ARDIMENTO.
Italian. 15th Century. *Plate XXV.*
(Waterton Colln.) 788–1871.

587. SILVER; octagonal bezel engraved with the Agnus Dei and the letter G.
15th Century.
(Waterton Colln.) 602–1871.

588. GOLD; octagonal bezel engraved with St. James the Great surrounded by the inscription IAQUES BOUCHIER; the hoop with slight spiral gadrooning.
French. 15th Century. *Plate XXV.*
(Waterton Colln.) 688–1871.

Ironmongers' Hall Exhibition, 1861, ii. 502.

589. SILVER; oval bezel engraved with a couchant dog and the inscription IAME S'GEEIN̄ (perhaps for *j'aime songeant*, "I love in my dreams"); the hoop engraved with an inscription (unread).
French. 15th Century. *Plate XXV.*
143–1907.

590. SILVER-GILT; transverse oval bezel engraved with the letters AN; the hoop chased with a magical inscription, +EADC·EU·PH·RUNASKHR +⁑+.
German. 15th Century.
(Waterton Colln.) 782–1871.

591. SILVER; circular bezel engraved with the letters L R; the hoop with wire edges.
Late 15th Century. *Plate XXV.*
(Waterton Colln.) 781–1871.

592. SILVER; octagonal bezel engraved with a T between two stars; ribbed shoulders and hoop.
15th Century.
(Waterton Colln.) 779–1871.

Above the junction of the limbs of the T is an annulet, as if a loop for suspension. It is possible, therefore, that this may be an example of the T cross (compare note to No. 542).

593. GILT BRONZE; oval bezel engraved with the figure of a saint surrounded by the inscription +KEROIΘITOC O ΔOVΛO ΘEOΔIΓI; the shoulders with coarse silver inlay of linear ornament.
Veneto-Greek. 15th Century.
Plate XXVI.
(Waterton Colln.) 982–1871.

594. SILVER; octagonal bezel engraved with a monogram.
16th Century. *Plate XXV.*
(Waterton Colln.) 778–1871.

Compare a ring in the British Museum (Dalton, 548).

595. SILVER; oblong bezel engraved with the letters I S in monogram; the hoop spirally fluted.
16th Century.
(Waterton Colln.) 776–1871.

596. SILVER; octagonal bezel engraved with a monogram; the hoop formed as twisted ribbons.
Early 16th Century. *Plate XXV.*
(Waterton Colln.) 777–1871.

597. SILVER; octagonal bezel engraved with the letter I surmounted by a crown and flanked by branches; the hoop spirally fluted.
16th Century.
(Waterton Colln.) 768–1871.

598. SILVER; circular bezel engraved with an R (not in reverse) between two quatrefoil flowers.
16th Century.
(Waterton Colln.) 780–1871.

CONTINENTAL SIGNET RINGS ENGRAVED WITH DEVICES: 13TH TO 16TH CENTURY

578		582*a*	583
576		584	577
579		581	580
589	586	588	596
582	591	594	599

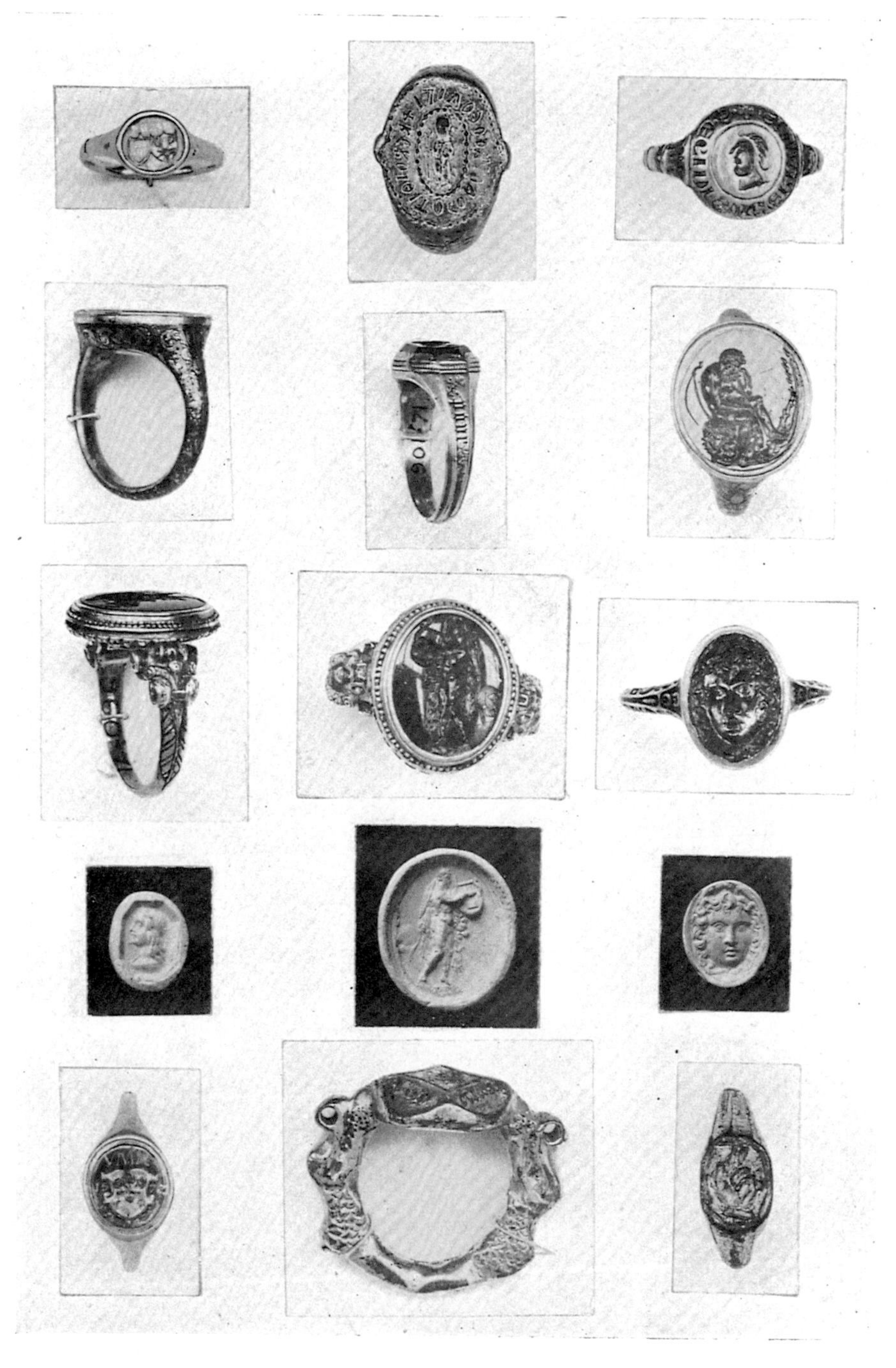

CONTINENTAL SIGNET RINGS ENGRAVED WITH DEVICES:
15TH TO 17TH CENTURY

601	593	607
613	606	613
612	612	306
606	612	306
602	616	611

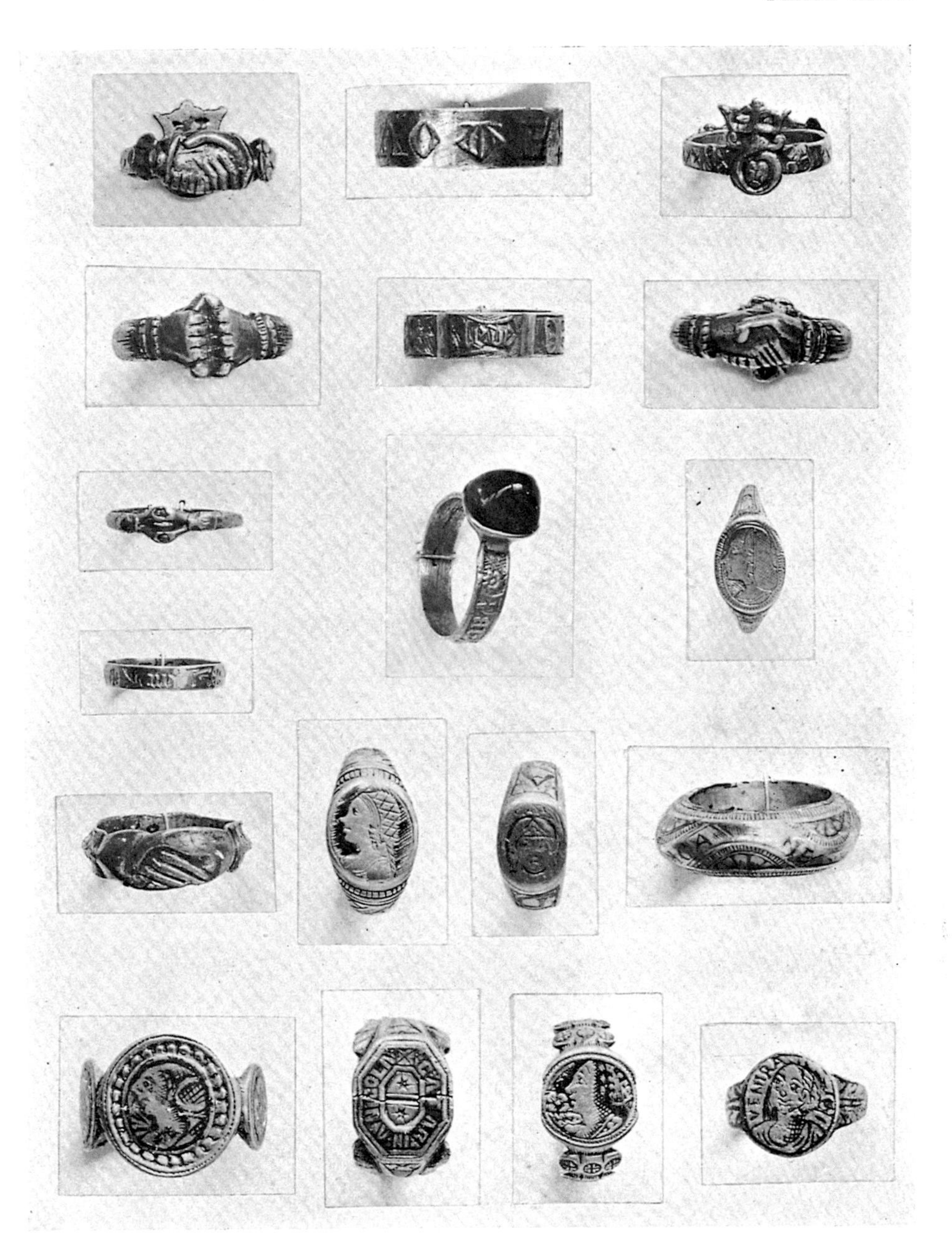

LOVE RINGS: 14TH AND 15TH CENTURY

630		623	630
636		624	636
625		624*a*	637
626			
632	650	652	653
640	638	648	651

PLATE XXVIII

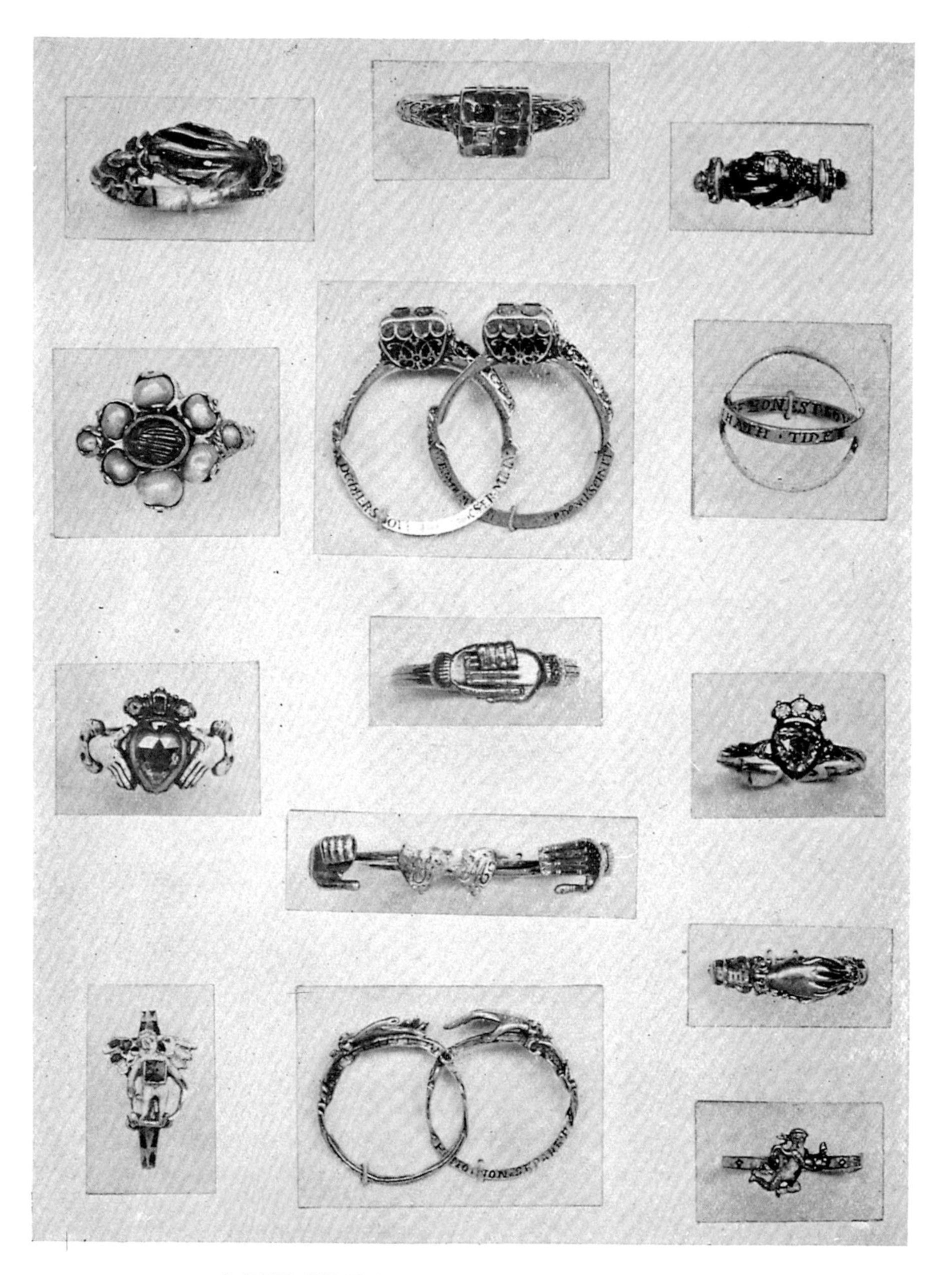

LOVE RINGS: 16TH TO 18TH CENTURY

661	663	665
667	663	676
697	668	701
	668	662
669	662	698

599. SILVER; oval bezel engraved with the letters I S bound by a true-lover's knot; the shoulders in the form of demi-figures.
16th Century. *Plate XXV.*
(Waterton Colln.) 838–1871.

600. SILVER; oval bezel engraved with a merchant's mark; the shoulders chased with leaves and scrolls.
16th Century.
(Waterton Colln.) 758–1871.

601. GOLD; oval bezel set with a gold-foiled crystal bearing two shields, the sinister engraved with a bunch of two forget-me-nots, the dexter inscribed IHS reserved in the foil; above are the letters FGMN (*fergiss mein nicht*, "forget me not") and below is a fleur-de-lys, all similarly reserved; the rest of the foil has been painted blue (?).
German. Late 16th Century.
Plate XXVI.
(Waterton Colln.) 815–1871.

A similar ring is illustrated in Debo, *Alte Ringe*, 1923, pl. V. Compare also the next.

602. GOLD; oval bezel set with a gold-foiled crystal engraved with a shield bearing two clasped hands holding a bunch of three forget-me-nots; further inscribed VMN (*vergiss mein nicht*, "forget me not") and date 1572; the foil is painted blue for the flowers and small details, and red for the general ground, the shield and inscriptions being reserved in the foil.
German. 16th Century. *Plate XXVI.*
(Waterton Colln.) 736–1871.

Said to have been found in the Seine at Paris in 1859. Waterton MS., p. 259. *Proc. Soc. Ant.*, iv. 1859, p. 309.

Compare the foregoing. Other rings with varieties of the same device and inscription are in the British Museum (Dalton, 317, 326, the latter with the date 1562), the Ashmolean Museum (Fortnum Colln., 516, with date 1579), the Bargello, Florence (Carrand Colln., 1036, with date 1582). Compare also one formerly in the Tarnóczy Collection (Szendrei, *Catalogue de la Collection de Bagues de Madame Gustave de Tarnóczy*, p. 273). A similar ring in the London Museum bears the letters VGMN with 1587.

603. GILT BRONZE; octagonal bezel engraved with a merchant's mark; the hoop spirally gadrooned.
16th Century.
(Waterton Colln.) 752–1871.

604. BRONZE; octagonal bezel engraved with a foul anchor between the letters G N.
15th Century.
(Waterton Colln.) 750–1871.

605. GILT BRONZE; circular bezel engraved with the letter W surmounted by a crown; gadrooned shoulders and hoop.
German. 16th Century.
(Waterton Colln.) 766–1871.

606. GOLD; octagonal bezel set with a garnet intaglio of a female bust to right; the shoulders engraved with sprays and POUR BIEN.
French or English. Early 16th Century. (The gem is Italian, 15th Century.) *Plate XXVI.*
(Waterton Colln.) 901–1871.

607. SILVER; circular bezel engraved with a male head in profile and inscribed +S·EGIDI·SACERDOTIS; wire hoop with palmette shoulders.
French. 16th Century. *Plate XXVI.*
(Waterton Colln.) 728–1871.

Ironmongers' Hall Exhibition, 1861, ii. 503.

608. SILVER; circular bezel engraved with a clover leaf; the shoulders chased with palmette ornament.
16th Century.
(Waterton Colln.) 746–1871.

609. BRASS ; octagonal bezel engraved with the letters M A crowned.
Italian. 16th Century.
(Waterton Colln.) 764–1871.

610. BRONZE ; octagonal bezel engraved with a hand holding an object, with two fingers raised ; on each shoulder a crown (stamped with a die).
16th Century.
(Waterton Colln.) 837–1871.

610*a*. BRONZE ; oval bezel engraved with the Virgin and Child ; on each shoulder a pair of conventional flowers.
16th or 17th Century.
Given by Dr. W. L. Hildburgh, F.S.A.
M. 170–1929.

610*b*. BRONZE ; oval bezel engraved with the Virgin and Child ; on each shoulder three diagonal bands.
16th or 17th Century.
Given by Dr. W. L. Hildburgh, F.S.A.
M. 171–1929.

610*c*. BRONZE ; oval bezel engraved with the Virgin and Child.
16th or 17th Century.
Given by Dr. W. L. Hildburgh, F.S.A.
M. 172–1929.

610*d*. BRONZE ; oval bezel engraved with a female head to left.
16th or 17th Century.
Given by Dr. W. L. Hildburgh, F.S.A.
M. 173–1929.

611. GILT BRONZE ; octagonal bezel engraved with a hand holding an object, with two fingers raised.
First half of 17th Century.
Plate XXVI.
(Waterton Colln.) 836–1871.

612. GOLD ; transverse oval bezel set with a sard intaglio of Hercules (?) playing a lyre ; shoulders elaborately chased with volutes and enamelled in various colours ; back of bezel chased as a sunflower and enamelled white with blue centre.
Italian. About 1600. *Plate XXVI.*
(Waterton Colln.) 960–1871.

613. SILVER ; oval bezel set with a cornelian intaglio of a resting Hercules ; hoop, shoulders and side of bezel nielloed with conventional flowers.
Italian. About 1600. *Plate XXVI.*
(Waterton Colln.) 968–1871.

614. SILVER-GILT ; oval bezel engraved with a merchant's mark accompanied by the letters MPS and surmounted by a conventional flower ; the shoulders chased with foliations.
17th Century.
(Waterton Colln.) 733–1871.

615. GILT BRONZE ; octagonal bezel engraved with the letter A within a tressure counterfleury ; fluted shoulders and hoop.
17th Century.
(Waterton Colln.) 783–1871.

616. SILVER-GILT ; circular bezel with raised quadrangular centre surrounded by the inscription GRAF SI FW URM (Count Siegfried Wurm ?) and bearing a shield charged with the letter S ; the shoulders in the form of dragon heads.
German. 17th Century. *Plate XXVI.*
(Waterton Colln.) 741–1871.

617. BRASS ; octagonal bezel engraved with a coat of arms (a merchant's mark with the letters P W, impaling a dimidiated double-headed eagle.)
German. 17th Century.
(Waterton Colln.) 757–1871.

618. BRONZE ; oval bezel engraved with a heart inscribed with the initials P B K and surmounted by a spray of three flowers.
French. 17th Century.
(Waterton Colln.) 732–1871.

619. BRONZE ; oval bezel engraved with a horseshoe on a dotted ground.
17th or 18th Century.
(Waterton Colln.) 747–1871.

620. GOLD ; the bezel set with a cornelian intaglio.
Italian (Roman). Late 18th Century.
(Waterton Colln.) 1002–1871.

The intaglio, in classical style, shows a ring with Silenus mask bezel and a hare inside the hoop, a grasshopper on an ear of corn, a cornucopia, and a male head to left.

621. GOLD ; set with a cornelian intaglio (a beardless male head to left).
Italian. Late 18th Century.
Given by Colonel D. H. Colnaghi.
M. 242–1924.

622. GOLD ; transverse oval bezel set with a sard intaglio of a draped female bust.
Late 18th Century. 3338–1856.

E. *BETROTHAL, WEDDING, AND LOVE RINGS*[1]

(1) 14TH TO END OF 15TH CENTURY

(N.B.—*The Darnley Ring, No.* 559, *is usually considered to be a Betrothal Ring. Apart from the section of Jewish Marriage Rings, Nos.* 703 *to* 716, *the following examples in this group may be definitely regarded as Wedding Rings : Nos.* 653, 660, 662. *Many other rings in the collection were probably also used as Betrothal, Wedding, or Love Rings, but for reasons explained in the Introduction it is no longer possible to identify them as such.*)

623. SILVER ; engraved ‡AMOVR‡MERCI.
French (?). 14th Century.
Plate XXVII.
(Waterton Colln.) 888–1871.

624. SILVER PARCEL-GILT ; a hollow hoop with six lobes chased with the words JE LE DE SIR (*je le désire*) alternating with crowns.
English. 14th Century.
Plate XXVII.
(Waterton Colln.) 890–1871.

624*a*. LATTEN ; plain bezel set with a projecting cabochon amethyst ; hoop stamped with two roses and PAR GRANT AMOUR.
English. Late 14th or early 15th Century. *Plate XXVII.*
(Harman-Oates Colln.)
M. 10–1929.

Found at Cardiff.

625. GOLD ; double bezel, each part formerly set with a stone ; the hoop engraved inside with +PENSEZ DE LI PARKI SVI CI (*pensez de lui par qui je suis ici*).
English. 15th Century.
Plate XXVII.
(Waterton Colln.) 889–1871.

Ironmongers' Hall Exhibition, 1861, ii. 506.

626. GOLD ; engraved with flowers and the words AUTRE NE VUEIL.
English. 15th Century.
Plate XXVII.
7125–1860.

Found at Bartlow in Essex. Other rings with the same inscription are in the British Museum (Dalton, 289, 966, 967).

627. GOLD ; a hollow hoop engraved with the words IN BONE FOY alternating with leaves.
English. Late 15th Century.
(Waterton Colln.) 891–1871.

[1] Other examples to which the description of Love Ring can definitely be applied will be found in the following sections :—
Early Teutonic-Continental, No. 235*a* (p. 137).
English Signets, Nos. 559, 569.
Continental Signets, Nos. 601, 602.
Peasant Rings, Nos. 380, 436, 448, 452, 462, 469, 470.

628. GOLD; concave hoop engraved POR TOUS IOURS alternating with flowers.
English. 15th Century.
(Waterton Colln.) 892–1871.

629. SILVER, with traces of gilding; engraved CEST MON PLESIR divided by clover leaves.
English. 15th Century.
(Waterton Colln.) 898–1871.

Ironmongers' Hall Exhibition, 1861, ii. 506.

630. SILVER-GILT; two applied bezels, one a fede [1] (clasped hands), the other a crowned Lombardic T enclosing a heart inscribed I; hoop engraved with X's.
English. 15th Century.
Plate XXVII.
(Waterton Colln.) 858–1871.

Found at Canterbury, 1854. Given to Waterton by William Burges, F.R.I.B.A. Waterton MS., p. 105.

630*a*. SILVER-GILT; a fede ring, with a second applied bezel of a quatrefoil charged with a heart; hoop inscribed IHC HELP.
English. 15th Century.
(Harman-Oates Colln.) M. 8–1929.

Found in Kent.

631. SILVER, with traces of gilding; a fede ring; inscribed IN ON IS AL.
English. 15th Century.
(Waterton Colln.) 845–1871.

Acquired at Norwich. The inscription is also found on a ring in the British Museum (Dalton, 293), and on the brass of Sir John Whylcote, 1410, at Great Tew, Oxon., where it is represented on three scrolls held in as many hands evidently symbolic of the Trinity. Waterton MS., p. 106.

[1] The term "fede," as applied to a ring with a representation of clasped hands, is derived from the Italian *mani in fede* (literally "hands in faith"); see Introduction, p. 21.

632. SILVER-GILT; a fede ring; ridged hoop with the inscription in two lines:
+IH'C·NAZAREN·REX
IVDEORVM+IASPAR.
English. 15th Century.
Plate XXVII.
(Waterton Colln.) 844–1871.

The combination of the inscription on the titulus with the names of the Magi shows that this is part of a charm for cramp. See the quotation from a 14th-century medical work given as a note to No. 754.

633. SILVER-GILT; a fede ring; hoop inscribed: +IHC+NAZAREN.
15th Century.
(Waterton Colln.) 842–1871.

In the *Revelation of the Monk of Evesham*, written in 1196, the magical significance of *Iesus Nazarenus* is given. In a conversation between a monk and a goldsmith in Purgatory the latter discloses that these words are a safeguard against sudden death. (Quoted in full in Joan Evans, *Magical Jewels*, pp. 128-9.)

634. SILVER-GILT; a fede ring; the hoop ridged and with traces of lettering (simulated ?).
German. 15th Century.
(Waterton Colln.) 843–1871.

635. SILVER-GILT; a fede ring; engraved with the letters IHESVS on six panels.
German. 15th Century.
(Waterton Colln.) 846–1871.

636. SILVER; a fede ring with second bezel in the form of hands holding a heart.
Italian. 15th Century. *Plate XXVII.*
(Waterton Colln.) 848–1871.

Obtained at Rome, 1857. Waterton MS., p. 105.

637. GOLD; oval bezel engraved with a woman's head to left.
Italian. Late 15th Century.
Plate XXVII.
(Waterton Colln.) 876–1871.

638. SILVER; octagonal bezel engraved and nielloed with the inscription +CATARINA NICOLA surrounding a coat of arms (?); the shoulders chased and nielloed.
Italian. 15th Century. *Plate XXVII.*
(Waterton Colln.) 833–1871.

Bought at the Monte di Pietà, Rome, 1857.

The arms: a fess fimbriated between two stars. It was suggested by Waterton that this ring may have belonged to Nicola di Rienzi, Tribune of Rome, or to Catarina di Raselli, his wife. Neither Rienzi nor his wife had arms, but he used as his device a star, so it was suggested that the stars represent both of them, and though these arms ought to have been impaled, space did not allow them to be put in this position (*South Kensington Museum, Catalogue of the Special Exhibition*, 1862, p. 630). It may be remarked that the arms as they stand are heraldically possible and were used by the family of Abate of Savigliano, and perhaps by others.

Ironmongers' Hall Exhibition, 1861, ii. 500.

639. SILVER; circular bezel formerly containing a nielloed plaque, the shoulders and hoop set with three pointed oval projections and enriched with niello.
North Italian. 15th Century.
(Waterton Colln.) 884–1871.

640. SILVER; parcel-gilt; flat circular bezel engraved with a woman's head to left within a beaded circle; the shoulders with two roundels filled with rosettes; the hoop formed by clasped hands with sleeves.
North Italian. 15th Century.
Plate XXVII.
(Waterton Colln.) 874–1871.

641. SILVER; flat circular bezel engraved and nielloed with a woman's head to left, within an octagon; the shoulders with roundels filled with rosettes; the hoop formed by clasped hands with sleeves.
North Italian. 15th Century.
(Waterton Colln.) 872–1871.

642. SILVER; flat circular bezel engraved and formerly nielloed with a woman's head to left within an octagon; the shoulders with roundels filled with rosettes; the hoop formed by clasped hands with sleeves.
North Italian. 15th Century.
(Waterton Colln.) 871–1871.

643. SILVER; flat circular bezel engraved with a woman's head to left (with a flower in front of the face), within an octagon; the shoulders with roundels filled with rosettes; the hoop formed by clasped hands with sleeves.
North Italian. 15th Century.
(Waterton Colln.) 875–1871.

644. SILVER; flat circular bezel engraved and nielloed with a woman's head to left with a flower in front of the face; the shoulders with roundels filled with rosettes; the hoop formed of conventional ornament (similar to that on the shoulders of Nos. 647 and 648).
North Italian. 15th Century.
7550–1861.

645. SILVER; flat circular bezel engraved and nielloed with a woman's head to left; plain narrow hoop.
North Italian. 15th Century.
(Waterton Colln.) 878–1871.

646. SILVER; flat oval bezel engraved with a woman's head to left, with a flower in front of the face. The plain hoop and the lining of shoulders and bezel are modern.
North Italian. 15th Century.
(Waterton Colln.) 877–1871.

647. SILVER; thin circular bezel engraved and formerly nielloed with a female bust to left, the shoulders with four roundels charged with rosettes arranged in pairs on each side.
North Italian. 15th Century.
(Waterton Colln.) 883–1871.

Compare Nos. 644 and 648 for the ornament on the shoulders.

647*a*. SILVER; thin circular bezel engraved and formerly nielloed with a female bust to left; the hoop with waved outline.
North Italian. 15th Century.
Given by Dr. W. L. Hildburgh, F.S.A. M. 162–1929.

648. SILVER; flat circular bezel engraved and nielloed with a woman's head to left, with a rose in front of the face; the hoop formed by clasped hands, the shoulders formed as in No. 647, but with nine roundels.
North Italian. 15th Century.
Plate XXVII.
(Waterton Colln.) 873–1871.

649. SILVER; flat circular bezel engraved and nielloed with a woman's head to left; the plain hoop and the lining of shoulders and bezel are modern.
North Italian. 15th Century.
(Waterton Colln.) 881–1871.

650. SILVER; flat oval bezel engraved and nielloed with a woman's head to left; the hoop with spiral scroll inscribed +A VE MA RIA.
North Italian. 15th Century.
Plate XXVII.
(Waterton Colln.) 882–1871.

651. SILVER; flat circular bezel engraved and nielloed with a woman's head three-quarters to left inscribed VENIRA; the shoulders with a leaf pattern.
North Italian. 15th Century.
Plate XXVII.
(Waterton Colln.) 879–1871.
Venira, possibly for *Venere* (Venus), or else the old form of *verra* ("he will come"). Waterton MS., p. 132.

652. SILVER; oval bezel engraved with a full-face female bust; the hoop inscribed LA VIRTV FA with floral ornament. On the shoulders A G.
North Italian. 15th Century.
Plate XXVII.
(Waterton Colln.) 880–1871.

The inscription, according to Waterton, is intended to read *la vertu fa l'amore*, the missing word being a a common name in Italian for the mignonette (Waterton, wrongly, "orpine"), the flower represented in the background.
Bought at Rome, 1857. Waterton MS., p. 132.

653. SILVER; ridged and nielloed with a wavy band inscribed ERVNT DVO IN CARNE VNA and clasped hands.
North Italian. 15th Century.
Plate XXVII.
(Waterton Colln.) 834–1871.
Ironmongers' Hall Exhibition, 1861, ii. 508.
Very similar to two rings in the Fortnum Collection at the Ashmolean Museum, inscribed respectively (420) AMORE VOLE VOLE FE, and (421) CHI CAMBIA LOCO DI CAMBIARE VSANZA.

654. SILVER; a fede ring; the shoulders nielloed with leaves.
North Italian. 15th Century.
(Waterton Colln.) 847–1871.

Obtained at Rome, 1860. Waterton MS., p. 106.

655. SILVER; a fede ring; the hoop with a simulated inscription in niello.
Italian. 15th Century.
(Waterton Colln.) 849–1871.

656. SILVER; oval bezel engraved and nielloed with a fede, the shoulders with leaves; plain narrow hoop.
North Italian. 15th Century.
(Waterton Colln.) 835–1871.

Bought at Rome, 1860. Waterton MS., p. 106.

(2) 16TH TO MIDDLE OF 17TH CENTURY

657. GOLD ; engraved inside UWER EYGEN (" your own " ?) with a cinquefoil and a heart pierced by an arrow.
German. Early 16th Century.
(Waterton Colln.) 896–1871.

658. GOLD ; the hoop inscribed outside +MY WORDELY IOYE+ALLE MY TRVST, and inside + HERT THOUGHT LYFE AND LUST.
English. Early 16th Century.
(Waterton Colln.) 895–1871.
Given to Waterton by the Bishop of Newcastle and Hexham.
Ironmongers' Hall Exhibition, 1861, ii. 506.

659. GOLD ; the hoop engraved inside with the letters C M joined by a true-lover's knot and DEVX·CORPS·VNG·CVER.
English. 16th Century.
(Waterton Colln.) 897–1871.
Found at Glastonbury Abbey.

660. GOLD ; the hoop engraved outside +OBSERVE WEDLOKE with scrolls, and inside +MEMENTO MORI with device.
English. 16th Century.
(Waterton Colln.) 905–1871.

661. SILVER ; a fede ring ; on each shoulder is a terminal figure.
16th Century. *Plate XXVIII.*
(Waterton Colln.) 850–1871.

662. GOLD ; a gimmel fede ring[1] ; the hoops with traces of enamel ; inscribed on the inside QVOD DEVS CONIVNVIT and HOMO NON SEPARET.
16th or 17th Century. *Plate XXVIII.*
(Waterton Colln.) 851–1871.
Ironmongers' Hall Exhibition, 1861, ii. 509.

[1] The gimmel ring (*gemellus*, a " twin ") was made with two interlacing or pivoted hoops capable of division so that each lover might keep half. Many gimmel rings have the bezel in the form of a fede. See Introduction, pp. 19, 22.

663. GOLD ; a gimmel ring ; square bezel set with a diamond, a ruby and two pastes ; the hoop chased with arabesques enamelled black and inscribed inside :
WER MICH VA——ER DENCK SEINIT.
(Wer mich (d)er denke seinit.)
(Who (verb) me let him think of { it.) / him.)
DECHTER S SOV——OSER MEIN
(Dächte er's so (conditional verb) er mein.)
(Were he to think it he would . . . of me.)
German. Early 17th Century.
Plate XXVIII.
22–1865.

664. GOLD, with traces of enamel ; a gimmel fede ring ; the hoops inscribed on the inside and nielloed ·CLEMEN· KESSELER and ·DEN·25·AVG·AO 1607.
German. Dated 1607.
Plate XXVIII.
(Waterton Colln.) 854–1871.
Ironmongers' Hall Exhibition, 1861, ii. 509.

665. GOLD ; a fede ring ; the hands enamelled black ; one finger is set with a ruby and the shoulders each with four diamonds (one wanting).
17th Century.
(Waterton Colln.) 852–1871.

666. GOLD, enriched with enamel ; a gimmel fede ring ; the shoulders with diamonds in silver settings.
17th Century. 112–1872.

667. GOLD ; lozenge-shaped bezel set with eight pearls surrounding a ruby engraved with clasped hands, the hoop and shoulders engraved and enamelled in black and white ; back of bezel enamelled with a red flower.
German (?) 17th Century.
Plate XXVIII.
(Waterton Colln.) 857–1871.

668. GOLD ; a gimmel fede ring with three pivoted hoops, the middle one set with two conjoined hearts, inscribed F and M, the others with clasped hands masking the hearts.
English. 17th Century.
Plate XXVIII.
(Waterton Colln.) 856–1871.

Compare No. 700.

669. GOLD ; the bezel in the form of an enamelled Cupid having a square garnet (?) on his breast.
Italian (?). 17th Century.
Plate XXVIII.
191–1864.

670. SILVER ; flat square bezel engraved with an L enclosing a heart ; the shoulders chased with masks above capitals, the hoop with leaves. Maker's mark, I G.
Italian. 17th Century.
(Waterton Colln.) 923–1871.

671. GOLD ; the bezel of double-trefoil shape set with seven diamonds in silver collets and inscribed at the back LOVE FOR LOVE ; the hoop engraved with foliage and enamelled.
English. Late 17th Century.
8540–1863.

672. GOLD ; a fede ring ; the shoulders enriched with enamel.
Italian. 17th Century.
(Murray Bequest.) M. 1015–1910.

673. GOLD, with traces of enamel ; engraved outside with a hare, a hound, a bird, a fly, and various plants ; inscribed inside LOYALTE NA PEUR.
English or French. 17th Century.
(Waterton Colln.) 906–1871.

Given to Waterton by Henry Cholmley in Rome, 1865. Waterton MS., p. 115.

674. GOLD, enamelled in translucent colours ; inscribed inside AS TRUE TO THEE AS DEATH TO MEE. Maker's mark, R.
English. 17th Century.
Given by the Rev. R. Brooke.
662–1864.

675. GOLD, with traces of enamel ; the hoop chased outside with a hare pursued by two hounds, and inscribed inside TIME LESSENETH NOT MY LOVE.
English. 17th Century.
(Waterton Colln.) 911–1871.

676. GOLD ; a double hoop opening on two pivots, inscribed inside ACCEPT·THIS·GIFT OF HONEST·LOVE WHICH·NEVER ·COVLD·NOR·CAN·REMOVE, and outside I HATH·TIDE 2 MEE·SURE 3 WHILST·LIFE 4 DOTH·LAST.
English. 17th Century.
Plate XXVIII.
(Waterton Colln.) 909–1871.

Acquired at Bury St. Edmunds, 1854. Waterton MS., p. 124.

677. GOLD ; chased with scrolls ; inscribed inside TIME·DEVM·ME·AMA.QD: R IE
English. 17th Century.
(Waterton Colln.) 904–1871.

Ironmongers' Hall Exhibition, 1861, ii. 509.

678. GOLD ; plain ; inscribed inside in two lines *SEITHE·GOD·HATHE WROUGHT THIS.CHOICE·IN·THE·
SO·FRAME·THYSELFE·TO·COMFOURTH·ME.
English. First half of 17th Century.
Given by the Rev. R. Brooke.
384–1864.

(3) Middle of 17th to 19th Century

679. GOLD; plain; inscribed inside AS GOD DECREED SO WE AGREED.
English. 17th Century.
Given by the Rev. R. Brooke.
377–1864.

680. GOLD; plain; inscribed inside AS GOD DECREED SO WEE AGREED.
English. 17th Century.
Given by the Rev. R. Brooke.
383–1864.

681. GOLD; plain; inscribed inside CAREFULL I'LE BE TO COMFORT THEE.
English. 17th Century.
Given by the Rev. R. Brooke.
382–1864.

682. GOLD; plain; inscribed inside GODS PROUIDENC IS OUR INHERITANC I EA.
English. Middle of 17th Century.
M. 369–1923.

For other rings with this inscription, see British Museum (Dalton, 1179–81).
Catalogue of the Antiquities in Norwich Castle Museum, No. 1096.

683. GOLD; plain; inscribed inside MB (altered from ME) REMEMBAR THE ♡ THAT IS IN PAYNE, the letters filled in with black.
English. 17th Century.
(Waterton Colln.) 910–1871.

Ironmongers' Hall Exhibition, 1861, ii. 506.

684. GOLD; plain; inscribed inside VERTUE PASSETH RICHES.
English. 17th Century.
Given by the Rev. R. Brooke.
385–1864.

685. GOLD; plain; inscribed inside WHERE ♡TS AGREE THERE GOD WILL BEE.
English. 17th Century.
Given by the Rev. R. Brooke.
381–1864.

686. GOLD; plain; inscribed inside YOV HAVE ME HART.
English. 17th Century.
(Waterton Colln.) 915–1871.

687. SILVER-GILT; plain; inscribed inside IN CONSTANCIE I LIVE & DIE.
English. 17th Century.
(Waterton Colln.) 912–1871.

688. SILVER-GILT; formed of ten bosses with roped borders; inscribed inside LET·LIKING·LAST.
English. 17th Century.
(Waterton Colln.) 907–1871.

Ironmongers' Hall Exhibition, 1861, ii. 506.

689. BRONZE, with traces of gilding; plain; inscribed inside LOVE TRUE TIS JOYE.
English. Late 17th Century.
(Waterton Colln.) 917–1871.

Found at Troston, near Bury St. Edmunds. Waterton MS., p. 124.

690. BRONZE; plain; inscribed inside LOVE EVER.
English. 17th or 18th Century.
(Waterton Colln.) 916–1871.

691. BRONZE; plain; inscribed inside LOVE ME.
English. 17th or 18th Century.
(Waterton Colln.) 918–1871.

692. GOLD; plain; inscribed inside A FAITHFULL WIFE PRESER[V]ETH LIFE.
English. 18th Century.
Given by the Rev. R. Brooke.
380–1864.

693. GOLD; plain; inscribed inside LET US SHARE IN JOY & CARE. Maker's mark, Bu.
English. 18th Century.
Given by the Rev. R. Brooke.
379–1864.

694. GOLD; plain; inscribed inside LOVE & LIVE HAPPILY.
English. 18th Century.
Given by the Rev. R. Brooke.
386–1864.

695. GOLD; plain; inscribed inside MY PROMISE PAST SHALL ALWAYS LAST.
English. 18th Century.
(Waterton Colln.) 914–1871.
Formerly in the possession of Waterton's maternal grandfather, Charles Edmonstone, of Cardross Park, N.B. Waterton MS., p. 124.

696. GOLD; plain; inscribed inside VNITED HEARTS DEATH ONLY PARTS.
English. 18th Century.
Given by the Rev. R. Brooke.
378–1864.

697. GOLD; the bezel in the form of a crowned heart set with diamonds in silver collets held by two white-enamelled hands; inscribed inside DUDLEY & KATHERINE UNITED 26 MAR 1706.
Plate XXVIII.
302–1867.

698. GOLD; the bezel in the form of a small enamelled Cupid holding a heart formed by a ruby; the thin hoop inscribed STOP THIEF in gold letters on white enamel.
English. 18th Century.
Plate XXVIII.
215–1870.

699. GOLD; the bezel in the form of an enamelled Cupid sideways with quatrefoil above and below; plain thin hoop.
English. 18th Century. 216–1870.

700. GOLD; a gimmel fede ring with three pivoted hoops, the middle one, with milled edges, set with two conjoined hearts, the others with clasped hands masking the hearts.
French. 18th Century.
(Waterton Colln.) 859–1871.
Compare No. 668.

701. GOLD; the bezel in the form of a crowned heart set with diamonds; the thin hoop roped.
English. Late 18th Century.
Plate XXVIII.
8545–1863.

702. STAINED GUT; red and black, embroidered in white quill with ANN CHILCOTT and a heart.
English. 18th Century.
Given by Miss Elizabeth Alice Chilcote. 374–1908.

(4) Jewish Marriage Rings[1]

703. GOLD; the bezel in the form of a square building, with battlemented roof on which is a group of four pellets; hoop split at shoulders, with voluted ends.
Italian. 16th Century. *Plate XXIX.*
(Waterton Colln.) 864–1871.

704. GOLD; the bezel in the form of a square building with stepped roof; cusped and foliated shoulders.
Italian. Middle of 16th Century.
Plate XXIX.
(Waterton Colln.) 863–1871.

705. GOLD; the bezel in the form of a gabled building surmounted by two revolving vanes; wide hoop, with heavily roped edges and pounced ground, and the Hebrew inscription *Mazzāl tōb* ("Good Luck") in raised cloisonné enamel.
German. 16th Century.
Plate XXIX.
(Waterton Colln.) 866–1871.

706. GOLD; the bezel in the form of a gabled building inscribed *Mazzāl tōb*; flat filigree hoop of plain and twisted wire.

[1] Compare Introduction, p. 18.

Italian (Venetian). 16th Century.
Plate XXIX.
(Waterton Colln.) 865–1871.

707. GOLD ; the bezel in the form of a gabled building with two finials ; the roof inscribed with the initials of the words *Mazzāl tōb* ; flat hoop with roped edges and ten repoussé bosses. Mark, |B|.
German. 17th Century. 453–1873.

708. GOLD ; the bezel in the form of a gabled building surmounted by two vanes ; wide hoop with heavily roped edges and pounced ground, and the Hebrew inscription *Mazzāl tōb* in raised cloisonné enamel.
German. 16th Century. 4100–1855.

709. GOLD ; a wide hoop set with six filigree bosses separated by groups of leaves enamelled blue and white, with small pendent rings ; heavily roped edges ; engraved inside with the initials of the words *Mazzāl tōb*.
16th Century. *Plate XXIX.*
32–1894.

710. GOLD ; a wide hoop set with six filigree bosses separated by groups of leaves partly enamelled in blue, with small pendent rings ; heavily roped edges ; engraved inside with the words *Mazzāl tōb*.
16th Century.
(Waterton Colln.) 868–1871.

Illustrated in *Jewish Encyclopedia*, x. 429.

711. GOLD ; a wide hoop with five filigree bosses and a compartment engraved with the beginning of the phrase *Mazzāl tōb* (which is continued inside) ; two rows of ornaments (quatrefoil and other) in blue raised cloisonné enamel ; roped edges.
16th Century. 80–1872.

Compare Museé de Cluny, 20692.
Illustrated in *Jewish Encyclopedia*, x. 429.

712. GOLD ; a wide hoop set with two rows of filigree bosses separated by roped borders ; engraved inside with the initials of the words *Mazzāl tōb*.
16th Century. *Plate XXIX.*
2746–1855.

Illustrated in *Jewish Encyclopedia*, x. 429.

713. GILT BRONZE ; the hoop set with eight bosses with pellets in the angles, plain or granulated ; square bezel with applied foliage, provided with a hinge and clasp and opening to reveal the inscription *Mazzāl tōb*.
German. 17th Century.
Plate XXIX.
(Waterton Colln.) 867–1871.

714. SILVER-GILT ; a flat hoop set with six filigree bosses and a plate engraved with the inscription *Mazzāl tōb*.
17th Century. *Plate XXIX.*
(Waterton Colln.) 869–1871.

715. GILT BRONZE ; a flat hoop with pounced ground, set with three simple filigree bosses and engraved with the inscription *Mazzāl tōb* ; roped edges.
17th Century.
(Waterton Colln.) 870–1871.

716. GILT BRONZE ; a flat hoop set with four simple filigree bosses ; engraved inside with the initials of the words *Mazzāl tōb* ; roped edges.
17th Century. 81–1872.

F. *RELIGIOUS AND MAGICAL RINGS*

(1) Religious Subjects and Emblems [1]

717. BRONZE; oval bezel inscribed *yhs*, the centre letter crossed.
Italian. 15th Century.
(Waterton Colln.) 696–1871.

718. SILVER, with traces of gilding; applied bezel consisting of a heart between two death's-heads; the hoop inscribed +IOH'ES GODEFRAY.
English. 15th Century.
Plate XXX.
(Waterton Colln.) 900–1871.

719. SILVER, with traces of gilding; ridged bezel roughly engraved on one side with the Virgin and Child, on the other with a female saint; shoulders chased with branches; hoop spirally gadrooned and pearled.
English. 15th Century.
(Waterton Colln.) 687–1871.

720. SILVER, with traces of enamel and gilding; ridged bezel roughly engraved on one side with St. Joseph seated, the Infant Christ on his knees, on the other with St. Catherine; shoulders chased with branches; hoop spirally gadrooned and pearled.
English. 15th Century.
Plate XXX.
(Waterton Colln.) 686–1871.

St. Catherine was especially popular in the Middle Ages as the patron saint of young girls.

[1] Other rings to which this description might be applied will be found in the following sections:—
Early Christian, Nos. 203-205, 210.
Byzantine, Nos. 216-218, 224.
Peasant Rings, Nos. 430, 431, 446, 447, 457, 458.
English Signets, Nos. 484, 485, 542, 565, 567.
Continental Signets, Nos. 587, 588, 592, 601.
Fancy Rings, No. 947.

721. SILVER-GILT; ridged bezel roughly engraved on one side with St. Barbara, on the other with an unidentified saint; shoulders chased with sprays.
English. 15th Century.
(Waterton Colln.) 685–1871.

St. Barbara was especially venerated in the later Middle Ages for her supposed power to protect from sudden death, and especially from death before receiving the *viaticum*. On the rings she is shown with her usual emblem, the tower in which she was imprisoned. See E. Mâle, *L'Art Religieux de la Fin du Moyen Age en France*, 1922, p. 186.

722. SILVER-GILT; the ridged bezel roughly engraved with two saints, the shoulders with two busts, one of a crowned woman; hoop spirally gadrooned.
English. 15th Century.
Plate XXX.
(Waterton Colln.) 683–1871.

723. GOLD; a decade ring [2] (thirteen knobs); ridged bezel engraved on one side with St. Barbara, on the other with St. Christopher; inscribed A MA VYE.
English. 15th Century.
Plate XXX.
(Waterton Colln.) 690–1871.

To St. Christopher, as to St. Barbara, was attributed in the Middle Ages the power of protecting from sudden death. It was only necessary to see a representation of St. Christopher to be secure from death for the rest of the day.

Christophori faciem die quacunque tueris
Illa nempe die morte mala non morieris.

[2] For decade rings, see Introduction, p. 23.

JEWISH MARRIAGE RINGS: 16TH AND 17TH CENTURY

714	706	713
704	705	703
709	707	712

PLATE XXX

ENGLISH RELIGIOUS AND MAGICAL RINGS:
15TH TO 17TH CENTURY

720		718		722
723	735	735	735	728
724		731		729
727		726		741

RELIGIOUS AND MAGICAL RINGS: 16TH TO 18TH CENTURY

732		736		733
738		742		743
740*a*	739	737	739	740
		744		
746		750		748

PLATE XXXII

RELIGIOUS AND MAGICAL RINGS: 14TH TO 18TH CENTURY

	751		755	
	763		764	
756	759		757	757
758	767		771	768
		774		
772		776		778

See E. K. Stahl, *Die Legende vom Heil. Riesen Christophorus in der Graphik des 15. und 16. Jahrhunderts*, Munich, 1920; and E. Mâle, *L'Art Religieux de la Fin du Moyen Age en France*, 1922, p. 185. It is not at all unusual for rings of this sort to bear amorous inscriptions. Compare Nos. 729 and 731. Some were probably used as wedding rings.

724. SILVER-GILT, with traces of enamel; the ridged bezel roughly engraved with St. John the Baptist between St. Barbara and another saint; the hoop spirally gadrooned and pearled; the shoulders each with a T cross.
English. 15th Century.
Plate XXX.
(Waterton Colln.) 681–1871.

For the use of the T cross, see the note to No. 542.

725. SILVER-GILT; the ridged bezel roughly engraved with St. Catherine, St. Barbara and another saint, the shoulders with branches; the hoop spirally gadrooned and pearled.
English. 15th Century.
(Croft Lyons Bequest.) M. 818–1926.

Acquired at Preston, Lancs.

726. SILVER-GILT; transversely ridged bezel roughly engraved with the three Magi (?); ridged shoulders engraved with sprigs.
English. 15th Century.
Plate XXX.
(Waterton Colln.) 680–1871.

For the Magi or Three Kings of Cologne, see the note to No. 754.

727. GOLD, hollow; oval bezel engraved with the Virgin and Child and formerly enamelled.
English. 15th Century.
Plate XXX.
(Waterton Colln.) 691–1871.

728. GOLD, hollow; a decade ring (eleven knobs); oval bezel engraved with St. Christopher.
English. 15th Century.
Plate XXX.
(Waterton Colln.) 689–1871.

729. GOLD; hexagonal bezel engraved with St. Christopher; shoulders obliquely ridged and pearled, engraved with flowers; hoop spirally gadrooned and pearled; inscribed inside DE BON COR.
English. 15th Century.
Plate XXX.
(Waterton Colln.) 692–1871.

For other rings with this inscription, see No. 731 and others in the British Museum (Dalton, 730, 731, 767, 939).

730. BRASS; a decade ring (eleven knobs); oval bezel engraved with St. Catherine.
English. 15th Century. 5575–1901.

Transferred from the Museum of Practical Geology, Jermyn Street.

Possibly identical with one illustrated in Jones, *Finger-ring Lore*, p. 249, which was found in the bed of the Thames at Kingston; but another ring of the same type was also shown at a meeting of the Archaeological Institute at Norwich in 1847.

731. GOLD, with traces of enamel; plain circular bezel; shoulders ridged, with pearled edges, each engraved with a female saint (Barbara and another crowned) between flower-sprays; hoop spirally gadrooned and pearled; inscribed inside DE BON COR.
English. 15th Century.
Plate XXX.
(Waterton Colln.) 902–1871.

Found near York in 1855 (*South Kensington Museum, Catalogue of the Special Exhibition*, 1862, p. 630).
Compare No. 729.

732. GOLD; crescent-shaped bezel inscribed IHS, the hoop with MARIA IOHANNIS.
English. 15th Century.
Plate XXXI.
(Waterton Colln.) 677–1871.

733. GOLD; heart-shaped bezel inscribed IHS; a hatched triangle on each shoulder.
English. Early 16th Century.
Plate XXXI.
740–1877.

Found near the site of Mynchin Buckland Priory.

Ironmongers' Hall Exhibition, 1861, ii. 510.

734. GOLD; heart-shaped bezel inscribed IHS.
Early 16th Century.
(Waterton Colln.) 678–1871.

735. GOLD; oblong bezel engraved with the Trinity, one shoulder with the Virgin and the dead Christ, the other with St. Anne and the Virgin.
English. Early 16th Century.
Plate XXX.
(Waterton Colln.) 693–1871.

Found at Orford Castle. Formerly in the possession of the Rev. S. Blois Turner. *Arch. Journal*, vii. 1850, p. 89, *South Kensington Museum Catalogue of Special Exhibition*, 1862, p. 630.

Illustrated in Jones, *Finger-ring Lore*, p. 254.

736. SILVER; octagonal bezel engraved IHS; the hoop chased with pearled chevrons.
Italian. 16th Century. *Plate XXXI.*
(Waterton Colln.) 697–1871.

737. GOLD; oval bezel inscribed IHS; the shoulders boldly chased with terminal figures and volutes.
English (?). 16th Century.
Plate XXXI.
1582–1902.

738. BRONZE; a decade ring (eleven knobs); bezel in the form of a capital S.
English. 16th Century.
Plate XXXI.
(Waterton Colln.) 775–1871.

A similar ring from Dunwich is in the collection of Sir Arthur Evans.

738*a*. [See p. 138.]

739. GOLD; revolving circular bezel having on one side a skull in white enamel and on the other a signet of a merchant's mark; inscribed round the edge NOSSE TE IPSVM; shoulders boldly chased with volutes.
English. Late 16th Century.
(Harman-Oates Colln.) *Plate XXXI.*
M. 18–1929.

Found at Guildford.

740. GOLD; hexagonal bezel with incurved sides, enamelled with a death's-head surrounded by the inscription ×BEHOLD·THE·ENDE and (on the edge) ×RATHER·DEATH THEN FALS·FAYTH, and on the reverse the letters M L bound by a true-lover's knot; the shoulders and hoop chased in foliations, with black enamel.
English. Late 16th Century.
Plate XXXI.
Given by Miss Charlotte Frances Gerard. 13–1888.

Said to have been presented to Bishop Juxon by Charles I. on the day of his execution.

A ring in the Ashmolean Museum (Fortnum Colln., 642) is very similar in appearance and has the same inscription, but without anything on the margin.

740*a*. GOLD; hexagonal bezel with incurved sides, enamelled with a death's-head surrounded by the inscription +NOSSE TE YPSVM, and (on the edge) +DYE TO LYVE; the shoulders chased in foliations, with black enamel.
English. Late 16th Century.
Plate XXXI.
(Waterton Colln.) 920–1871.

Ironmongers' Hall Exhibition, 1861, ii. 507.
Compare No. 740 and British Museum (Dalton, 813).

741. SILVER; a decade ring (ten projecting knobs); circular bezel with a crucifix in relief.
English (?). 17th Century.
Plate XXX.
(Croft Lyons Bequest.) M. 814–1926.

742. SILVER; a decade ring (ten projecting knobs); circular bezel engraved with the Sacred Monogram and the three nails; inside, an engraved inscription (unread).
17th Century. *Plate XXXI.*
(Croft Lyons Bequest.) M. 817–1926.

743. SILVER; a decade ring (ten projecting knobs); oval bezel engraved with the Sacred Monogram and the three nails.
English (?). 17th Century.
Plate XXXI.
(Croft Lyons Bequest.) M. 816–1926.
Compare an example found in Durham Cathedral and exhibited in the Cathedral Library.

744. SILVER-GILT; a decade ring (ten projecting knobs); circular bezel cast with the Madonna of the Rosary, and the letters R·S·R.
Italian. 17th Century. *Plate XXXI.*
(Croft Lyons Bequest.) M. 815–1926.

745. GOLD; the bezel a skull and crossbones in white enamel set with diamonds, the hoop enamelled black and white.
17th Century.
(Waterton Colln.) 922–1871.

746. GOLD; the bezel a skull and crossbones in white enamel, the shoulders with ornament in white and black enamel.
17th Century. *Plate XXXI.*
172–1872.

747. GOLD; the bezel a skull and crossbones in white enamel, the shoulders with knotted ribbons in the same; set with two diamonds.
17th Century. 528–1868.

748. GOLD; the bezel a skull and crossbones in white enamel on openwork cartouche, the shoulders with pierced floral designs; set with diamonds, some in silver collets.
English. Late 17th Century.
Plate XXXI.
211–1870.

749. SILVER-GILT; oval bezel set with a crystal enclosing a painting on vellum of the Crucifixion; the shoulders and hoop chased with palmettes.
Spanish. 18th Century.
(Waterton Colln.) 699–1871.

750. SILVER; circular openwork bezel with the Chi Rho monogram.
French (?). 18th Century.
Plate XXXI.
(Waterton Colln.) 700–1871.

(2) Religious and Magical Inscriptions, and Amuletic Materials [1]

751. BRONZE; in the form of a buckled strap inscribed O : MATER : DEI : MEMANTO.
English. 14th Century.
Plate XXXII.
(Waterton Colln.) 995–1871.
For similar rings, compare British Museum (Dalton 696-9); London Museum (A 1630); Marquet de Vasselot (No. 296); Cluny (9072); Norwich Castle Museum (*Catalogue*,

[1] Other rings which might have been included here will be found in the following sections:—
English Signets, No. 483.
Foreign Signets, Nos. 582, 590.
Betrothal, Wedding, and Love Rings, Nos. 632, 633, 660.

1909, No. 1125); Canterbury, Beaney Institute (found in the Franciscan Gardens, 1912); an example formerly belonging to a Mr. Davis, of Hampton, Oxfordshire (Jones, *Finger-ring Lore*, p. 263); another found at Hethersett, Norfolk, in 1845 (Ironmongers' Hall Exhibition, 1861, ii. 485); and one formerly in the Bateman Collection.

752. GOLD; stirrup-shaped; the hoop with thirteen transverse grooves inscribed +AVE MAR' GRACIA.
English (?). Late 14th Century.
(Waterton Colln.) 635–1871.

753. GOLD; inscribed outside +MARCUS: LVCAS+MATEVS: IOHES, and inside AVE: MARIA-: G C·: PLENA: DNS:
14th Century.
(Waterton Colln.) 679–1871.

754. SILVER; a ridged hoop engraved in two lines with + GASPAR· MELCHION· BALTHAZAR.
Italian (?). 14th Century.
(Waterton Colln.) 706–1871.

Bought in Rome, 1856. Waterton MS., p. 318.

C. W. King (*Arch. Journal*, xxvi. 234) considers that the names of the Magi or Three Kings of Cologne may be of Mithraic origin and represent the titles of "the White One," "the King of Light," and "the Lord of Treasures," applied to Mithras himself.

The amuletic powers of the Three Kings were very widely believed in, and were made use of in England down to the middle of the 18th century (*Arch. Journal*, xxx. 371). In the 13th-century *Lilium Medicinæ* of Bernard of Gordon is the following passage: *Si aliquis est in paroxismo. Si ponat os supra orem patientis et dicat ter istos tres versus procul dubio statim surgit:*

Gaspar fert mirram, thus Melchior, Baldasar aurum:
Hæc tria qui secum portabit nomina regum
Solvitur a morbo Christi pietate caduco.

(*Lilium Medicinæ*, pt. II., ch. xxv., *De Epilepsia*; Lyons, 1486. Quoted from E. Le Blant, *Rev. Arch.*, 1892, pt. I., p. 60.)

The following passage is quoted in Waterton MS., p. 317, from a 14th-century medical treatise (MS. Arundell, 275, fol. 23) as a cure for cramp:—

Tak and ger gedir on Gude Fridai at fyfe parische kirkes fyfe of the first penyes that is offered at ye Crosse, of ilke a kirke the first penye: than tak them al and ga befor ye Crosse and say fyfe pater nosters in the worschip of fyfe wondes and beyre thaym on ye V dais and say ilk a day also mekil on the same wyse and then ger mak a ryng thar of with outen alay of other metal and writ within IASPER, BATASAR ATTRAPA and writ with outen Ihc Nazarenus and sithin take it fra the goldsmyth up on a Fridai and say fyfe pater nosters als did before, and use it ever afterward.

The Stockholm MS. gives the names of the Three Kings as efficacious against fevers (*Archaeologia*, xxx. 1844, p. 400).

755. SILVER; engraved and nielloed; on the bezel a cross pattée; the hoop inscribed outside T·E·A·L·E·V·T·A·V·X·Y·+ ·A·P, and inside O·E·R·O S·5·A·P·H·I·E· L·X·D·A·P.
Italian. 14th Century.
Plate XXXII.
(Waterton Colln.) 708–1871.

756. SILVER-GILT; stirrup-shaped; the bezel and shoulders each crowned with a cluster of five pellets; the hoop with twelve transverse grooves inscribed AVE MARIA.
14th Century. *Plate XXXII.*
(Waterton Colln.) 676–1871.

Compare *Catalogue of the Finger Rings in the Collection of the Royal Irish Academy in the National Museum, Dublin*, 1914, Nos. 20-22.

757. GOLD; heart-shaped bezel set with a wolf's tooth (?); the shoulders with foliations in high relief and crowns in openwork; inscribed inside +BURO +BERTO+BERNETO+ƆSVM̄ATM̄ E.
English (?). 14th Century.
Plate XXXII.
816–1902.

Compare Joan Evans, *Magical Jewels*, p. 126. The inscription is a charm for toothache and to appease tempests. See the note to No. 765.

758. GOLD; the hoop inscribed GOD·HELP ANN̄ MARIA; the shoulders chased with hearts charged with crosses and with two supports for the cup-shaped bezel set with a round pebble of green porphyry held by four claws.
English. Late 14th Century.
Plate XXXII.
(Waterton Colln.) 675–1871.

Joan Evans, *Magical Jewels*, p. 129.

759. SILVER, BRASS and IRON; formed by two bands of twisted wire, with silver-gilt interior inscribed JASPAR✶ MELCHIAR✶BALTAZAR.
German. 14th Century.
Plate XXXII.
(Waterton Colln.) 719–1871.

Compare a ring in the British Museum (Dalton, 909), with a plaited band of bronze and iron, also bearing an amuletic inscription.

760. SILVER; the hoop nielloed outside with +ADROS VDROS ID, and inside with +ADROS VDROS.
Italian. Early 15th Century.
(Waterton Colln.) 707–1871.

For suggested interpretations of this charm, see *Arch. Journal*, xxvi. 1869, p. 232.

For other rings where these words occur, see British Museum (Dalton, 866), and *Gentleman's Magazine*, 1841, p. 416.

761. SILVER; the hoop engraved and nielloed with +AGIOS O DEIOS A outside, and ATANATOS inside.
Italian. 15th Century.
(Waterton Colln.) 709–1871.

Intended for ἅγιος ὁ θεὸς ἀθάνατος, a contracted form of a passage which occurs in the Service of the Mass, and is found in magical books. See *Brit. Archaeol. Assoc.*, xl. 1884, pp. 321 *f*.

For rings with the same inscription, see British Museum (Dalton, 892) and Pichon Collection (*Catalogue*, Paris, 1897, Nos. 82, 83).

762. SILVER; inscribed inside +AI·EBEL· DIABEL+GUGUL+GUGUL.
15th Century.
(Waterton Colln.) 705–1871.

763. SILVER; roughly engraved; on the square bezel, IHS with cross; on the flat hoop, +HCER+S+DIA+BIZ+SA+ S+I, and (inside) ABIZ+SAN+HCBERBN.
Italian. 15th Century.
Plate XXXII.
(Waterton Colln.) 710–1871.

Perhaps the initials of a lengthy formula of prayers against the plague, transcribed in full in Waterton MS., pp. 321-324. This has been traced back to 1564, and was printed at Ronciglione in 1631.

764. GOLD; circular bezel engraved with an heraldic rose rudely scored with a cross (perhaps with the intention of cancelling its use as a signet); the hoop inscribed outside +IHESUS NASARENUS REX IVDEORUM✶ and inside +IASPAR MELCHIOR BALTASAR.
English. Late 15th Century.
Plate XXXII.
(Waterton Colln.) 701–1871.

Found in Ireland. Waterton MS., 317.

Ironmongers' Hall Exhibition, 1861, ii. 505.

The inscription is a charm for cramp. Compare note to No. 754.

765. GOLD; the hoop inscribed outside (apparently) +A+NA+NI+ZAP+TA, and inside +BURO+BERTO+BERNETO+ CONSUMATUM+EST.
English. Early 16th Century.
(Waterton Colln.) 703–1871.

Arch. Journal, xxvi. 1869, 231. Waterton MS., p. 311.

Ironmongers' Hall Exhibition, 1861, ii. 505.

In a 14th-century English MS. in the Royal Library, Stockholm, from which extracts are printed in *Archaeologia*, xxx. 1844, is the following mention of *Ananizapta* as a cure for the falling sickness:—"Sey yis word anamzaptus in his ere qhwā he is fallyn dow̄ in yt ewyll, and also in awōmānys ere anamzapta, t yei schall nevere more aftir fele y[t] ewyll."

For other rings with this inscription, see British Museum (Dalton, 870, 876). A ring formerly in Waterton's possession (MS., p. 308) bore the inscription:—

Est mala mors capta dum dicitur Ananiszata
Ananiszatam ferit ile qui quem ledere querit.

Guarini in his *Vocabularium* (1491) explains *Ananisapta* as follows:—

"Ananisapta mala mors interpretatur et quae libet littera repraesentat unam dictionem, scilicet: Antidotum Nazareni Auferat Necem Intoxicationis Santifice Alimenta Pocula Trinitatis Alma" (Evans, *Magical Jewels*, p. 123).

In the Stockholm MS. "BORO BERTO BRIORE" forms part of a charm to cure toothache. A ring found at Agincourt has the words BORO BERTO BERIORA (*Arch. Journal*, iv. 1847, 78).

Consummatum est, the last words of Our Lord on the cross, seems to have been used to calm storms; see Thiers, *Traité des superstitions*, i. 435: "*Appaiser la tempête en scrivant Consummatum est, d'une certaine manière et en le mettant ensuite sur la pointe d'un couteau à manche noir.*"

766. SILVER; the hoop engraved +EC+ EBER+DIABIR+SABAVC (repeated inside).
Italian. Early 16th Century.
(Waterton Colln.) 704–1871.

Ironmongers' Hall Exhibition, 1861, ii. 505.

No suggestion has been offered in explanation of this charm, unless it is a variety of that on No. 763.

767. HORN (or HOOF?); with outer band and octagonal bezel of silver, the latter set with a toadstone.
English. 15th or 16th Century.
Plate XXXII.
(Waterton Colln.) 711–1871.

Found at Richmond, Yorks. Waterton MS., p. 346.

Ironmongers' Hall Exhibition, 1861, ii. 505.

Proc. Soc. Ant., 2nd series, i. 278.

For the toadstone, see Introduction, p. 26.

Ass's hoof was considered efficacious against epilepsy.

768. HORN (or HOOF?); with lining, outer band, and circular bezel of silver, the last set with a toadstone.
15th or 16th Century.
Plate XXXII.
(Waterton Colln.) 712–1871.

769. SILVER; circular bezel set with a toadstone, the shoulders engraved with foliations.
German. 16th Century.
(Waterton Colln.) 713–1871.

770. SILVER; circular bezel set with a toadstone.
16th Century.
(Waterton Colln.) 714–1871.

771. HORN; the hoop mounted with a copper wire; circular silver bezel engraved with a coat of arms beneath the letters PP.
German (?). 16th Century.
Plate XXXII.
(Waterton Colln.) 717–1871.

The arms: an estoile above a crescent. The Pomeranian family of Pietrorche is amongst those bearing these arms.

772. IRON ; small conical bezel set with a piece of fossil tooth ; hoop with simple scale ornament.
16th Century. *Plate XXXII.*
(Waterton Colln.) 721–1871.

773. SILVER ; three oval bezels each set with a wolf's tooth ; shoulders with applied flowers ; hoop with oblique engraved gadroons and pearled bands.
South German. 16th Century.
(Waterton Colln.) 720–1871.

A wolf's tooth is a hunting charm to secure success in sport.

Compare British Museum (Dalton, 912–14).

774. GOLD ; originally circular bezel set with a toadstone ; hoop engraved inside *A friend at need doth gould exceed.*
English. 17th Century.
Plate XXXII.
(Waterton Colln.) 715–1871.

775. GOLD ; circular bezel set with a toadstone.
English. 17th Century.
Given by the Rev. R. Brooke.
389–1864.

776. GOLD ; circular bezel set with a toadstone, the inner side of the stone bare to the finger ; the hoop enamelled blue.
Italian. Second half of 17th Century.
Plate XXXII.
(Waterton Colln.) 716–1871.

Anselmus Boetius de Boot specially mentions that toadstones were worn in pierced rings, for they would warm the skin when in the presence of poison (*Gemmarum et Lapidum Historia*, p. 303).

777. SILVER-GILT ; a double bezel set with two wolf's teeth, the shoulders set with small pastes ; the hoop pearled and gadrooned.
German. 18th Century. 170–1872.

778. SILVER ; the shoulders with applied openwork ; the bezel set with a piece of bone (?) imitating a wolf's tooth.
German. 18th Century.
Plate XXXII.
173–1872.

Illustrated in Jones, *Finger-ring Lore*, p. 153.

779. GOLD encasing horn ; plain.
(Waterton Colln.) 718–1871.

Waterton MS., 347.

Ironmongers' Hall Exhibition, 1861, ii. 505.

780. SILVER ; the hoop covered with small circular knops.
Irish. 18th Century.
(Waterton Colln.) 722–1871.

Said to have been worn as a charm against rheumatism.

G. *OFFICIAL RINGS (ECCLESIASTICAL)*

(1) PAPAL

781. GOLD ; slender moulded hoop, forked at the shoulders, where a human head is applied ; large oval bezel set with a bloodstone engraved with St. Peter in a boat drawing a net.
Italian. 18th Century.
Plate XXXIII.
(Waterton Colln.) 749–1871.

The "Anulus Piscatoris" (see Introduction, p. 33) is the investiture ring and privy seal of a Pope. The name of the Pope has never been added to this specimen, and it was probably prepared for a Papal election, but not used.

(2) Cardinalitial

782. GOLD; long octagonal bezel set with a table-cut sapphire over foil; on the reverse the enamelled arms of Lambertini with the tiara and crossed keys, for Pope Benedict XIV. (1740-1758); openwork shoulders; richly chased hoop, hinged and opening with a spring. Italian. Middle of 18th Century.
Plate XXXIII.
(Waterton Colln.) 674–1871.

Perhaps the cardinalitial ring of Giorgio Doria, Cardinal of San Lorenzo in Panisperna (1743-1759). Given to Waterton by Prince Doria Pamphilj in 1857.

South Kensington Museum, Catalogue of Special Exhibition, 1862, p. 628.

Ironmongers' Hall Exhibition, 1861, ii. 498.

See Introduction, p. 34.

H. *COMMEMORATIVE RINGS*[1]

(1) Miscellaneous

783. LEAD; circular bezel with busts of the Emperors Charles V. and Ferdinand I. in profile to right; the hoop and bezel pierced to serve as a whistle. German. Middle of 16th Century.
Plate XXXIII.
(Waterton Colln.) 919–1871.

Ironmongers' Hall Exhibition, 1861, ii. 509.

784. ENAMELLED GOLD; transverse oval bezel with revolving centre having on one side a portrait of Anne of Austria, on the other her son the young Louis XIV., the hoop enamelled with coloured flowers on a white ground.
French. Middle of 17th Century.
Plate XXXIII.
103–1865.

785. GOLD; oval bezel set with a crystal enclosing a profile portrait in gold and enamel of Gustavus Adolphus. Inscribed at the back SIC REDIT.
English (?). 17th Century.
Plate XXXIII.
(Waterton Colln.) 925–1871.

Ironmongers' Hall Exhibition, 1861, ii. 502.

786. GOLD; transverse oval bezel set with an enamel portrait of Charles I. surrounded by diamonds in silver collets; back of bezel and hoop enamelled in black with floral and other ornament.
English. About 1650. *Plate XXXIII.*
(Waterton Colln.) 924–1871.

Ironmongers' Hall Exhibition, 1861, ii. 502.

786*a*. GOLD; oval bezel with a skull in white enamel above C R in black, the sides chased with scrolls; shoulders chased with masks and enamelled black.
English. About 1650.
Plate XXXIII.
(Harman-Oates Colln.) M. 22–1929.

A memorial ring for Charles I.

787. GOLD; transverse oval bezel set with a contemporary miniature of Charles I. under crystal.
English. 18th Century.
Plate XXXIII.
Bequeathed by Miss A. Cameron.
M. 1–1909.

788. SILVER, with traces of gilding; circular bezel set with a crystal enclosing a gold medal of Innocent XI. (1676-1689); the shoulders set with garnets.
Italian (?). Late 17th Century.
Plate XXXIII.
(Waterton Colln.) 928–1871.

[1] Other rings to which this description might be applied will be found under Peasant Rings, Nos. 384-388*a*, 481.

789. GOLD ; oval bezel set with a crystal enclosing a portrait of the Old Pretender on vellum ; shoulders chased in openwork with scrolls and leaves.
French (?). First half of 18th Century.
Plate XXXIII.
6–1899.

790. GOLD ; octagonal bezel set with a crystal enclosing a portrait of the Old Pretender on ivory.
French (?). First half of 18th Century.
Plate XXXIII.
(Waterton Colln.) 926–1871.

791. IRON ; the hoop chased and pierced with holes ; oval silver bezel engraved with four portrait-busts divided by clasped hands holding a caduceus. Beneath is the inscription (in reverse) BORBONVM FOEDVS.
Italian. Middle of 18th Century.
Plate XXXIII.
(Waterton Colln.) 930–1871.

The bezel seems to commemorate the family compact of 1761.

The busts are, (left) Ferdinand IV., King of the Two Sicilies, and Philip, Duke of Parma, and (right) Louis XV., King of France, and Charles III., King of Spain.

792. GOLD ; transverse octagonal bezel set with a crystal enclosing a grisaille miniature of a young man, under crystal.
French. About 1785.
Plate XXXIII.
527–1868.

792*a*. GOLD ; oval bezel set with a glass enclosing a painted silhouette on ivory of the head of a woman to left. In the manner of John Miers.
English. About 1790.
Given by Captain Desmond Coke.
P. 171–1922.

792*b*. GOLD ; oval bezel, with a border of seed pearls and violet enamel surrounding a glass enclosing a painted silhouette on ivory of a man's head to right. Signed by John Miers.
English. About 1790.
Given by Captain Desmond Coke.
P. 172–1922.

792*c*. GOLD ; oval bezel set with a Wedgwood cameo in blue-and-white jasper ware of a profile head to right.
English. Late 18th Century.
(Schreiber Colln., 1299.)

793. GOLD ; oval bezel set with an onyx cameo in three strata, the bust of an old man to right, with two diamond buttons in his coat. Signed on the truncation, WHITLEY F.
English. About 1790.
Plate XXXIII.
Given by Colonel Guthrie.
7128–1860.

W. Whitley, medallist and cameo-cutter, worked in Old Bond Street in the late 18th and early 19th century (Forrer, *Dictionary of Medallists*, vi. 464).

794. GOLD ; the hoop inscribed in reserve on blue enamel with SOYEZ HEUREUX and the oval bezel with two interlaced Y's.
English. 1791. *Plate XXXIII.*
Given by Mrs. Frederica Jane Halse.
325–1907.

Presented by Frederick, Duke of York, on the occasion of his marriage, September 29, 1791, to John Marling. See Introduction, p. 38.

795. SILVER ; a broad thin hoop with applied bezel stamped with portraits of Jean Paul Marat (murdered 13th July 1793) and Louis Michel Lepelletier de Saint Fargeau (murdered 20th January 1793).
French. Late 18th Century.
Plate XXXIII (inverted by error).
(Waterton Colln.) 931–1871.

Other rings of this type, and variants, are in the Musée Carnavalet and Musée des Arts Décoratifs, Paris.

(2) Mourning Rings

796. GOLD; oval bezel set with a crystal enclosing plaited hair and the letters CR KR beneath a crown in gold wire; the hoop with foliations formerly filled in with black enamel.
English. About 1685.
Plate XXXIV.
(Waterton Colln.) 927–1871.
Supposed to be a memorial ring for Charles II. and Catherine of Braganza.

797. GOLD; bezel set with a crystal enclosing the monogram J R in gold wire beneath a crown supported by two angels in coloured silk; the shoulders with foliations in black enamel.
English. About 1701.
Plate XXXIV.
(Harman-Oates Colln.) M. 21–1929.
A memorial ring for James II.

798. GOLD; oval bezel set with a crystal over plaited hair and the initials SJ in gold filigree; the hoop with foliations in black enamel.
English. Late 17th or early 18th Century. *Plate XXXIV.*
Given by the Rev. R. Brooke.
1110–1864.

798*a*. GOLD; circular bezel set with a crystal enclosing the letters C P in gold filigree; the shoulders formerly enamelled in foliations.
English. Late 17th or early 18th Century.
Given by Messrs. Child and Child.
M. 95–1913.

799. GOLD; circular bezel set with a crystal enclosing a monogram in gold filigree; the hoop with a skeleton and crossbones reserved on a ground of black enamel and inscribed within M FREND OB^T. 9' MAY 1709 AETA 59.
English. 1709. *Plate XXXIV.*
Given by Miss Anna Newton.
1639–1903.

800. GOLD; oval bezel set with a crystal enclosing a gold filigree monogram over red foil; the shoulders with foliations in black enamel.
English. Early 18th Century.
Given by the Rev. R. Brooke.
1114–1864.

801. GOLD; oval bezel set with a crystal framed in silver enclosing a gold filigree monogram on blue silk; the back of the bezel inscribed IMS; the shoulders with foliations in black enamel.
English. Early 18th Century.
526–1868.

802. GOLD; octagonal bezel set with a crystal enclosing a gold filigree monogram on yellow silk; the shoulders with foliations in black enamel.
English. Early 18th Century.
Given by the Rev. R. Brooke.
Plate XXXIV.
1124–1864.

803. GOLD; octagonal bezel set with a crystal enclosing a monogram in gold wire on red foil; inscribed inside the hoop HOPES.
English. Early 18th Century.
Given by the Rev. R. Brooke.
1109–1864.

804. GOLD; set with an oblong crystal covering a skull and crossbones; the hoop enamelled black with floral patterns and inscribed within MB OB^T 16 AUG: 1720 AETĀ: 63. Maker's mark, RU.
English. 1720.
Given by the Rev. R. Brooke.
1119–1864.

805. GOLD; set with three diamonds; inscribed within M B OB^T. 16 AUG^T 1720.
English. 1720.
Given by the Rev. R. Brooke.
1118–1864.

806. GOLD; set with a crystal enclosing a piece of black silk; the hoop with a skeleton and bones reserved on a ground of black enamel and the inscription MEMENTO MORI; engraved within the hoop S SPILLER OB 14 MAY 1719 AET 39. Maker's mark, T. T.
English. 1719. *Plate XXXIV.*
M. 371–1923.

807. GOLD; set with an oblong crystal covering the initials M C B in gold filigree; the hoop with three flowers in black enamel and inscribed within M C B OB^{T} 21 NOV: 1721 AETĀ 24.
English. 1721.
Given by the Rev. R. Brooke.
1121–1864.

Mary Catharine Hammond married Walter Brooke (Poulson's *Holderness*, i. 241).

808. GOLD; set with an oblong crystal covering a skull and crossbones; the hoop enamelled black with floral patterns and inscribed within C.M.B. OB^{T} 21 NOV. 1721. Maker's mark, D E.
English. 1721. *Plate XXXIV.*
Given by the Rev. R. Brooke.
1120–1864.

Probably for Mary Catharine Brooke (see the foregoing).

809. GOLD; set with an oblong crystal covering the initials W B in gold filigree; the hoop enamelled black with floral patterns and inscribed within W B OB^{T} 15 NOV: 1722 ÆT 27. Maker's mark, R U.
English. 1722.
Given by the Rev. R. Brooke.
1122–1864.

For Walter Brooke (see Poulson's *Holderness*, i. 241).

810. GOLD; inscribed ELIZ: HORSMAN OB: 7 JUNE 1740 Æ: 3 in reserve on five white-enamelled scrolls; hexagonal bezel set with a crystal covering a skull.
English. 1740. *Plate XXXIV.*
Given by Mr. Martin Travers.
M. 351–1927.

811. GOLD; a hoop of five scroll-shaped panels inscribed in reserve on black enamel ROB: POCKLEY· AR. OB 19 NOV 1744.
English. 1744.
Given by the Rev. R. Brooke.
661–1864.

See Poulson's *Holderness*, i. 241.

812. GOLD; square bezel set with a paste diamond; the hoop of six scroll-shaped panels inscribed in reserve on black enamel RACH BRAIN OB 26 JUN 1746 Æ: 3.
English. 1746. *Plate XXXIV.*
M. 373–1923.

Compare Introduction, p. 40.

813. GOLD; silver heart-shaped bezel set with a diamond; the hoop of six scroll-shaped panels formerly enamelled and inscribed RICH^{D} PERRY OB 22 APR: 1754 Æ 76.
English. 1754.
Given by Mr. C. B. Farmer.
138–1906.

814. GOLD; a hoop of five scroll-shaped panels inscribed in reserve on white enamel ROBINSON MORLEY ARM: OB 28 SEP: 1756 ÆT 22.
English. 1756. *Plate XXXIV.*
Given by the Rev. R. Brooke.
660–1864.

815. GOLD; a hoop of five scroll-shaped panels inscribed in reserve on black enamel MARY SELLAR OB: 21 MAR: 1762 Æ 65.
English. 1762. *Plate XXXIV.*
M. 372–1923.

816. GOLD; a wavy hoop inscribed in reserve on black enamel ANNA MITFORD OB: 6 MAY 1763 Æ 38.
English. 1763.
Given by the Rev. R. Brooke.
655–1864.

817. GOLD; scroll-shaped bezel inscribed in reserve on black enamel MEMENTO, the hoop with RICH: EPIS: LONDON· OB: 15· MAY· 1764 ÆT. 75.
English. 1764. *Plate XXXIV*.
Given by the Rev. R. Brooke.
654–1864.

Richard Osbaldeston, Bishop of London, 1762-1764.

818. GOLD; inscribed in reserve on white enamel THO: MORLEY· ESQ: OB: 20 AUG: 1766 Æ 30.
English. 1766.
Given by the Rev. R. Brooke.
658–1864.

819. GOLD; inscribed in reserve on white enamel W: OSBALDESTON: ESQ: OB: 5· SEP: 1766. Æ 79.
English. 1766.
Given by the Rev. R. Brooke.
659–1864.

820. GOLD; oval bezel set with a crystal enclosing a landscape executed in hair on white enamel; the hoop inscribed in reserve on white enamel RICHD. TOWNSEND· ESQ: OB: 12 MAR: 1768. Æ 44.
English. 1768. *Plate XXXIV*.
Given by Miss Anna Newton.
1630–1903.

Compare British Museum (Dalton, 1580).

821. GOLD; a hoop of six scroll-shaped panels inscribed in reserve on white enamel RICH TOWNSEND ESQ: OB 12 MAR 1768 Æ: 44. Maker's mark, J.W.
English. 1768.
Given by Miss Anna Newton.
1631–1903.

822. GOLD; set with a crystal; inscribed in reserve on black enamel S: E: BROOKE: OB: 27 FEB: 1769· Æ 85.
English. 1769.
Given by the Rev. R. Brooke.
1123–1864.

823. GOLD; inscribed in reserve on black enamel S. E. BROOKE. OB: 27· FEB: 1769· Æ 85.
English. 1769.
Given by the Rev. R. Brooke.
651–1864.

824. GOLD; inscribed in reserve on white enamel F: W: OSBALDESTON. ESQ: OB: 10· JUNE· 1770 Æ 76.
English. 1770.
Given by the Rev. R. Brooke.
657–1864.

825. GOLD; inscribed in reserve on white enamel RT STAVELEY· OB: 6· AUG: 1771· Æ 26.
English. 1771.
Given by the Rev. R. Brooke.
656–1864.

826. GOLD; inscribed in reserve on black enamel JOHN· HUDSON· ESQ: OB: 17 OCT: 1772 Æ 45.
English. 1772.
Given by the Rev. R. Brooke.
648–1864.

827. GOLD; inscribed in reserve on black enamel BOYNTON· LANGLEY· ESQ: OB: 5· JAN 1772 Æ 32.
English. 1772.
Given by the Rev. R. Brooke.
647–1864.

828. GOLD; inscribed in reserve on black enamel THOS. HASSELL. ESQ: DIED. 29· MAY· 1773· AGED· 54.
English. 1773.
Given by the Rev. R. Brooke.
645–1864.

829. GOLD; inscribed in reserve on black enamel JAMES HEBLETHWAYTE· ESQ: OB: 2. NOV: 1773 Æ 46.
English. 1773.
Given by the Rev. R. Brooke.
649–1864.

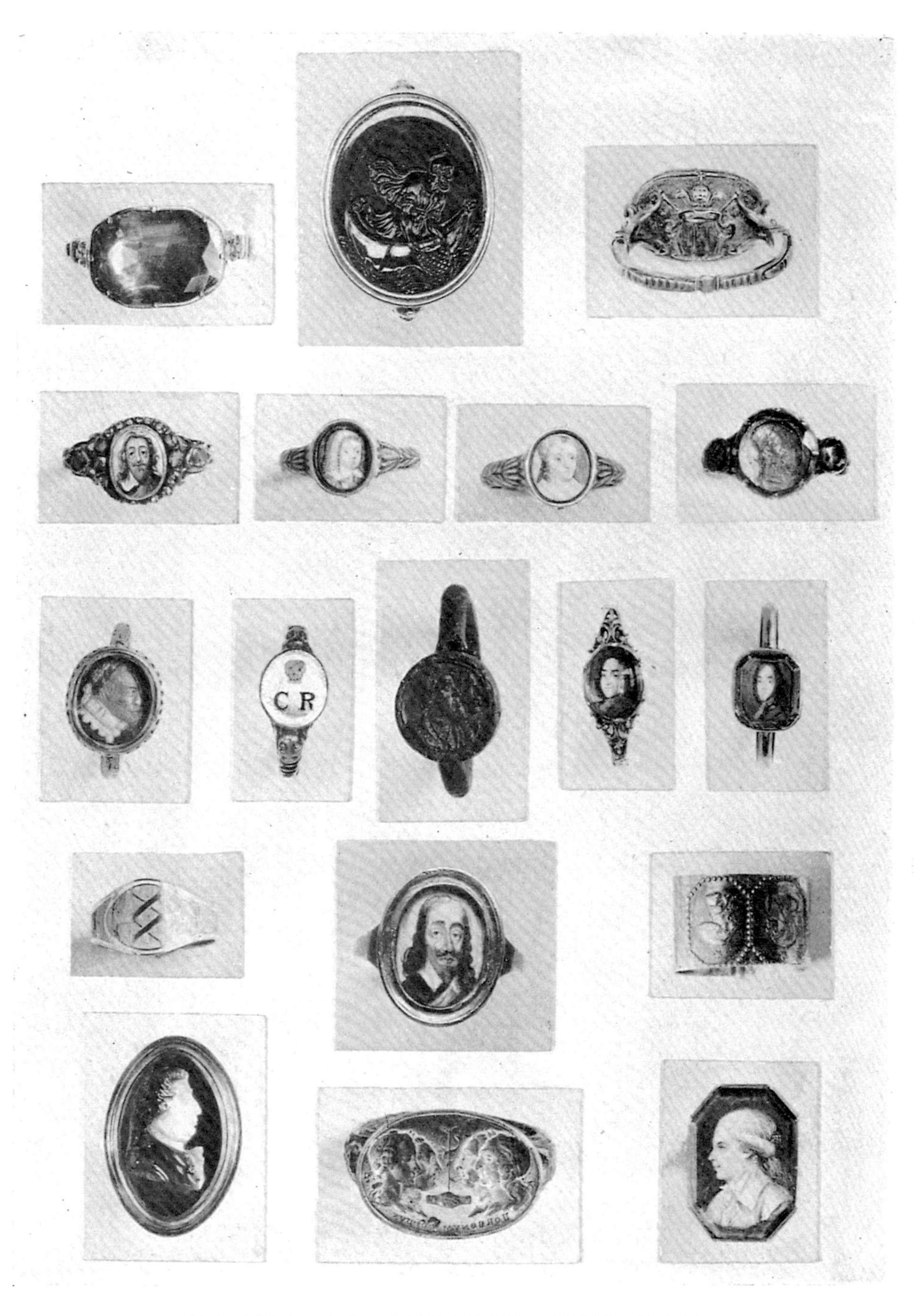

OFFICIAL AND COMMEMORATIVE RINGS

782		781		782
786	784		784	788
785	786*a*	783	789	790
794		787		795
793		791		792

PLATE XXXIV

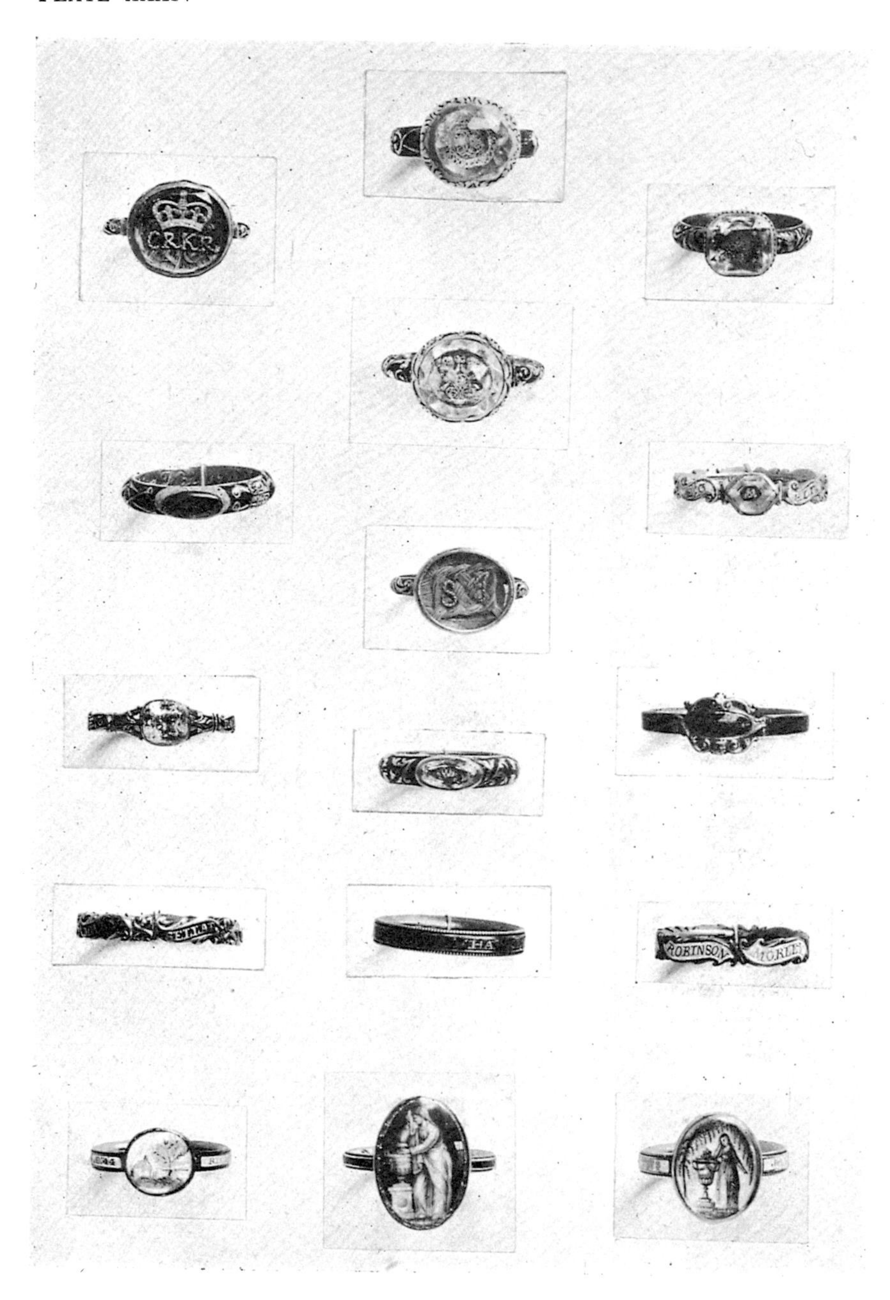

MOURNING RINGS: 17TH AND 18TH CENTURY

796	799	802
806	797	810
	798	
812	808	817
815	831	814
820	835	837

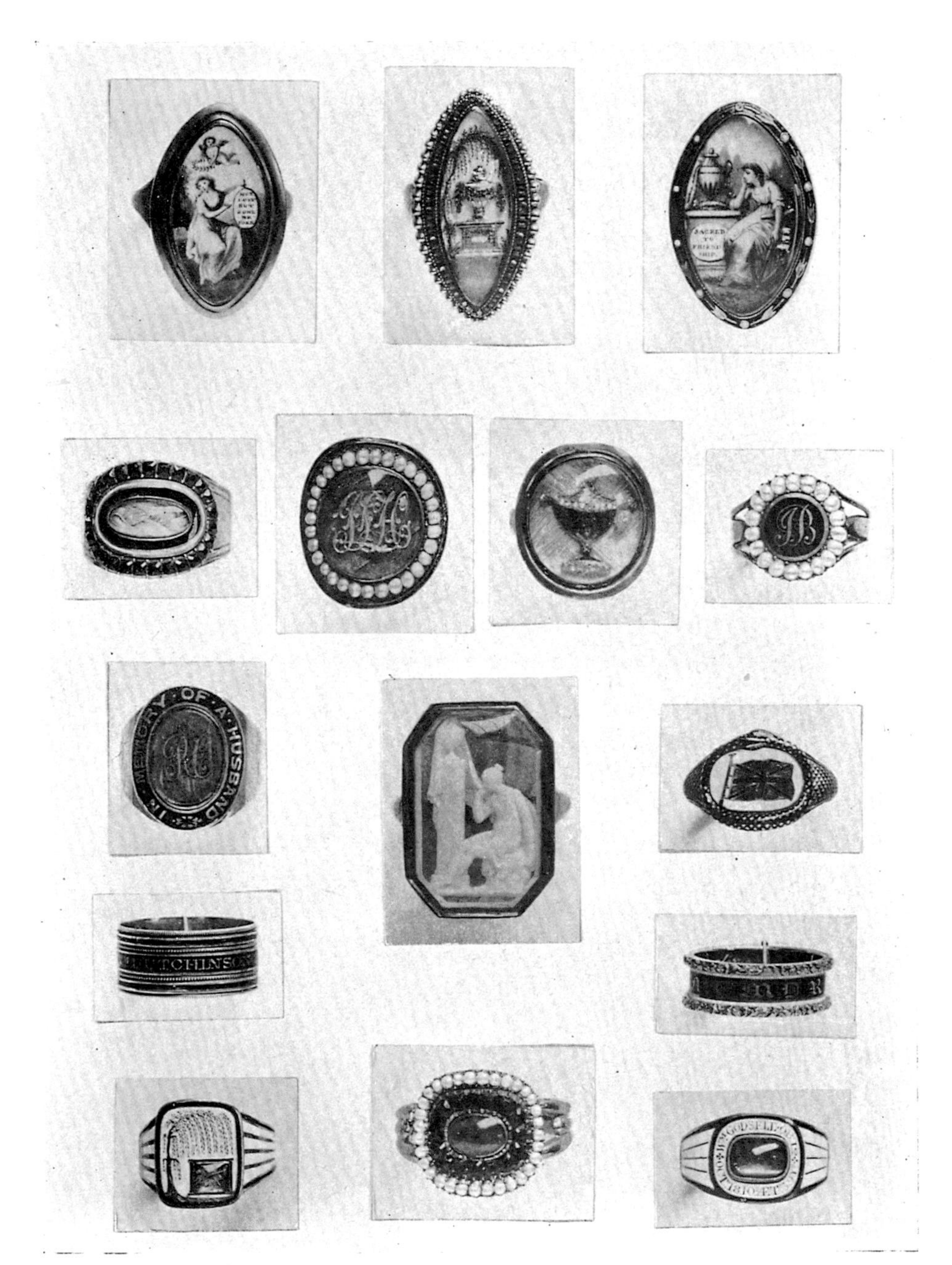

MOURNING RINGS: 18TH AND 19TH CENTURY

864		847		853
893	879		883	892
902		915		909
905				912
907		895		908

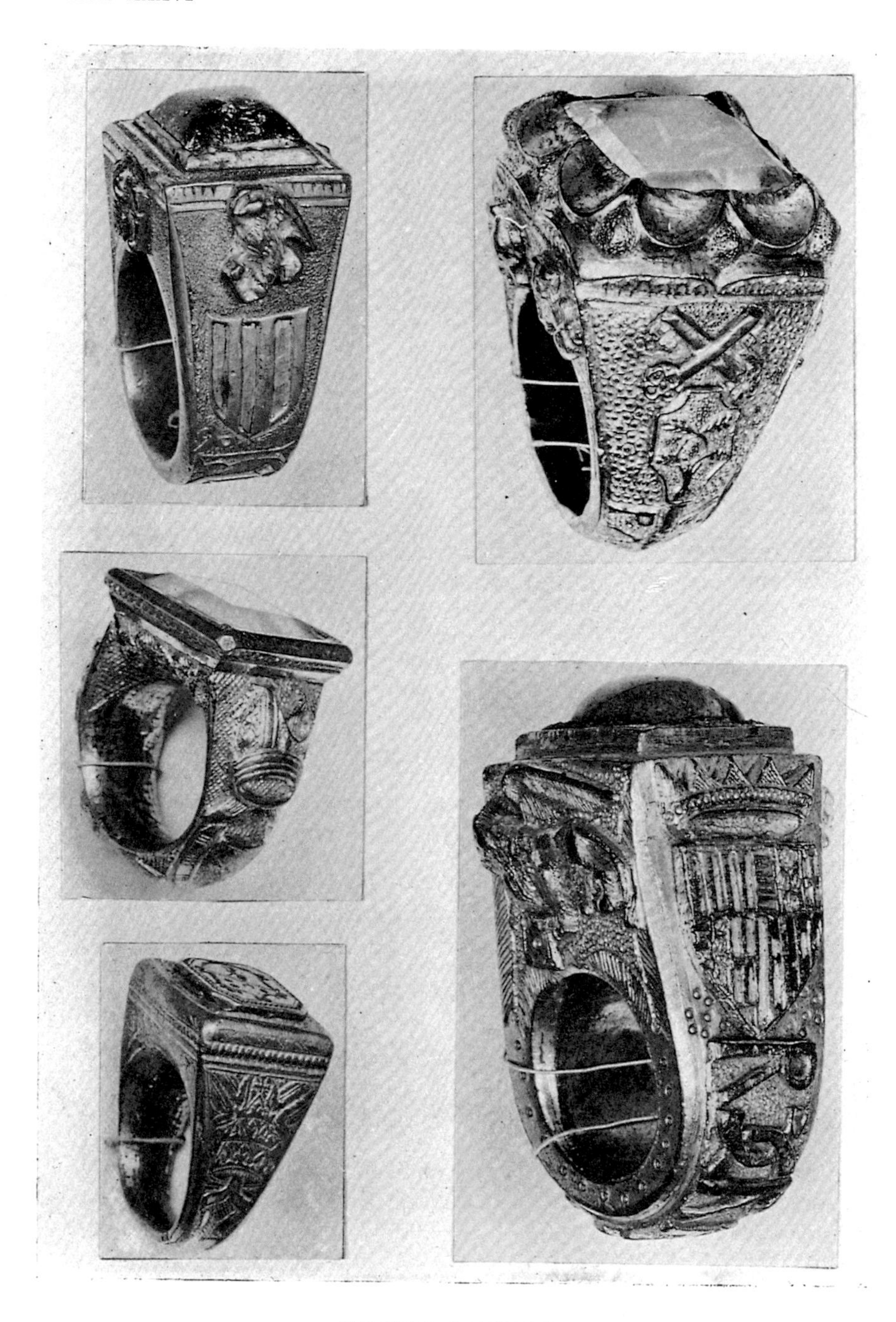

"PAPAL" RINGS

921 927
920
917 922

830. GOLD; inscribed in reserve on black enamel MATT^{W} SMITH. ESQ: OB: 4 NOV: 1777 Æ: 56.
English. 1777.
Given by the Rev. R. Brooke.
646–1864.

831. GOLD; inscribed in reserve on black enamel EDW^{D} LORD· HAWKE OB: 17 OCT: 1781· Æ: 76.
English. 1781. *Plate XXXIV.*
Given by the Rev. R. Brooke.
650–1864.

Lord Hawke married a member of the family of Brooke; see Poulson's *Holderness*, i. 241.

832. GOLD; vesica-shaped bezel set with a glass enclosing a painting of a woman seated by an urn on a pedestal inscribed REST IN PEACE; and on the back MICK^{L} NORTON DIED 13 FEB^{Y} 1770 AGED 60. ANN NORTON DIED 4 NOV^{R} 1768 AGED 60.
English. 1770. 905–1888.

833. GOLD; oval bezel set with a glass enclosing a painting of a youth standing by an urn and pedestal worked in hair and inscribed WB 1777 EB 1779 and on the back W. BALLANTINE OB. 29 MAR. 1777 Æ. 82. ELIZ BALLANTINE OB 19 OCT^{R} 1779 Æ 68.
English. 1779. 904–1888.

834. GOLD; vesica-shaped bezel surrounded by seed pearls and set with a glass enclosing a painting of a woman laying a wreath on an altar inscribed M. B. and set with seed pearls.
English. Late 18th Century.
861–1888.

835. GOLD; oval bezel set with a glass enclosing a painting of a woman weeping by an urn; inscribed on the back E DAVY OB: 28 OCT^{R} 1779 ÆT 71; the hoop enamelled black.
English. 1779. *Plate XXXIV.*
876–1888.

836. GOLD; oval bezel enamelled black with an urn inscribed DAN: DANIEL surrounded by the inscription in reserve MARTHA· MYERS· OB: 8· OCT: 1779. ÆT 38; the hoop inscribed in reserve on black enamel SAM^{L} MYERS· OB: 10. AUG: 1777. ÆT: 62; the back of the bezel engraved OB^{T} 25 AUG^{T} (erasure) Æ 61.
English. 1779. 852–1888.

837. GOLD; oval bezel set with a glass enclosing a painting of a woman weeping by an urn; the hoop inscribed JOHN. PRINCE. OB: 11 SEP: 1779· Æ: 7 W^{S}.
English. 1779. *Plate XXXIV.*
875–1888.

838. GOLD; oval bezel set with a glass enclosing an urn worked in hair; inscribed on the back FRANCES BLAKE OB· 5 JULY 1780. ÆT 14.
English. 1780. 850–1888.

839. GOLD; oval bezel set with a glass enclosing an urn of plaited hair and gold; inscribed at the back GABRIEL BROOKE ESQ^{R} OB. 12 APR. 1781. ÆT. 71.
English. 1781.
Given by the Rev. R. Brooke.
1125–1864.

840. GOLD; oval bezel set with a glass enclosing an urn worked in hair.
English. Late 18th Century.
847–1888.

841. GOLD; circular bezel set with a glass enclosing plaited hair, surrounded by two bands of black and white enamel; the hoop inscribed in reserve on black enamel ELIZ: DENMAN· OB: 7· NOV: 1781· Æ 59.
English. 1781. 868–1888.

842. GOLD; vesica-shaped bezel set with a glass enclosing a painting of a woman standing by an urn worked in hair, on a pedestal inscribed EVER TO BE REMEMBER,D; on the back AMOS ANGLES OB. 9. JUNE 1782. ÆT. 73.
English. 1782. 917–1888.

843. GOLD; oblong bezel with rounded corners, set with a glass enclosing a piece of silk, surrounded by a border of pearls; the hoop dividing into three at the shoulders; inscribed on the back of the bezel THOS BORROW DIED 9 AUG^{T} 1783, AGED 62.
English. 1783. 869–1888.

844. GOLD; oval bezel set with a glass enclosing a piece of silk, surrounded by a border of pearls; the hoop dividing into three at the shoulders.
English. Late 18th Century.
891–1888.

845. GOLD; vesica-shaped bezel set with a glass enclosing a painting of an urn on a pedestal; the hoop inscribed in reserve on black enamel FRANCES· CRABTREE OB: 27, SEP: 1783 Æ: 72.
English. 1783. 853–1888.

846. GOLD; vesica-shaped bezel set with a glass enclosing a painting of a woman standing by an altar inscribed A S D; on the back SAMUEL DURRANT DIED SEP^{T} 4 1783 AGED 62.
English. 1783. 857–1888.

847. GOLD; vesica-shaped bezel set with a glass enclosing an urn in blue and white enamel and a weeping willow worked in hair, surrounded by a blue enamel border; inscribed on the back JOHN DAVYS ESQ^{R} OB. 22 APRIL 1783 ÆT. 70 ELIZ. DAVYS OB^{T} 7 DEC 1784 ÆT 55.
English. 1784. *Plate XXXV.*
911–1888.

848. GOLD; oval bezel set with a glass enclosing a painting of a woman standing by an urn on a pedestal inscribed E M in monogram; on the back E M MAR^{D} 14 MAY 1779 OB 23 AUG. 1783 A'T 25.
English. 1783. 903–1888.

849. GOLD; vesica-shaped bezel set with a glass enclosing an urn worked in hair with gold fittings; on the back E TEMPEST. OB: JULY 3: 1784 A. . . 70 (?).
English. 1784. 871–1888.

850. GOLD; vesica-shaped bezel set with a glass enclosing a painting of a woman standing by an urn on a pedestal inscribed M H; on the back MARTHA HOLWORTHY OB 13 SEP. 1785 Æ^{T} 65.
English. 1785. 915–1888.

851. GOLD; vesica-shaped bezel set with a glass enclosing a painting of an urn on a pedestal surrounded by the inscription FORGIVE THE WISH THAT WOULD HAVE KEPT THEE HERE.
English. Late 18th Century.
874–1888.

852. GOLD; vesica-shaped bezel set with a glass enclosing a painting of an obelisk.
English. Late 18th Century.
870–1888.

853. GOLD; vesica-shaped bezel set with a glass enclosing a painting of Hope seated by an urn on a pedestal inscribed SACRED TO FRIENDSHIP, surrounded by a border of laurels in black and white enamel; the back engraved with JOHN CHALMERS ESQ^{R} OB. 28 March 1786 ÆT. 57.
English. 1786. *Plate XXXV.*
909–1888.

854. GOLD; oval bezel set with a glass enclosing an urn in relief in brown enamel mounted with gold; inscribed on the back JAMES STEWART OB: 9 MAY 1786 Æ 29.
English. 1786. 854–1888.

855. GOLD; oval bezel set with a glass enclosing an urn surrounded by the inscription NOT· LOST· BUT· GONE· BEFORE.
English. Late 18th Century.
848–1888.

856. GOLD; vesica-shaped bezel set with a glass enclosing plaited hair, over

which are worked the initials S W H and willow leaves partly in seed pearls; inscribed on the back SARAH HETHERINGTON OB: 7 APR. 1786 ÆT 7 MS WM HETHERINGTON OB 31 JULY 1786 ÆT 8 YRS 9 MS.
English. 1786. 864–1888.

857. GOLD; vesica-shaped bezel set with a glass enclosing a painting of a woman standing by an urn on a pedestal inscribed W B; on the reverse WM BARBER OB: 26 JAN 1787 Æ 71.
English. 1787. 916–1888.

858. GOLD; vesica-shaped bezel set with a glass enclosing a representation of two doves perched on a vase worked in hair and set with seed pearls, above which is the word AMITIE; inscribed on the back with the letters SS, JLH in monogram, and 1787.
English. 1787. 856–1888.

859. GOLD; oval bezel set with a glass enclosing a painting of an urn surrounded by the inscription SAML. CHARLSON OBT. MAY 23RD 1788 AGED 72.
English. 1788. 851–1888.

860. GOLD; vesica-shaped bezel set with a glass over a painting of a woman standing by an urn; on the back THOS. DARVILL OB 16 APL 1788 ÆT 25.
English. 18th Century. 860–1888.

861. GOLD; vesica-shaped bezel set with a glass enclosing a painting of a woman weeping by an urn on a pedestal inscribed VIRTUE ALONE IS HAPPINESS BELOW.
English. Late 18th Century.
914–1888.

862. GOLD; oblong bezel with rounded ends, with a border of seed pearls surrounding a white-enamelled urn, inscribed W E and set with diamond sparks, on a blue ground; inscribed on the back WILLM FAUQUIER ESQR OBT DECR. 15 1788 ÆT. 80.
English. 1788. 849–1888.

863. GOLD; oval bezel set with a glass enclosing a piece of silk, surrounded by a border of pearls; the hoop formed of a central band and two wires joining together at the back.
English. Late 18th Century.
895–1888.

864. GOLD; vesica-shaped bezel set with a glass enclosing a painting of a seated woman holding a plaque inscribed NOT·LOST·BUT·GONE·BEFORE; engraved on the reverse JOHN GRIFFITHS ESQ. OBT 9 AUG 1788 Æ 50.
English. 1788. *Plate XXXV.*
Given by Miss Marie Langton.
364–1890.

865. GOLD; octagonal bezel set with a glass enclosing a painting of a woman seated by an urn on a pedestal inscribed NOT LOST BUT GONE BEFORE; above is a hovering angel with a scroll reading TO BLISS; inscribed on the back HARRIOT WILLOCK OB 18 DECR. 1788 ÆT 15.
English. 1788. 902–1888.

866. GOLD; oblong bezel with rounded ends set with a glass enclosing a painting of an urn above which are two angels holding a crown and the inscription NOT LOST BUT GONE BEFORE.
English. Late 18th Century.
873–1888.

867. GOLD; oval bezel set with a glass enclosing plaited hair covered by an enamelled urn on a pedestal inscribed E P; on the back IN MEMORY OF MRS ELIZ. PARTRIDGE OBT. 30TH MAY 1789 ÆT 27.
English. 1789. 919–1888.

868. GOLD; oval bezel set with a glass enclosing an urn worked in hair set with seed pearls and diamonds, surrounded by a border of seed pearls.
English. Late 18th Century.
846–1888.

869. GOLD; curved circular bezel set with a glass enclosing plaited hair and a white-enamelled plaque inscribed I H E, surrounded by a border of pearls.
English. Late 18th Century.
867–1888.

870. GOLD; vesica-shaped bezel set with a glass enclosing plaited hair behind a bird on a willow-tree worked in seed pearls.
English. Late 18th Century.
863–1888.

871. GOLD; oval bezel set with a glass enclosing a piece of silk, surrounded by pearls; the hoop formed by three bands separating at the shoulders.
English. Late 18th Century.
901–1888.

872. GOLD; oval bezel set with a glass enclosing plaited hair surrounded by a border of blue and white enamel.
English. Late 18th Century.
881–1888.

873. GOLD; oblong bezel with rounded ends, set with a glass enclosing an urn worked in hair; inscribed on the back LADY MAWBEY OB 19TH AUG: 1790 Æ. 45.
English. 1790. 855–1888.

874. GOLD; vesica-shaped bezel set with a glass enclosing a painting of a woman seated by an urn on a pedestal inscribed NOT LOST BUT GONE BEFORE; on the back, ANN SCURFIELD OB 20 OCTR 1790 ÆT 49.
English. 1790. 858–1888.

875. GOLD; vesica-shaped bezel set with a glass enclosing a painting of a weeping willow and an urn on a pedestal inscribed SACRED TO LOVE; on the back, JNO AMEY OB 18 MAR 1791 ÆT 64.
English. 1791. 872–1888.

876. GOLD; the hoop inscribed in reserve on black enamel ELIZ: CARTER. OB: 31. DEC 1797. Æ; added bezel set with a glass enclosing a painting of a woman standing by an urn inscribed C E H, under a willow. Maker's mark, I P.
English. London hall-mark for 1791-2.
862–1888.

877. GOLD; oblong bezel set with a glass enclosing a painting of a girl with a dove, surrounded by a blue enamel border.
English. Late 18th Century.
910–1888.

878. GOLD; oblong bezel with rounded ends, set with a glass enclosing plaited hair and an enamelled urn on a pedestal surrounded by an inscription reserved on blue enamel, GABL WIRGMAN· DIED· 12· SEP: 1791· AGED· 53; inscribed on the back THOS GARLE. ARM: OBT 5 SEPR 1789 ÆT 67.
English. 1791. 907–1888.

879. GOLD; curved circular bezel with a border of blue enamel and seed pearls, set with a glass enclosing plaited hair and a monogram in gold.
English. Late 18th Century.
Plate XXXV.
Given by Mr. S. P. Avery. 585–1892.

880. GOLD; curved circular bezel with border of pearls, set with a glass enclosing plaited hair and a monogram T L B in gold, surrounded by a border of blue and white enamel.
English. Late 18th Century.
866–1888.

881. GOLD; vesica-shaped bezel set with a glass enclosing a painting of a girl seated by an obelisk inscribed TO JOY & HAPPINESS I RISE ELIZA CLARK OB: 9 OCT 1792 Æ 15 YRS; from the monument rises her spirit about to be crowned by an angel.
English. 1792. 918–1888.

882. GOLD; oval bezel set with a glass enclosing a painting of a woman and a girl weeping beside an urn on a pedestal inscribed SACRED TO THE BEST OF HUSBANDS, surrounded by an in-

scription reserved on blue enamel, WM HEMBROW. OB: 8. OCT: 1792. ÆT: 31.
English. 1792. 908–1888.

883. GOLD ; curved oval bezel set with a glass enclosing an urn of blue enamel with diamond sparks over plaited hair ; inscribed at the back JOHN WILLIAMS, OBT. 6 APL. 1793. ÆT. 57.
English. 1793. *Plate XXXV.*
630–1872.

884. GOLD ; oval bezel set with a glass enclosing a painting of a woman standing by an obelisk inscribed E·N OB: 9 AP: 1794 Æ: 32 ; on the back IN MEMY. OF A DEAR COMPANION.
English. 1794. 859–1888.

885. GOLD ; oval bezel set with a glass enclosing a painting of a woman seated by an urn on a pedestal inscribed W W ; on the back WM WARRINGTON OBT. 17 SEPR. 1794 ÆT 54.
English. 1794. 906–1888.

886. GOLD ; oval bezel set with a glass over a painting of two birds perched on a chalice ; above is the word AMITIE.
English. Late 18th Century.
Given by Mr. S. P. Avery. 586–1892.

887. GOLD ; circular bezel with recessed centre containing an urn in white enamel on a black ground ; inscribed on the back JNO BROWN OB: 24. NOVR 1795 ÆT: 66.
English. 1795. 877–1888.

888. GOLD ; circular bezel set with a glass enclosing plaited hair and the letters E H in seed pearls, surrounded by the inscription EDWARD· HARPER· DIED· 20· MAY· 1795· AGED· 58.
English. 1795. 886–1888.

889. GOLD ; curved oval bezel set with a glass enclosing a painting of a woman seated by an urn on a pedestal inscribed I H, surrounded by the inscription MR ISAAC· HITCHIN· OB: 14 JAN. 1796 ÆT: 71.
English. 1796. 913–1888.

890. GOLD ; oval bezel set with a crystal enclosing plaited hair and a white-enamelled urn on a pedestal set with diamond sparks and inscribed M R ; on the back, MAURICE RANDLE OBT. 7 OCTR. 1796 ÆT 48.
English. 1796. 912–1888.

891. GOLD ; oval bezel set with a glass enclosing plaited hair and the letters M G in gold, surrounded by the inscription IN MEMORY OF MARY GRISSIN.
English. Late 18th Century.
879–1888.

892. GOLD ; circular bezel with the initials J B reserved on black enamel, surrounded by seed pearls ; the hoop composed of three bands separating at the shoulders.
English. Late 18th Century.
Plate XXXV.
880–1888.

893. GOLD ; oval bezel set with a glass enclosing plaited hair, surrounded by bands of black and white enamel and cut jet ; inscribed inside BARBARA TOWNELEY OB, 25 DECR. 1797 ÆT 66.
English. 1797. *Plate XXXV.*
899–1888.

894. GOLD ; curved octagonal bezel with the initials M W surrounded by the inscription MARY· WHITE· OB: 10. FEB: 1798. Æ. 73 in reserve on black enamel within white borders.
English. 1798. 883–1888.

895. GOLD ; rounded bezel set with a glass enclosing plaited hair, surrounded by borders of cut jet and pearls ; open shoulders.
English. Late 18th Century.
Plate XXXV.
896–1888.

896. GOLD ; oval bezel set with a glass covering a piece of silk, surrounded by pearls, the hoop formed of wire with a fleur-de-lys on each shoulder.
English. Late 18th Century.
887–1888.

897. GOLD; oblong bezel with rounded corners, set with a glass surrounded by a double border of pearls; the hoop formed of four wires separating at the shoulders.
English. Late 18th Century.
900–1888.

898. GOLD; oval bezel set with a glass enclosing plaited hair, surrounded by graduated pearls; the shoulders with wirework decoration.
English. Late 18th or early 19th Century.
893–1888.

899. GOLD; oblong bezel set with a glass enclosing plaited hair, surrounded by pearls; the hoop branching into two at the shoulders.
English. Late 18th or early 19th Century.
894–1888.

900. GOLD; oval bezel placed diagonally, set with a glass enclosing plaited hair and surrounded by seed pearls.
English. Late 18th or early 19th Century.
897–1888.

901. GOLD; octagonal bezel set with a glass enclosing plaited hair, surrounded by diamond pastes; inscribed on the back with the initials D P and E K.
English. Late 18th or early 19th Century. (The hoop modern.)
865–1888.

902. GOLD; oval bezel set with a glass enclosing plaited hair with the initials R C in wire; surrounded by the inscription IN· MEMORY· OF· A· HUSBAND in reserve on black enamel.
English. Early 19th Century.
Plate XXXV.
885–1888.

903. GOLD; curved circular bezel set with a glass enclosing plaited hair surrounded by the inscription M^RS MARY-ANN GOODHART OB· 19 OCT 1802 Æ 18 in reserve on white enamel and a border of cut jet; similar inscription engraved inside. Made by Henry Sardet.
English. London hall-mark for 1802-3.
882–1888.

904. GOLD; oval bezel set with a glass enclosing a piece of silk surrounded by a border of pearls; the shoulders enamelled black and white; inscribed inside W^M RAVEN OB^T 22, AUG^T 1804 ÆT 39.
English. 1804. 888–1888.

905. GOLD; inscribed in reserve on black enamel W^M HUTCHINSON· ESQ: OB: 17. DEC: 1808: Æ: 48. Made by Robert Cattle and J. Barber.
English. York hall-mark for 1807-8.
Plate XXXV.
Given by the Rev. R. Brooke.
652–1864.

906. GOLD; curved circular bezel set with a glass enclosing plaited hair and the initials E W L. in gold; on the back the inscription E.W.L. OB: 16 MAY 1809 ÆT 9 Y^RS.
English. 1809. 884–1888.

907. GOLD; the hoop enamelled with bands of white and black; oblong bezel with a weeping willow on a white ground and a square set with a glass covering plaited hair; inscribed inside, ANNA SEWARD, OB. 25 MARCH, 1809, ÆT 66.
English. 1809. *Plate XXXV.*
Given by Mr. Cecil Crofton.
M. 326–1922.

908. GOLD; rounded oblong bezel set with a glass enclosing plaited hair, surrounded by a border of black and white enamel with the inscription W^M GODSELL· OB: 12 ∵ OCT: 1810 ÆT: 39 Y^S; the shoulders similarly enamelled.
English. 1810. *Plate XXXV.*
889–1888.

909. GOLD; oval bezel enamelled with the Union Flag surrounded by a serpent; inscribed inside CAPT^N JAMES NEWMAN

NEWMAN, LOST OFF THE HAAK IN THE HERO 74. DEC 24, 1811, AGED 46.
English. 1812. *Plate XXXIV.*
Given by Mrs. G. H. Goodman.
M. 314–1926.

910. GOLD; oblong bezel set with a glass enclosing plaited hair, surrounded by a border of pearls; the shoulders each with three pearls; inscribed inside, ANN ATKINSON, OB. 5, SEPT. 1815 ÆT 26.
English. 1815. 890–1888.

911. GOLD; oblong bezel set with a glass enclosing plaited hair surrounded by cut jet and a chased border; the hoop with a similar border and the inscription IN· MEMORY· OF in reserve on black enamel; inscribed inside, JAMES CLARKE OB^T 10 AUG^T 1820 ÆT 66.
English. 1820. 892–1888.

912. GOLD; inscribed in reserve on black enamel IN·MEMORY·OF and engraved inside JAMES SELBY PENNINGTON OB^T NOV^R 1ST 1831, Æ 88. Made by Barber, Cattle and North.
English. York hall-mark for 1824-5.
Plate XXXV.
Given by the Rev. R. Brooke.
653–1864.

913. GOLD; oblong bezel set with a glass enclosing plaited hair, surrounded by an inscription reserved on black enamel AS · IN · LIFE · BELOVED · IN · DEATH · LAMENTED; the shoulders with white urns on a black ground.
English. Early 19th Century.
878–1888.

914. GOLD; oblong bezel with lobed sides, set with a glass enclosing plaited hair and surrounded by pearls and a black-enamelled border; the shoulders branching into three and chased with flowers.
English. Early 19th Century.
898–1888.

915. GOLD; large octagonal bezel enclosing a cameo under crystal (nude figure seated at the foot of a column supporting an urn). Signed: BABOUOT.
French. Early 19th Century.
Plate XXXV.
(Waterton Colln.) 929–1871.

Babouot did work for the Paris mint in the early 19th century. L. Forrer, *Biographical Dictionary of Medallists*, i. 40.

915*a*. GOLD; transverse oval bezel with a border of diamonds framing a 19th-century painted enamel plaque of Psyche by Lepec; the hoop enamelled blue; the shoulders edged with diamond sparks.
French. Late 18th Century.
Bequeathed by Mrs. Harriet Bolckow.
746–1890.

Probably originally a mourning ring.

I. *MISCELLANEOUS RINGS*

(1) RING OF A SERJEANT-AT-LAW

916. GOLD; a plain hoop inscribed REX LEGIS TVTAMEN, the motto used at the call of 1669. Maker's mark, C over W.
English. 1669. *Plate XXXIX.*
Given by the Rev. R. Brooke.
388–1864.

Compare Introduction, p. 41. The following anecdote probably refers to the call of 1669: "Seventeen serjeants being made the 14th day of November (1669 ?), a daye or two after, Serjeant Powis, the junior of them all, coming to the King's Bench Bar, Lord Chief Justice Kelynge told him 'that he had something to say to him, viz., that the rings that he and the rest of the serjeants had given weighed but eighteen shillings apiece; whereas Fortescue, in his book *De Laudibus Legum Angliae*, says " the rings given to the Chief Justices and to the Chief Baron ought to weigh twenty shillings apiece," and that he spoke not this expecting a recompence, but that it might not be drawn into a precedent, and that the young gentlemen there might take note of it ' " (Jones, *Finger-ring Lore*, p. 188).

(2) " Papal " Rings

917. GILT BRONZE ; engraved on one side with the crown and column of the Colonna family for Pope Martin V. (1417-31), on the other the tiara ; on either side of the bezel, the initials P M (for Papa Martinus); the original stone has been replaced by an armorial seal-matrix.
Italian. 1417-31. (The signet 17th Century.) *Plate XXXVI.*
(Waterton Colln.) 87–1899.

The arms on the signet : a bend sinister, in chief three stars and a crescent, in base a dog sejant with head raised. Another example of the conversion of one of these rings into a signet is in the British Museum (Dalton, 834).

918. GILT BRONZE ; on the shoulders, in delicate pointillé engraving, the tiara surmounting the arms of Pope Eugenius IV. (1431-46), and a crown surmounting those of Aragon, for Alfonso the Magnanimous, King of Aragon and Sicily (1416-58) ; on one side the crossed keys, on the other a pastoral staff ; the bezel set with a dark green paste.
Italian. 1431-46.
(Waterton Colln.) 668–1871.

Ironmongers' Hall Exhibition, 1861, ii. 497.

919. GILT BRONZE ; in relief on one shoulder the tiara above the arms of Pope Eugenius IV. (1431-46) ; on the other, the crossed keys ; square bezel, the upper part and the stone wanting ; under the bezel, two crowns.
Italian. 1431–46.
(Waterton Colln.) 657–1871.

Ironmongers' Hall Exhibition, 1861, ii. 497.

Compare an example in the Museo Correr, Venice (V. Lazari, *Notizie, etc., della Raccolta Correr*, No. 1001) ; a similar ring is in the British Museum (Dalton, 845).

920. GILT BRONZE ; in relief on one shoulder a mitre above the arms of Condulmerio ; on the other a cardinal's (?) hat with tassels ; square bezel set with a crystal ; under the bezel, two crowns.
Italian. 15th Century.
Plate XXXVI.
(Waterton Colln.) 658–1871.

Attributable either to Gabriele Condulmerio, Cardinal 1408-31, afterwards Pope Eugenius IV., or to his nephew Francesco Condulmerio, Cardinal 1431-53. Compare British Museum (Dalton, 837-8).

921. GILT BRONZE ; the hoop engraved with a crown, the name RAGONAS, and the arms of Aragon ; oblong bezel set with a brown granular stone and having the symbols of the Evangelists in relief on the four sides.
Italian. 1416-58. *Plate XXXVI.*
(Waterton Colln.) 663–1871.

Attributed to Alfonso the Magnanimous, King of Aragon and Sicily (1416-58) and Naples (1442-58).

Compare an example in the Museo Correr, Venice (Lazari, *op. cit.*, No. 1003).

922. GILT BRONZE; the hoop with raised inscription RXRAGONA; on each shoulder the arms of Alfonso the Magnanimous, King of Aragon and Sicily, as King of Naples (1442-58); on the other two sides, the lion of St. Mark; square bezel set with a green chalcedony.
Italian. Middle of 15th Century. *Plate XXXVI.*
(Waterton Colln.) 664–1871.

Ironmongers' Hall Exhibition, 1861, ii. 501.

923. GILT BRONZE; the hoop engraved with the arms of Aragon, the name RE ALFŌSO, and a crown, for Alfonso the Magnanimous, King of Aragon and Sicily (1416-58) and Naples (1442-58); oblong bezel set with a crystal and having on the four sides the symbols of the Evangelists in relief.
Italian. 1416-58.
(Waterton Colln.) 662–1871.

Ironmongers' Hall Exhibition, 1861, ii. 501.

924. GILT BRONZE; on the hoop in relief the crossed keys surmounting the arms of Pope Pius II. (1458-64), the name PAPAPIO (AP joined, O as 8), and the tiara; oblong bezel set with a red-foiled paste and having on the four sides the symbols of the Evangelists.
Italian. 1458-64. *Plate XXXVIII.*
(Waterton Colln.) 666–1871.

Ironmongers' Hall Exhibition, 1861, ii. 497.

Compare other rings in the Palazzo Piccolomini at Pienza; in the Kunsthistorische Sammlung, Vienna (illustrated in the Vienna *Jahrbuch*, 1893, xiv., pt. 1., p. 4); and in the Louvre (Marquet de Vasselot, 211).

925. GILT BRONZE; on the hoop in relief the tiara, the crossed keys, and the name PAPA PIVS divided by the arms of Pope Pius II. (1458-64); oblong bezel set with a crystal over pink foil and having on the four sides the symbols of the Evangelists.
Italian. 1458-64.
(Waterton Colln.) 667–1871.

Ironmongers' Hall Exhibition, 1861, ii. 497.

926. GILT BRONZE; on the hoop in relief the crossed keys surmounting the arms of Pope Pius II. (1458-64), the name PAPA PIO (O as 8), and the tiara; oblong bezel set with a projecting green paste and having on the four sides the symbols of the Evangelists.
Italian. 1458-64. *Plate XXXVIII.*
(Waterton Colln.) 665–1871.

Formerly in the collection of Thomas Windus, F.S.A. (*Gentleman's Magazine*, vol. clxxxiii. 1848, p. 599; Fairholt's *Rambles of an Archaeologist*, pp. 108-9).

Compare examples in the British Museum (Dalton, 855-6) and the Bargello, Florence.

927. GILT BRONZE; on the hoop the raised inscription in two lines SIXTVS PAPA QVARTVS; on the shoulders in relief the tiara and the arms of Pope Sixtus IV. (1471-84) surmounted by the crossed keys; on the other two sides, the symbols of the Evangelists; oblong bezel set with a crystal in imitation claw setting.
Italian. 1471-84. *Plate XXXVI.*
(Bernal Colln.) 2107–1855.

928. GILT BRONZE; on one shoulder in relief a mitre surmounting the engraved arms of della Rovere, on the other a cardinal's (?) hat with tassels; on the two other sides the inscription PAPA SISTVS for Pope Sixtus IV. (1471-84); oblong bezel set with a modern paste crystal.
Italian. 1471-84.
(Waterton Colln.) 669–1871.

There were three cardinals of the della Rovere family who used these arms during the pontificate of Sixtus IV.: Giuliano (afterwards Pope Julius II.), who received the dignity in 1471,

Domenico in 1477, and Cristoforo in 1478, who lived only a month after his elevation.

929. GILT BRONZE; on the hoop is the inscription SISTVS I, and, applied in silver-gilt, the tiara and crossed keys surmounting the arms of Pope Sixtus IV. (1471-84); large circular bezel of flower form (the stone missing), with the symbols of the Evangelists similarly applied.
Italian. 1471-84. *Plate XXXVII.*
(Waterton Colln.) 670–1871.

Ironmongers' Hall Exhibition, 1861, ii. 497.

Compare a ring of similar form in the Kunsthistorische Sammlung, Vienna, illustrated in the Vienna *Jahrbuch*, 1893, xiv., pt. I., p. 9.

930. GILT BRONZE; on one shoulder in relief a mitre above a coat of arms, on the other a cardinal's (?) hat with tassels; oblong bezel set with a yellow paste.
Italian. 15th Century.
Plate XXXVII.
(Waterton Colln.) 659–1871.

The arms: a bend chequy, on a chief a cross of St. John, doubtless a misreading of the arms of Cibo, which have a plain cross. The same mistake is made on three rings in the British Museum (Dalton, 835, 836, 860). This chief was granted to the Genoese family of Cibo in the 13th century by the Republic of Genoa. The ring is most probably attributable either to Giovanni Battista Cibo, afterwards Pope Innocent VIII. (1484-92), who became cardinal in 1473, to his nephew Lorenzo Cibo, who was raised to the cardinalate in 1488 and died in 1504, or to his grandson Innocentio, who received the dignity in 1515 and died in 1540.

931. GILT BRONZE; on the hoop in low relief are the tiara and the crossed keys; oblong bezel set with a green tourmaline (?) and having on the four sides the symbols of the Evangelists.
Italian. 15th Century.
(Waterton Colln.) 661–1871.

Possibly intended for the arms of Pope Nicholas V. (1447-55), who, not having any family arms, used the crossed keys.

932. GILT BRONZE; the hoop engraved on one side with the tiara, on the other with a cross above a coat of arms; square bezel set with a crystal and having in relief on the four sides the symbols of the Evangelists.
Italian. 15th Century.
Plate XXXVII.
(Waterton Colln.) 660–1871.

The arms: two keys in saltire, the bows uppermost and linked.

932*a*. GILT BRONZE; triple-grooved hoop engraved on each shoulder with a mitre above crossed keys and a cardinal's hat, between two mitres; bezel re-set with an oval amethyst in notched collet.
Italian. 15th Century.
Given by Dr. W. L. Hildburgh, F.S.A.
M. 161–1929.

933. GILT BRONZE; on one of the shoulders in low relief the Virgin and Child seated with a flower-pot containing a lily, on the other the half-figure of an abbess holding a book and having a branch beside her; on the two sides a hat with tassels surmounting a coat of arms; on the hoop the raised inscription EPISC. LVGDVN; oblong bezel set with a pyramidal crystal.
Italian. 15th Century.
Plate XXXVII.
741–1877.

The arms: two keys crossed in saltire.

Compare a very similar ring with the same arms and inscription in the British Museum (Dalton, 861). Many conjectures have been made regarding these two rings (compare O. Morgan,

Arch. Journal, 1857, p. 178). No Archbishop of Lyons nor any Bishop of Laon (*Lugdunum Clavatum*), or of St. Bertrand de Comminges (*Lugdunum Convenarum*), is known to have used these arms. A certain John, who was Bishop of St. Bertrand de Comminges in 1465, and was not of armorial family, may possibly have adopted them.

The arms are those in use for the "*sede vacante*" administration of the Holy See.

(3) RINGS BEARING MISCELLANEOUS INSCRIPTIONS

934. SILVER; engraved outside + QUANT·DIEU·PLERA·MELIOR·SERA.
15th Century. *Plate XXXIX.*
(Waterton Colln.) 899–1871.

Ironmongers' Hall Exhibition, 1861, ii. 507.

935. GOLD; chased outside with foliations and two scrolls inscribed NUL·SANS·PEYN; engraved inside SANS MAL DESYR.
English. Early 16th Century. *Plate XXXIX.*
(Waterton Colln.) 893–1871.

Ironmongers' Hall Exhibition, 1861, ii. 506.

936. GOLD; a child's ring; small circular bezel set with a diamond, slender hoop engraved inside THIS SPARK WILL GROW.
English. 17th Century. *Plate XXXIX.*
(Waterton Colln.) 908–1871.

937. SILVER; engraved inside LOUE THE TRUTH.
English. 17th Century.
(Waterton Colln.) 913–1871.

938. GOLD; engraved inside NEVER TO BEE FORGOTEN 12 JAN 77.
English. 1777.
Given by the Rev. R. Brooke. 387–1864.

(4) FANCY RINGS

939. GILT BRONZE; massive; inscribed "mur" in large Gothic letters divided by two projecting settings with antique pastes of profile heads of Marcus Aurelius and Hadrian.
Italian. 15th Century. *Plate XXXIX.*
(Waterton Colln.) 654–1871.

Compare a ring of similar material and shape, set with a small red paste and engraved with M+M, in the Musée de Cluny (No. 19972).

940. GILT BRONZE; oblong bezel set with a large pyramidal crystal over foil.
Italian. 15th Century. *Plate XXXVIII.*
(Waterton Colln.) 656–1871.

Compare a very similar example in the Ashmolean Museum (Fortnum Collection, 787). In the Bargello, Florence, is another example (Carrand Collection, 1019); the crystal here is foiled red and flat instead of pyramidal; its lower side is faceted as in the two other examples. All three are very reminiscent of the "Papal" rings.

941. BRONZE; octagonal bezel chased with a mask of Silenus, the plain hoop hollow with a projecting tube for use as a squirt.
Italian. 17th Century. *Plate XXXIX.*
(Waterton Colln.) 959–1871.

Ironmongers' Hall Exhibition, 1861, ii. 507.

Illustrated in Jones, *Finger-ring Lore*, p. 494.

942. GOLD; a dial ring; circular locket bezel enclosing a removable compass

engraved round the edge with the numerals from 1 to 12; the lid set with a ruby and five diamonds in the form of a flower; the shoulders and sides of the bezel chased in scrolls and enamelled.
German. Late 16th Century.
Plate XXXIX.
4300–1857.

Compare other dial rings in the British Museum (Dalton, 1703-7), and the Ashmolean Museum (Fortnum Collection, 516).

943. GOLD; opening to form an armillary sphere, with four hoops fitting together in pairs, the outer pair engraved with cross-hatching.
English. 17th Century.
Plate XXXIX.
M. 368–1923.

Compare British Museum (Dalton, 1700-2).

944. GOLD; the hoop formed by three chains decorated with faceting and small rosettes; the large transverse oval bezel contains a revolving setting with a discoloured turquoise engraved on one side with Venus and Cupid, and on the other with a Gnostic inscription.
Italian. 17th Century. (The gem Roman, 2nd or 3rd Century A.D.)
Plate XXXIX.
(Waterton Colln.) 613–1871.

945. GOLD; in the form of a snake, composed of fourteen hinged joints, twelve of them each set with a diamond and enamelled inside with black and white; the head joint unscrews and passes through a loop in the tail.
Italian. 17th Century.
Plate XXXIX.
(Waterton Colln.) 961–1871.

Ironmongers' Hall Exhibition, 1861, ii. 507.

946. IRON, plated with gold; octagonal box-shaped bezel with hinged lid; the hoop penannular, with volutes at the shoulders.
Italian. 17th Century.
Plate XXXIX.
(Waterton Colln.) 962–1871.

947. SILVER-GILT; of very large size; plain narrow hoop, a cherub and foliations applied to each shoulder; large circular bezel set with a rounded crystal, and engraved at the back with the Crucifixion.
Italian. 17th Century.
Plate XXXVIII.
(Waterton Colln.) 673-1871.

Illustrated in Jones, *Finger-ring Lore*, p. 264.

948. GILT BRONZE; the shoulders chased as demi-figures; large octagonal bezel (the stone and upper part wanting).
Italian. 17th Century.
(Waterton Colln.) 672–1871.

949. BRONZE; oval bezel engraved with a fleur-de-lys; the hoop with projecting tobacco-stopper.
Probably German. 17th Century.
Plate XXXIX.
(Waterton Colln.) 745–1871.

950. BRONZE; oval bezel engraved with the letters A.D. in reverse, the hoop with projecting tobacco-stopper.
Probably German. 17th Century.
(Waterton Colln.) 744–1871.

951. BRONZE; oval bezel engraved with a double-headed eagle displayed, the hoop with projecting tobacco-stopper.
Probably German. 17th Century.
(Waterton Colln.) 743–1871.

952. SILVER; massive; the hoop and shoulders chased with grapes and foliage; projecting plain circular bezel with moulded side.
Tyrolese. 17th Century.
Plate XXXVIII.
(Waterton Colln.) 971–1871.

For use as a weapon. Compare No. 457 and a ring in the Tarnóczy Collection (Szendrei, *Collection de Bagues de Madame de Tarnóczy*, pp. 119-20).

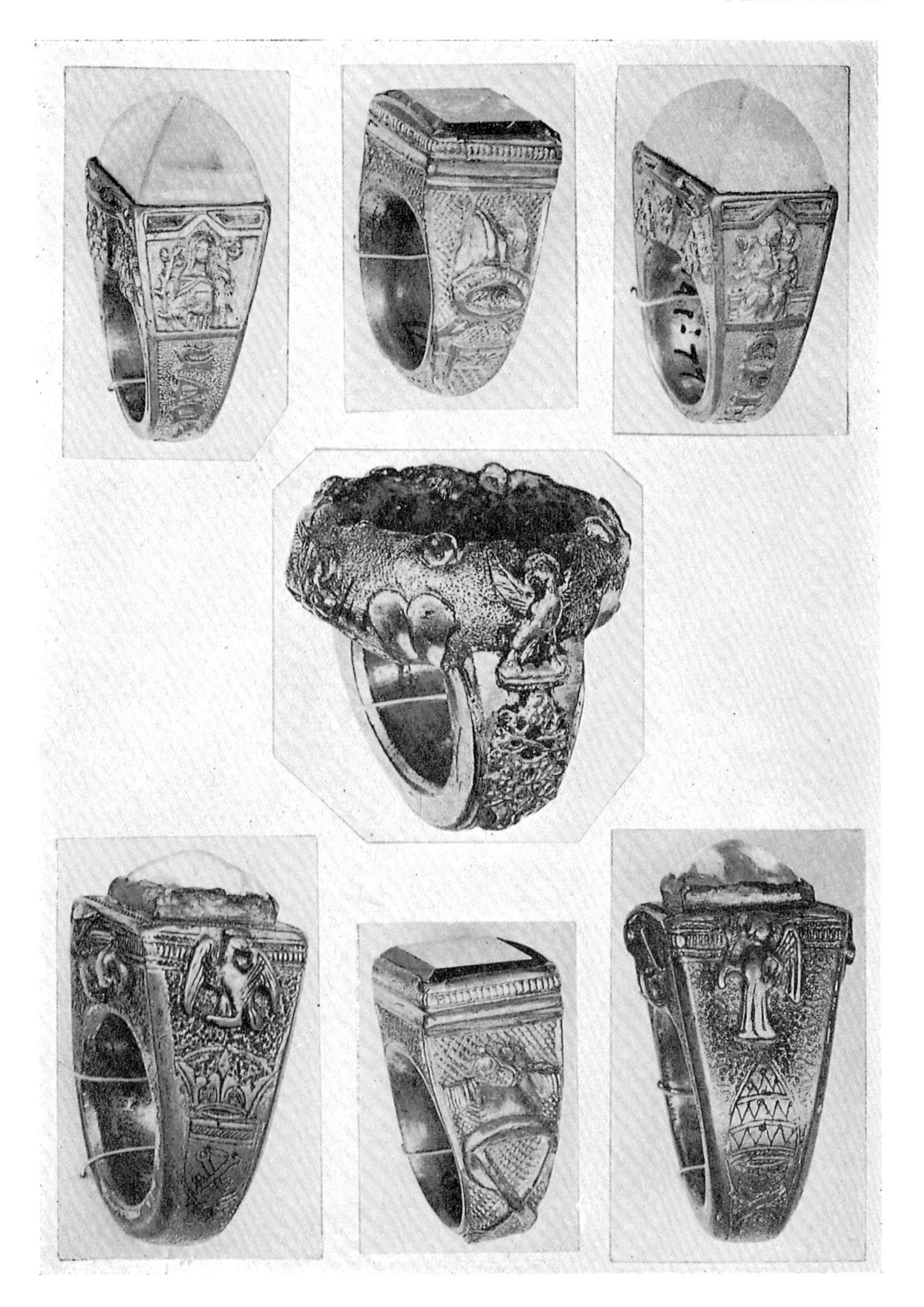

"PAPAL" RINGS

933	930	933
	929	
932	930	932

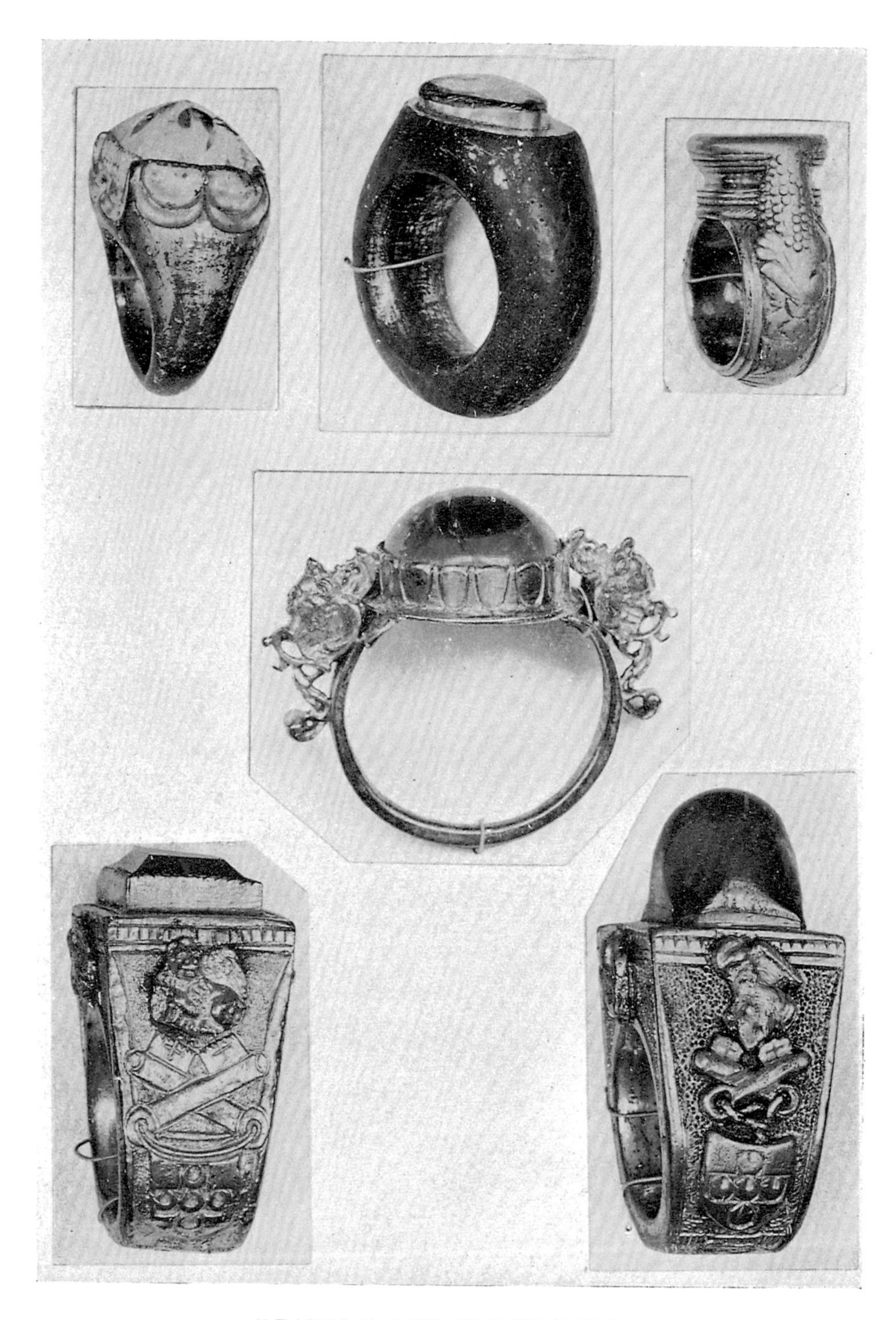

"PAPAL" AND FANCY RINGS

940 961 952

947

924 926

INSCRIBED AND FANCY RINGS

916   934, 935   958
943   945   942
936   941
946   944   957
953   939   949

953. SILVER; flat square bezel surmounted by two transversely trained cannon; the hoop chased with scrolls.
German. 18th Century.
Plate XXXIX.
(Waterton Colln.) 987–1871.

954. SILVER; a puzzle ring; three hoops, each set with a square plaque engraved with a cross between four amulets; the three plaques, united by a group of three pellets, form the bezel.
German (?). 18th Century.
(Waterton Colln.) 861–1871.

955. WHITE METAL; massive octagonal bezel set with five short spikes, the shoulders chased with scrolls.
German (Upper Bavarian). 18th Century. 916–1872.

For use as a weapon.

Illustrated in Jones, *Finger-ring Lore*, p. 84.

956. GOLD; five pivoted hoops, alternately beaded and plain; lozenge-shaped bezel set with a garnet, pearls, and two pastes.
Spanish. Late 18th Century.
113–1870.

957. PAINTED ENAMEL ON COPPER; a broad band with four figure subjects.
Austrian (Vienna). Late 18th Century. *Plate XXXIX.*
(Waterton Colln.) 1003–1871.

The scenes represent three musicians, a man and woman dancing, three men gambling, and two savages.

958. GOLD; in the form of a snake in three coils, with rubies for eyes.
English. Early 19th Century.
Plate XXXIX.
Bequeathed by Mrs. A. B. Woodcroft.
476–1903.

Said to have been the favourite ring of King George IV. In the painting by Sir Thomas Lawrence in the Wallace Collection (559) the King appears to be wearing this ring.

959. CHISELLED STEEL AND GOLD; composed of openwork foliage, the bezel with seated figure of a Muse between two Cupids. Made by Froment Meurice, of Paris.
French. About 1850.
Bought at the Paris Exhibition, 1856.
2658–1856.

960. SILVER; a flexible band of fine multiple chainwork, each link set with four pellets, forming a close diaper on the outside.
Maltese. About 1870.
(Annual International Exhibition, 1872.) 1459–1873.

961. GILT BRONZE; large and massive; the flat bezel set with a triangular crystal.
Plate XXXVIII.
(Waterton Colln.) 655–1871.

(5) Oriental Rings

(a) *Near Eastern*

962. BRONZE; the hoop swelling towards the circular bezel which is engraved with a duck.
(Waterton Colln.) 729–1871.

963. HAEMATITE; the flattened shoulders and the oblong bezel engraved with inscriptions in Arabic (?).
Mediaeval Egyptian.
(Waterton Colln.) 1012–1871.

964. SILVER; a signet ring; octagonal bezel engraved with a bird surrounded by an inscription in Hebrew.
Jewish. 17th Century (?).
(Waterton Colln.) 742–1871.

965. SILVER; octagonal bezel set with a projecting faceted crystal engraved with two lines of inscription; other inscriptions (of Arabic type) on the shoulders and sides of the bezel.
(Waterton Colln.) 1011–1871.

966. SILVER; oval bezel engraved with a line of Arabic (?) inscription on a band between nielloed scrolls.
(Waterton Colln.) 984–1871.

967. GOLD FILIGREE; the hoop of plaited wire with five pendants, three hung with pearls.
Syrian (Beyrout). 1872. 98–1873.

968. BRONZE; projecting circular bezel engraved with a cross patty surrounded by symbols (?).
(Waterton Colln.) 610–1871.

969. SILVER; oblong filigree bezel set with a large turquoise inscribed in Arabic lettering; the hoop with filigree decoration, set with fragments of turquoise and cornelian.
(St. Maurice Colln.) 957–1884.

From Cairo.

970. GOLD, openwork; the hoop composed of scrolls, the large mitre-shaped bezel closely set with emeralds and garnets.
Turkish. 19th Century. 214–1892.

971. GOLD; with filigree decoration, set with turquoises and coloured pastes; large projecting hemispherical bezel.
Turkish. 19th Century. 213–1892.

972. GOLD; the shoulders set with eight diamonds; oval bezel set with a turquoise engraved with an Arabic inscription.
(St. Maurice Colln.) 958–1884.

From Cairo.

(b) *Middle Eastern*

973. GOLD; set with an emerald, the bezel and shoulders pierced with foliage and set with garnets.
Persian. 19th Century. 424–1884.

Made at Teheran.

974. JADE; a bowman's ring; hoof-shaped, carved in low relief with floral ornament (*sausan* lily).
Indian (Delhi). 2nd half of 17th Century.
(Waterton Colln.) 1022–1871.

975. JADE; a bowman's ring; hoof-shaped, inlaid inside with an Arabic inscription in gold.
Indian (Delhi). Dated 1733.
(Waterton Colln.) 1023–1871.

976. GOLD; the bezel in the form of a six-petalled flower set with foiled blue and red pastes; hoop and back of bezel richly enamelled.
Indian (Jaipur). 19th Century.
(Waterton Colln.) 1018–1871.

977. GOLD; with fourteen turquoises in heart-shaped settings; enamelled inside white and translucent red.
Indian (Jaipur). 19th Century.
(Waterton Colln.) 1016–1871.

978. GOLD; oval bezel enamelled with a peacock in white and green on a red ground, the hoop coming to a point behind.
Indian (Jaipur). 19th Century.
(Waterton Colln.) 1019–1871.

979. GOLD; large oval bezel with relief of Lakshmi attended by two lustrating elephants.
Indian. 19th Century.
(Waterton Colln.) 1014–1871.

980. GOLD; flat octagonal bezel decorated with a chequer of fine filigree; hoop,

shoulders and sides of bezel with similar ornament.
Indian. 19th Century.
(Waterton Colln.) 1017–1871.

981. SILVER; large projecting octagonal bezel engraved with an inscription; the hoop with the initials L F.
Southern Indian. 19th Century.
(Waterton Colln.) 1013–1871.

982. SILVER; curved circular bezel engraved with a head in profile.
(Waterton Colln.) 1015–1871.

(c) *Far Eastern*

983. GOLD; a wide band chased with branches of prunus.
Chinese. 19th Century.
Given by Mr. Victor Ames.
216–1891.

984. GOLD; large curved oblong bezel embossed with a bat and prunus blossoms; the hoop formed of two overlapping pointed strips.
Chinese. 19th Century.
M. 431–1911.

Part of a collection given by Miss Edith J. Hipkins in memory of her parents, A. J. Hipkins, F.S.A., and J. S. Hipkins.

985. SILVER; large curved oblong bezel embossed with three figures and a pavilion, with traces of blue and green enamel; the hoop formed of two overlapping pointed strips.
Chinese. 19th Century.
Given by Mrs. E. S. Sanders.
589–1908.

986. SILVER; a band chased with floral ornament enriched with translucent enamel (blue, green and manganese).
Chinese. 19th Century.
(Waterton Colln.) 1020–1871.

987. SILVER; a band chased with pavilions and trees. Maker's mark of Chang Hsin.
Chinese. 19th Century.
(Waterton Colln.) 1021–1871.

988. SILVER; a band of filigree between two blue-enamelled borders with milled edges.
Chinese (Hakka). 19th Century.
Given by the Rev. Arthur S. Adams.
M. 116–1913.

989. SILVER; a hoop of beaded wire.
Chinese (Hakka). 19th Century.
Given by the Rev. Arthur S. Adams.
M. 120–1913.

ADDENDA

225. Additional note. Compare also the illustrations of the nielloed gold armlet (now lost) and ring (in the Museo Civico, Bologna) found in the Rio Reno, near Bologna (P. Ducati, *Bolletino D'Arte*, 2nda Serie, iii., 1923-4, pp. 241-7).

235*a*. GOLD; small; the hoop widening to form the bezel, which is set with filigree of two lozenges separated by beading.
Lombard. 6th or 7th Century.
Plate III.
(Waterton Colln.) 439–1871.

Seven silver and six gold rings with similar decoration of lozenges and filigree were discovered in the excavation of the sixth and seventh-century Lombard cemetery at Castel Trosino, near Ascoli Piceno. As all these examples were found in the graves of women it has been suggested that they were love rings of some sort, a supposition which seems to be supported by the discovery at Ripatransone of a gold ring on which one of the lozenges is inscribed GERONTIVS and the other REGINA (see R. Mengarelli, *La necropoli barbarica di Castel Trosino* in *Monumenti Antichi*, xii., 1902). See also, two rings, one of silver (720), the other of gold (722), found in 1821 by Canon Michele della Torre in his excavations in the barbaric cemetery near the Rio Emiliano and now in the museum at Cividale del Friuli (see Gino Fogolari, *Cividale del Friuli*, p. 29).

738*a*. LEAD ; a decade ring (eleven knobs) ; bezel in the form of a projecting crucifix.
English. 16th Century.
M. 220–1929.

Found at Lyme Regis.

The size of this ring (external diameter of hoop $1\frac{5}{8}$ in., projection of bezel $1\frac{5}{16}$ in.) emphasises the fact that many decade rings were not intended for ordinary wear.

NUMERICAL INDEX

Registered Number.	Catalogue Number.	Registered Number.	Catalogue Number.
649–1864	829	455–1868	422
650–1864	831	457–1868	403
651–1864	823	458–1868	434
652–1864	905	461–1868	413
653–1864	912	462–1868	417
654–1864	817	465–1868	419
655–1864	816	471–1868	410
656–1864	825	476–1868	396
657–1864	824	477–1868	418
658–1864	818	478–1868	421
659–1864	819	479–1868	420
660–1864	814	481–1868	435
661–1864	811	482–1868	399
662–1864	674	483–1868	425
1109–1864	803	484–1868	426
1110–1864	798	485–1868	428
1111–1864	341	487–1868	406
1112–1864	328	488–1868	409
1113–1864	336	525–1868	242
1114–1864	800	526–1868	801
1115–1864	334	527–1868	792
1116–1864	337	1817–1869	112
1117–1864	340	1831–1869	481
1118–1864	805	113–1870	956
1119–1864	804	211–1870	748
1120–1864	808	212–1870	344
1121–1864	807	213–1870	338
1122–1864	809	214–1870	343
1123–1864	822	215–1870	698
1124–1864	802	216–1870	699
1125–1864	839	697–1870	438
22–1865	663	65–1871	251
23–1865	326	401–1871	14
103–1865	784	402–1871	5
129–1865	489	403–1871	7
112–1866	475	404–1871	8
113–1866	477	405–1871	4
114–1866	473	406–1871	6
115–1866	474	407–1871	3
116–1866	476	408–1871	10
302–1867	697	409–1871	9
427–1868	408	410–1871	2
428–1868	402	411–1871	1
429–1868	427	412–1871	11
431–1868	430	413–1871	12
435–1868	436	414–1871	13
436–1868	404	415–1871	16
440–1868	433	416–1871	15
441–1868	412	418–1871	17
449–1868	411	419–1871	21
454–1868	407	420–1871	18

Registered Number.	Catalogue Number.	Registered Number.	Catalogue Number.
529–1871	193	609–1871	147
530–1871	194	610–1871	968
531–1871	198	613–1871	944
532–1871	195	614–1871	161
533–1871	196	615–1871	220
534–1871	105	616–1871	224
535–1871	75	617–1871	215
539–1871	91	618–1871	216
541–1871	124	619–1871	217
542–1871	136	620–1871	236
543–1871	141	621–1871	208
544–1871	142	622–1871	213
545–1871	166	623–1871	214
546–1871	167	624–1871	239
547–1871	168	625–1871	238
548–1871	169	626–1871	237
549–1871	170	627–1871	227
550–1871	171	628–1871	225
551–1871	172	629–1871	228
552–1871	78	630–1871	138
553–1871	123	631–1871	229
554–1871	130	632–1871	230
555–1871	92	633–1871	250
557–1871	115	634–1871	251
559–1871	93	635–1871	752
560–1871	116	636–1871	252
564–1871	150	637–1871	254
565–1871	135	638–1871	255
566–1871	95	639–1871	257
567–1871	75	640–1871	256
568–1871	96	641–1871	258
575–1871	71	642–1871	259
586–1871	231	643–1871	262
587–1871	201	644–1871	244
588–1871	221	645–1871	245
589–1871	206	646–1871	247
590–1871	202	647–1871	260
591–1871	200	648–1871	243
592–1871	233	649–1871	578
593–1871	234	650–1871	249
594–1871	159	651–1871	583
595–1871	137	652–1871	263
598–1871	165	653–1871	264
599–1871	108	654–1871	939
601–1871	156	655–1871	961
602–1871	587	656–1871	940
603–1871	199	657–1871	919
604–1871	203	658–1871	920
605–1871	204	659–1871	930
606–1871	218	660–1871	932
608–1871	146	661–1871	931

Registered Number.	Catalogue Number.	Registered Number.	Catalogue Number.
662–1871	923	713–1871	769
663–1871	921	714–1871	770
664–1871	922	715–1871	774
665–1871	926	716–1871	776
666–1871	924	717–1871	771
667–1871	925	718–1871	779
668–1871	918	719–1871	759
669–1871	928	720–1871	773
670–1871	929	721–1871	772
671–1871	309	722–1871	780
672–1871	948	723–1871	581
673–1871	947	724–1871	584
674–1871	782	725–1871	579
675–1871	758	726–1871	577
676–1871	756	727–1871	576
677–1871	732	728–1871	607
678–1871	734	729–1871	962
679–1871	753	730–1871	232
680–1871	726	731–1871	530
681–1871	724	732–1871	618
682–1871	267	733–1871	614
683–1871	722	736–1871	602
684–1871	268	737–1871	492
685–1871	721	738–1871	570
686–1871	720	739–1871	569
687–1871	719	741–1871	616
688–1871	588	742–1871	964
689–1871	728	743–1871	951
690–1871	723	744–1871	950
691–1871	727	745–1871	949
692–1871	729	746–1871	608
693–1871	735	747–1871	619
694–1871	485	748–1871	531
695–1871	484	749–1871	781
696–1871	717	750–1871	604
697–1871	736	751–1871	562
698–1871	565	752–1871	603
699–1871	749	753–1871	549
700–1871	750	754–1871	550
701–1871	764	755–1871	554
702–1871	483	756–1871	546
703–1871	765	757–1871	617
704–1871	766	758–1871	600
705–1871	762	759–1871	556
706–1871	754	760–1871	568
707–1871	760	761–1871	564
708–1871	755	762–1871	585
709–1871	761	763–1871	540
710–1871	763	764–1871	609
711–1871	767	765–1871	548*a*
712–1871	768	766–1871	605

Registered Number.	Catalogue Number.	Registered Number.	Catalogue Number.
767–1871	543	818–1871	491
768–1871	597	819–1871	558
769–1871	541	820–1871	532
770–1871	548	822–1871	533
771–1871	539	824–1871	131
772–1871	542	825–1871	155
773–1871	551	826–1871	148
774–1871	544	827–1871	145
775–1871	738	828–1871	160
776–1871	595	829–1871	125
777–1871	596	833–1871	638
778–1871	594	834–1871	653
779–1871	592	835–1871	656
780–1871	598	836–1871	611
781–1871	591	837–1871	610
782–1871	590	838–1871	599
783–1871	615	839–1871	573
784–1871	575	840–1871	572
785–1871	514	841–1871	559
786–1871	519	842–1871	633
787–1871	529	843–1871	634
788–1871	586	844–1871	632
789–1871	513	845–1871	631
790–1871	523	846–1871	635
791–1871	524	847–1871	654
792–1871	503	848–1871	636
793–1871	502	849–1871	655
794–1871	552	850–1871	661
795–1871	553	851–1871	662
796–1871	555	852–1871	665
797–1871	510	853–1781	380
798–1871	509	854–1871	664
799–1871	516	855–1871	470
800–1871	522	856–1871	668
801–1871	482	857–1871	667
802–1871	525	858–1871	630
803–1871	512	859–1871	700
804–1871	520	860–1871	383
805–1871	511	861–1871	954
806–1871	521	863–1871	704
807–1871	487	864–1871	703
808–1871	494	865–1871	706
809–1871	488	866–1871	705
810–1871	496	867–1871	713
811–1871	497	868–1871	710
812–1871	490	869–1871	714
813–1871	499	870–1871	715
814–1871	526	871–1871	642
815–1871	601	872–1871	641
816–1871	757	873–1871	648
817–1871	527	874–1871	640

Registered Number.	Catalogue Number.	Registered Number.	Catalogue Number.
875–1871	643	926–1871	790
876–1871	637	927–1871	796
877–1871	646	928–1871	788
878–1871	645	929–1871	915
879–1871	651	930–1871	791
880–1871	652	931–1871	795
881–1871	649	934–1871	308
882–1871	650	935–1871	307
883–1871	647	936–1871	298
884–1871	639	937–1871	241
885–1871	272	938–1871	300
886–1871	273	939–1871	299
887–1871	274	940–1871	304
888–1871	623	941–1871	323
889–1871	625	942–1871	324*a*
890–1871	624	943–1871	325
891–1871	627	944–1871	312
892–1871	628	945–1871	313
893–1871	935	946–1871	290
894–1871	266	947–1871	286
895–1871	658	948–1871	281
896–1871	657	949–1871	280
897–1871	659	950–1871	455
898–1871	629	951–1871	327
899–1871	934	952–1871	235
900–1871	718	953–1871	277
901–1871	606	954–1871	276
902–1871	731	955–1871	296
903–1871	560	956–1871	297
904–1871	677	957–1871	311
905–1871	660	958–1871	302
906–1871	673	959–1871	941
907–1871	688	960–1871	612
908–1871	936	961–1871	945
909–1871	676	962–1871	946
910–1871	683	963–1871	301
911–1871	675	965–1871	322
912–1871	687	966–1871	331
913–1871	937	967–1871	321
914–1871	695	968–1871	613
915–1871	686	969–1871	397
916–1871	690	970–1871	350
917–1871	689	971–1871	952
918–1871	691	972–1871	447
919–1871	783	973–1871	446
920–1871	740*a*	974–1871	464
921–1871	566	975–1871	480
922–1871	745	977–1871	472
923–1871	670	980–1871	471
924–1871	786	982–1871	593
925–1871	785	983–1871	479

Registered Number.	Catalogue Number.	Registered Number.	Catalogue Number.
984–1871	966	939–1872	460
985–1871	275	940–1872	459
986–1871	478	959–1872	361
987–1871	953	98–1873	967
990–1871	98	453–1873	707
992–1871	381	454–1873	377
993–1871	162	456–1873	293
995–1871	751	457–1873	456
1000–1871	382	1327–1873	466
1002–1871	620	1357–1873	467
1003–1871	957	1459–1873	960
1006–1871	398	1460–1873	437
1011–1871	965	1462–1873	431
1012–1871	963	4–1874	501
1013–1871	981	740–1877	733
1014–1871	979	741–1877	933
1015–1871	982	783–1877	545
1016–1871	977	2042*j*–1877	4*b*
1017–1871	980	21–1883	357
1018–1871	976	424–1884	973
1019–1871	978	957–1884	969
1020–1871	986	958–1884	972
1021–1871	987	13–1888	740
1022–1871	974	846–1888	868
1023–1871	975	847–1888	840
1214–1871	362	848–1888	855
1215–1871	316	849–1888	862
1216–1871	440	850–1888	838
1217–1871	439	851–1888	859
46–1872	458	852–1888	836
80–1872	711	853–1888	845
81–1872	716	854–1888	854
112–1872	666	855–1888	873
170–1872	777	856–1888	858
171–1872	339	857–1888	846
172–1872	746	858–1888	874
173–1872	778	859–1888	884
189–1872	285	860–1888	860
628–1872	504	861–1888	834
630–1872	883	862–1888	876
662–1872	384	863–1888	870
663–1872	384*a*	864–1888	856
664–1872	385	865–1888	901
665–1872	386	866–1888	880
666–1872	388	867–1888	869
667–1872	388*a*	868–1888	841
668–1872	387	869–1888	843
916–1872	955	870–1888	852
925–1872	461	871–1888	849
926–1872	454	872–1888	875
927–1872	453	873–1888	866

Registered Number.	Catalogue Number.	Registered Number.	Catalogue Number.
874–1888	851	585–1892	879
875–1888	837	586–1892	886
876–1888	835	597–1892	278
877–1888	887	746–1893	291
878–1888	913	25–1894	310
879–1888	891	26–1894	246
880–1888	892	27–1894	450
881–1888	872	28–1894	445
882–1888	903	29–1894	451
883–1888	894	30–1894	292
884–1888	906	31–1894	360
885–1888	902	32–1894	709
886–1888	888	507–1894	574
887–1888	896	621–1894	358
888–1888	904	65–1896	288
889–1888	908	397–1896	465
890–1888	910	398–1896	463
891–1888	844	1894–1897	209
892–1888	911	1894*a*–1897	211
893–1888	898	1894*e*–1897	157
894–1888	899	6–1899	789
895–1888	863	87–1899	917
896–1888	895	88–1899	582
897–1888	900	89–1899	534
898–1888	914	90–1899	261
899–1888	893	91–1899	495
900–1888	897	92–1899	207
901–1888	871	93–1899	163
902–1888	865	94–1899	253
903–1888	848	95–1899	205
904–1888	833	97–1899	187
905–1888	832	98–1899	197
906–1888	885	2245–1900	4*a*
907–1888	878	4917–1901	223
908–1888	882	5575–1901	730
909–1888	853	292–1902	444
910–1888	877	731–1902	289
911–1888	847	732–1902	318*a*
912–1888	890	733–1902	333
913–1888	889	776–1902	374
914–1888	861	777–1902	375
915–1888	850	778–1902	373
916–1888	857	779–1902	372
917–1888	842	817–1902	54
918–1888	881	949–1902	462
919–1888	867	1582–1902	737
364–1890	864	1583–1902	500
746–1890	915*a*	476–1903	958
216–1891	983	1000–1903	432
213–1892	971	1204–1903	271
214–1892	970	1205–1903	270

Registered Number.	Catalogue Number.	Registered Number.	Catalogue Number.
1206–1903	283	M. 431–1911	984
1207–1903	451*a*	M. 640–1911	400
1374–1903	538	M. 641–1911	424
1375–1903	561	M. 13–1912	401
1630–1903	820	M. 86–1913	369
1631–1903	821	M. 95–1913	798*a*
1636–1903	507	M. 107–1913	70
1639–1903	799	M. 116–1913	988
1644–1903	506	M. 120–1913	989
730–1904	295	M. 76–1917	94
903–1904	536	M. 102–1920	563
904–1904	469	M. 277–1920	226
1377–1904	210	M. 253–1921	265
1059–1905	371	M. 326–1922	907
1060–1905	370	M. 327–1922	378
138–1906	813	M. 328–1922	379
201–1906	284	M. 368–1923	943
638–1906	330	M. 369–1923	682
643–1906	19	M. 370–1923	359
142–1907	518	M. 371–1923	806
143–1907	589	M. 372–1923	815
325–1907	794	M. 373–1923	812
374–1908	702	M. 374–1923	493
589–1908	985	M. 242–1924	621
M. 1–1909	787	M. 236–1926	515
M. 131–1909	423	M. 237–1926	517
M. 135–1909	457	M. 314–1926	909
M. 149–1909	99	M. 814–1926	741
M. 150–1909	149	M. 815–1926	744
M. 151–1909	37	M. 816–1926	743
M. 446–1910	468	M. 817–1926	742
M. 552–1910	28	M. 818–1926	725
M. 553–1910	306	M. 819–1926	537
M. 554–1910	535	M. 1142–1926	212
M. 555–1910	305	M. 351–1927	810
M. 556–1910	282	M. 378–1927	567
M. 557–1910	376	M. 848–1927	508
M. 1008–1910	389	M. 249–1928	486
M. 1009–1910	390	M. 7–1929	248
M. 1010–1910	391	M. 8–1929	630*a*
M. 1011–1910	392	M. 9–1929	547
M. 1012–1910	393	M. 10–1929	624*a*
M. 1013–1910	394	M. 11–1929	550*a*
M. 1014–1910	395	M. 12–1929	544*a*
M. 1015–1910	672	M. 13–1929	583*a*
M. 1016–1910	332	M. 14–1929	480*a*
M. 1017–1910	405	M. 15–1929	317
M. 1018–1910	415	M. 16–1929	319
M. 1019–1910	416	M. 17–1929	319*a*
M. 1020–1910	414	M. 18–1929	739
M. 1021–1910	429	M. 19–1929	317*a*

INDEX

N.B.—*Only the more important inscriptions are included. Those on the later Love Rings or on the Mourning Rings will be found on pp.* 106-8 *and* 120-9 *respectively. References in ordinary figures are to pages, those in heavy type are the catalogue numbers.*